DIGITAL MAGNETIC RECORDING

DIGITAL MAGNETIC RECORDING

Second Edition

ALBERT S. HOAGLAND
JAMES E. MONSON

A Wiley-Interscience Publication
JOHN WILEY & SONS, INC.
New York / Chichester / Brisbane / Toronto / Singapore

Copyright © 1991 by John Wiley & Sons, Inc.

Library of Congress Cataloging in Publication Data:

Hoagland, Albert S.
  Digital magnetic recording/Albert S. Hoagland, James E. Monson—2nd ed.
     p.   cm.
  "A Wiley-Interscience publication."
  Includes bibliographical references and index.
    1. Computer storage devices. 2. Magnetic recorders and recording.
  I. Monson, James E. II. Title.
  TK7895.M3H6   1991
  621.39'76—dc20   90-39771
  ISBN 0-471-40144-7   CIP

Printed in the United States of America

10 9 8 7 6 5 4 3 2 1

CONTENTS

Preface   ix

List of Figures   xiii

1   MAGNETIC RECORDING AND DATA STORAGE   1

   1.1 Magnetic Recording, 4
       1.1.1 Modes of Recording, 6
       1.1.2 Magnetic Recording of Digital Information, 8
   1.2 Magnetic Data Storage Devices, 12
       1.2.1 Technology Objectives, 14
       1.2.2 The Beginning, 15
       1.2.3 Current Trends, 17
       1.2.4 The Future, 19
   1.3 Alternative Technologies, 19
   1.4 Summary, 20
   References, 21
       Pioneer Work, 21
       Other Material, 21

2   PRINCIPLES OF MAGNETICS   23

   2.1 Historical Background, 24
   2.2 Magnetic Field Relations, 26
       2.2.1 Units, 30

2.2.2 Magnetic Permeability, 31

2.2.3 Equivalence, Magnetic Shell–Current Loop, 31

2.3 Magnetic Fields Using the Concept of Magnetic Charge, 33

2.3.1 Image Fields, 33

2.3.2 Demagnetizing Fields, 35

2.3.3 Fields at Magnetic Circuit Air Gaps, 36

2.4 Magnetic Field Boundary Value Problems, 39

2.5 Magnetic Energy, 43

2.5.1 Self- and Mutual Induction, 44

2.6 Magnetic Circuits, 45

2.7 Eddy Currents In Magnetic Media, 48

2.8 Ferromagnetic Materials, 50

2.8.1 The Magnetization Process, 53

References, 58

3 THEORY OF THE DIGITAL MAGNETIC RECORDING PROCESS: READING
61

3.1 Principle Of Reciprocity, 63

3.2 Idealized Ring Head, 66

3.3 Step Function Change in Magnetization, 69

3.4 Finite Transition Width in the Magnetization Reversal, 74

3.5 Voltage Waveform Characteristics, 76

3.5.1 Three-Dimensional Factors, 78

3.6 Wavelength Response and Sine Wave Magnetization, 79

3.7 Alignment of Gap and Track, 84

References, 88

4 THEORY OF THE DIGITAL MAGNETIC RECORDING PROCESS: WRITING
89

4.1 Writing: The Transition, 89

4.1.1 Media Self-Demagnetization, 94

4.2 Transition Models, 96

4.2.1 Arctangent Model, 97

4.3 Write Process: Overwrite Phenomena, 103

4.3.1 Overwrite Criterion, 106

References, 108

5 MAGNETIC HEADS
111

5.1 Magnetic Heads—Magnetic Aspects, 111

5.1.1 Gap Fringing Field—General, 112

5.1.2 Idealized Ring Head, 114

5.1.3 Additional Pole-Tip Geometries, 121

5.1.4 Magnetic Circuit of the Magnetic Head, 124

5.1.5 Domain Structure in Film Heads, 130

5.1.6 Magnetoresistive Heads, 130

5.2 Electrical Characteristics of Magnetic Heads, 135

5.2.1 Ferrite Cores, 135

5.2.2 Metallic Head Cores, 136

5.2.3 Equivalent Lumped-Constant Electrical Circuit of the Magnetic Head, 139

5.2.4 Cross-Talk and Interhead Shielding, 141

5.3 Head-Track Registration, 141

References, 144

6 MAGNETIC RECORDING MEDIA   147

6.1 General Features of Recording Media, 147

6.1.1 Magnetic Properties and Design Considerations, 147

6.1.2 Noise Characteristics, 150

6.1.3 Mechanical Properties, 150

6.2 Particulate Media, 151

6.2.1 Signal-to-Noise Factors, 153

6.3 Thin Film Media, 154

6.3.1 Signal-to-Noise Factors, 154

6.4 Nonmagnetic Media Characteristics, 155

References, 156

7 DIGITAL RECORDING TECHNIQUES   159

7.1 The Digital Magnetic Recording Channel, 159

7.1.1 Qualitative Features of Digital Recording, 160

7.1.2 The Characteristic Voltage Pulse, 164

7.1.3 Pulse Superposition Theory, 166

7.2 Equalization of the Digital Magnetic Recording Channel, 175

7.2.1 Time Domain Factors, 182

7.2.2 Electrical Equalization: Summary, 182

7.3 Channel Modulation Coding, 183

7.3.1 NRZ Methods, 183

7.3.2 Phase Encoding, 185

7.3.3 Formal Characterization of Codes, 186

7.3.4 Additional Codes, including MFM, 2,7 and 1,7, 189

7.4 Readback Detection Techniques, 191

    7.4.1 Amplitude Detection, 193

    7.4.2 Peak Detection, 195

References, 198

8 DIGITAL RECORDING: NOISE SOURCES, ERROR RATES, AND ECC   201

8.1 Error Sources, 202

    8.1.1 Head Noise, 203

    8.1.2 Electronics Noise, 203

    8.1.3 Medium Noise, 204

8.2 Bit Error Rate, 209

    8.2.1 Noise-Induced Bit Shift, 209

    8.2.2 Intersymbol-Interference-Induced Bit Shift, 214

    8.2.3 Other Sources of Bit Shift, 216

    8.2.4 Window Margin Analysis, 216

    8.2.5 Bathtub Curve and TMR, 217

8.3 Reliability Through Redundancy, 217

    8.3.1 Error Detection and Correction, 219

References, 224

Index   **225**

PREFACE

This book was meant to be a second edition of *Digital Magnetic Recording* by A. S. Hoagland, first published in 1963 and reprinted in 1983. The term "second edition" may be a misnomer for almost all the original material has been revised and updated and a large amount of new material included. The decision to finally undertake a second edition nearly 30 years after its initial publication was a consequence of the return of Al Hoagland to the academic world and his formation of the Institute for Information Storage Technology (IIST) which provided both of us the opportunity and consequent challenge to teach the fundamentals of magnetic data recording to the growing number of professionals entering this field. The phenomenon of magnetic recording is in many ways a complex subject to grasp and yet is the key technology underpinning a huge data storage industry. The content of this second edition has benefitted from using the first edition supplemented by additional material in the teaching of undergraduate and graduate courses on magnetic recording theory at Santa Clara University.

The new text retains the basic approach to the subject matter, where concepts and principles are developed and clarified, and provides tools that can be directly applied to design situations. The overriding objective is to provide the reader with a basic understanding of magnetic recording for data storage. (This philosophy was taken in the first edition and accounts for the fact that there was a significant demand to bring it back into print as the reprint sales, although 20 years after first publication, exceeded those of the original issue.)

Digital magnetic recording is a unique application of magnetic recording technology and has become the technical base of a major new product category—devices for the mass storage of digital data.

The advent of the electronic computer with the concomitant growth in information processing has created a tremendous demand for the automated storage and retrieval of masses of data. Digital magnetic recording stands supreme in serving this need and is now an exceedingly important field of applied magnetics. This book presents a unified treatment of this subject in its own right.

There are many possible ways to approach the subject of digital magnetic recording, for it involves a range of engineering disciplines and has been built primarily upon practice rather than on theory. After considerable reflection, we came to the following two points of view. First, the essence of this method for recording and reproducing digital data lies in the field of magnetics. Second, in a subject like digital magnetic recording, which has been and still is under intensive development, the most valuable contribution a book can make is to provide a comprehensive understanding and perspective on this storage technology. Therefore, this text stresses digital magnetic recording principles and, through the emphasis on an integrated approach to the subject matter, attempts to illuminate the interrelation and significance of design parameters on the storage of digital information.

The individual merely searching for "cookbook" material will be disappointed. Should he or she peruse the contents, however, we believe that will be time well spent. Digital magnetic recording is occasionally disparaged as a "black art" precisely because circumstances rarely permit an effective realization of an overall system without close and continuous interaction between the component design activities.

The book should prove useful to professionals working or just beginning in digital magnetic recording, to students who desire to enhance their understanding in the engineering science of applied magnetics, and to engineers or scientists investigating the basic problems of data storage. Further, this book should be of value to those in the computer field who are designing or using data processing systems, for it gives a perspective on the factors setting the status and future potential of digital magnetic recording for mass storage. It should also serve as an important addition to the fundamental reference sources available to those active in other applications for magnetic recording.

The Introduction gives a descriptive presentation of the phases of the overall magnetic recording operation, along with definitions of common terms. The inherent characteristics of the process of "digital" magnetic recording are presented and elaborated. The influence of mass storage devices on the design environment is indicated. Then a brief review of the evolution, present status, and future trends in mass data storage is given. Chapter 1 serves as a valuable background, giving relevance and orientation to the body of the text. Chapter 2 reviews the fundamental principles and relations of magnetics relevant to phenomena in magnetic recording. The principles discussed in Chapter 2 form a base for the later theoretical developments. The last section is a presentation of the physical basis of ferromagnetism in terms of magnetic domain behavior.

Chapter 3 covers the theory of the overall magnetic recording process and readback of recorded information, from the perspective of both pulse and wavelength response. Chapter 4 covers the write process and the limitations on performance due to writing, which are reflected in the transition that characterizes a reversal in magnetization. Media parameters, head field gradient, and demagnetization are all included.

Chapter 5 goes into considerable detail on the design and role the magnetic head plays in digital magnetic recording. The head is viewed both from the magnetic and electrical circuit point of view as well as in terms of the magnetic coupling with the storage medium for writing and reading. Ferrite, thin film, MIG (metal-in-gap), and magnetoresistive head devices are treated.

Magnetic and mechanical factors that relate to the choice of the storage medium are the subject of Chapter 6. Signal to noise factors are also examined. Both particulate and thin film media are discussed.

Chapter 7 considers the topic of digital magnetic recording techniques. This subject represents the "bridge" between recording resolution and bit density. A deliberate attempt has been made to achieve generalizations so that the reader may secure an appreciation of and insight into this facet of digital magnetic recording, rather than merely a compilation of methods that have been used. The subjects of magnetic recording channel equalization and the use of recording codes are addressed.

Chapter 8 discusses bit error rate, and performance from the point of view of disk drive design. Margin analysis is covered. Then error correction and detection are presented to provide an overall picture of how these aspects are applied to achieve a reliable and high-performance data storage subsystem.

The second edition would not have been possible without the continuing support given by Santa Clara University through IIST. We are grateful to a number of individuals whose efforts made the completion of this endeavor possible and in particular: the dedicated administrative support provided by Mardi Gerdes; the commitment shown by Annie Yarbrough in converting text for computer word processing; and graduate student, Yenyu Hsieh, for taking hand sketches and preparing initial drawings by computer. Finally, we thank those graduate students who took the courses on magnetic recording theory over the last two years and willingly served as an "experimental laboratory" for the testing and evaluation of approaches to the treatment of the subject material.

ALBERT S. HOAGLAND
JAMES E. MONSON

Santa Clara, California
Claremont, California
March 1991

LIST OF FIGURES

Figure Number	**Page Number**
1.1 Storage hierarchy	2
1.2 Magnetic recording	5
1.3 Modes of recording	7
1.4 Ring head structure, showing magnetic coupling field	8
1.5 Magnetic saturation hysteresis phenomena	10
1.6 Input current–output voltage relationship	11
1.7 Elementary digital recording unit (disk)	13
1.8 RAMAC	16
1.9 Density versus time—disk storage	18
2.1 Incremental field arising from a current element	25
2.2 **B** and **H** fields of a permanent magnet	29
2.3 Resolution of current loop C into a network of elementary current loops	32
2.4 Image fields. (a) Point charge above a magnetic material. (b) Image charge added for calculating field above magnetic material. (c) Image charge for finding field within magnetic material	34
2.5 Uniformly magnetized sphere	36
2.6 Recording head showing field lines and magnetic charge in gap region	37
2.7 Approximation of gap charge by uniform charge sheets	38
2.8 Solenoid equivalent of charge sheets for producing head fields	39
2.9 Graphical development of a magnetic field configuration	41

Figure Number   **Page Number**

2.10 Mesh point and surrounding neighbors   43
2.11 Magnetic coupling between solenoid and enclosed loop   45
2.12 Equivalent magnetic circuit for toroid   47
2.13 Domain behavior—magnetostatic energy   51
2.14 Torque on a magnet in an external field   52
2.15 The magnetization process   54
2.16 *B–H* cyclic characteristic: ferromagnetic material   55
2.17 Single-domain particle aligned with applied field   56
2.18 Total particle energy as a function of magnetization angle θ for
      several values for applied field H 57
2.19 Hysteresis loop for single-domain particle aligned with applied
      field   58

3.1   Magnetic recording process   62
3.2   Magnetic ring head and medium, longitudinal recording   63
3.3   Idealized ring head   66
3.4 H_x and H_y in terms of angle and distances   68
3.5   Step response output signals   73
3.6   Output signal when both components of magnetization are
      present   75
3.7   Model for finite width of magnetization reversal   76
3.8   Selected path of line integral of fringing field   77
3.9   Recording process transfer function block diagram   82
3.10 Frequency response and effects of parameters   85
3.11 Azimuth alignment   86

4.1   Idealized ring head: saturation reversal   91
4.2   Graphical determination of $M_x(x)$ for a saturation reversal   92
4.3   Write field as function of current   93
4.4   Medium self-demagnetization   94
4.5 $M–H$ characteristic and demagnetizing factor   96
4.6 $M–H$ loop and parameter definitions   99
4.7   Nonlinear bit shift due to previous state of medium   105

5.1   Idealized ring head geometry   113
5.2   Attenuation of gap fringing field with spacing   116
5.3a Fringing field zones   117
5.3b Fringing field components H_x and H_y 119
5.4   Fringing field components H_x and $H_y(y' < g)$ 120
5.5   Head with finite-length pole tips   122
5.6   Probe head for perpendicular recording   123
5.7   Influence of read coil location on magnetic coupling field   123
5.8   Magnetic head circuit analog   125
5.9   Metal-in-gap (MIG) head structure   127

Figure Number   **Page Number**

5.10 Film head showing (*a*) cross section, (*b*) pole piece while
     reading, (*c*) pole piece while writing   129
5.11 Magnetoresistive sensor   131
5.12 Shielded MR head   134
5.13 Plot for two different materials of ferrite complex permeability
     versus frequency   137
5.14 Simplified equivalent electrical circuit of magnetic head   139
5.15 Write-wide read-narrow head   142
5.16 Write-wide read-narrow positioning tolerance   143

6.1 Hysteresis loop showing magnetic medium parameters   149
6.2 Noise spectra for particulate media   153
6.3 Zigzag transitions in a thin film disk at an average spacing of
     2.5 μm between transitions   155
6.4 Signal and noise spectra for thin film media   156

7.1 Digital magnetic recording channel   160
7.2 Write current waveforms for recording binary data   162
7.3 Current–voltage relations, digital magnetic recording   163
7.4 Block diagram of recording channel model   164
7.5 Gaussian pulse response waveform   166
7.6 A roll-off curve of output voltage amplitude versus pulse
     (transition) density   168
7.7 Two adjacent saturation reversals and resultant signal showing
     peak shift effect   169
7.8 Peak shift displacement s versus current reversal interval h 171
7.9 Output signal from three adjacent magnetization transitions   172
7.10 Output signal from four successive saturation reversals   172
7.11 Unique saturation reversal combinations about a given current
     switching point, including the two nearest neighbors on both
     sides   174
7.12 Pulse interference in terms of pulse width and pulse density   175
7.13 Examples of Nyquist pulses having zero intersymbol
     interference   176
7.14 Tapped delay line equalizer   177
7.15 Frequency response of pulse-slimming equalizer   180
7.16 Unequalized and equalized frequency spectra   181
7.17 NRZ and NRZI binary coding   184
7.18 Phase-encoding waveforms   185
7.19 Comparison of several RLL (d,k) codes   188
7.20 State diagram and code generation for MFM code   190
7.21 Threshold detection limits for amplitude detection of NRZI
     signals   195

Figure Number	**Page Number**

7.22 Block diagram of peak detector	196
7.23 Signal distortion from tracking tolerances	197
7.24 Differentiated signal zero-crossing	198
8.1 Johnson noise equivalent circuit and noise power density	204
8.2 Magnetization noise power spectral density. (a) Particle magnetic moment. (b) Moment autocorrelation function. (c) Power spectral density	206
8.3 Slot noise-to-signal ratio versus wave number k	207
8.4 Effective medium volume sensed by head	209
8.5 Shifting of peak detector zero-crossing by noise	210
8.6 Soft bit error rate versus detection window	214
8.7 Two-dimensional parity to correct single error	220
8.8 Layout of code words	221
8.9 Interleaving to improve burst error correction	223

DIGITAL MAGNETIC RECORDING

CHAPTER 1

MAGNETIC RECORDING AND DATA STORAGE

The expanding applications for information processing systems are increasingly dependent upon the economic availability of on-line storage of extremely large capacity. Banking and airline reservations systems are two examples of interactive on-line transaction processing that require response times of milliseconds to a very few seconds. Removable storage for backup, archives, data and software distribution and interchange, and so on, are also essential to information processing systems. The trend to communications-oriented data processing systems with remote terminals and emphasis on "real-time" response and continuous data availability greatly magnifies the importance of reliability as well as cost per megabyte and access time of storage subsystems.

High-performance magnetic disk and tape subsystems have played an essential role in meeting these needs for many years in larger computer systems. A qualitative as well as quantitative change occurred with the advent of the personal computer in the early 1980s. The PC has had an enormous impact on the growth of magnetic data storage, and particularly the hard disk drive, which has now become a standard feature of low-end systems, including laptops.

Mass storage is a term used here to identify the levels of storage outboard of main memory. Typically, three levels of storage are identified as making up a storage hierarchy. These levels of storage represent different trade-offs in terms of access time and cost per byte. The first level is main memory, magnetic disk serves as the second level, and removable magnetic tape storage is the tertiary store. The high-speed semiconductor memory interacts directly with the processor and is volatile, while both magnetic disk and tape are non-

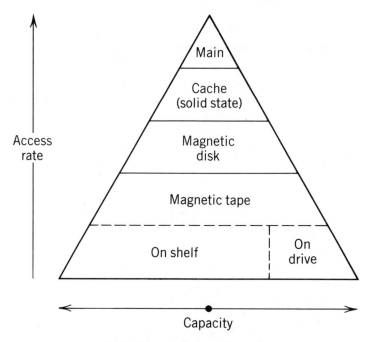

FIGURE 1.1   Storage hierarchy.

volatile. For data integrity, information in memory is frequently backed up to disk and in turn the data on disk drives, which are normally powered and operational, is backed up onto removable tape cartridges. Since cost considerations dictate that the size of electronic memory is limited, data is transferred (or staged) up and down the hierarchy to maintain a work load for the processor. While some applications, like payroll, can be scheduled and therefore their associated data fetched in a preplanned manner, many applications, especially transaction-oriented data processing, require the continuous and rapid availability of masses of data. For this reason continuing progress in rigid disk technology has become vital to the growth in new computer system applications. In the PC arena the hard disk has now become standard, whereas the magnetic floppy disk here serves the roles played by removable storage.

The storage subsystem is designed to provide an overall balance in cost/performance, since solid-state memory, offering submicrosecond access times, is much more expensive than disk, but disk drives only offer access times of a few milliseconds. Disk storage in turn is much more expensive than tape, when measured in terms of off-line storage, but with tape, access times range from seconds (if the cartridge happens to be mounted on a tape drive) to minutes when manual loading is required. Figure 1.1 shows these levels in the form of a pyramid, with the base representing capacity and the height providing a measure for access speed.

Solid-state memory provides high-speed (submicrosecond) access to any memory address location, needed for accomplishing both data and instruction manipulations by a central processor. In contrast, for mass storage, slower, mechanical devices such as disk and tape are exploited. Relative motion is, of course, required for access to storage locations. Very large capacities are practical, but access times are in milliseconds to many seconds, since mass storage devices involve mechanical movement. Disk provides on-line direct access while tape provides low cost off-line storage. The access time variability to storage locations, arising from the requisite mechanical motion, makes the structuring and data organization of mass storage a key factor to effective systems utilization. The recording density (bits per square inch) has proven to date to be principally a function of the mechanical registration tolerances that can be realized between the storage medium (or layer) and the coupling transducer. Secondly, signal-to-noise ratios become an increasing challenge with higher recording densities, particularly as track widths are reduced.

A head positioning actuator provides a single "path" to all the data on the disk surfaces it serves. With the continuing dramatic increases in areal density, the capacity associated with this path, and hence the number of associated data requests, can become so large that queuing leads to unacceptable response times. With downsizing of the disk drive and with these more modular units, the assembly of drives into arrays through sophisticated controllers is the evolving direction in storage subsystem design. For many years "disk farms" consisting of many drives have been utilized to meet total capacity needs, but each physical drive was also a logical drive. With smaller and more economical disk drives, large groups of drives can be organized to transfer data in parallel at extremely high rates, while other sets of disks are accessed independently, to maximize transaction processing rates by offering many concurrent paths to the data stored. The addition of redundant or parity drives and "hot spares" also becomes attractive as a means to assure reliability of the whole storage subsystem.

The need for operational reliability of mass storage units, devices that involve the integration of complex mechanical and electronic assemblies, has been and still remains one of the major challenges to be faced in the further development of mass storage. The need to make the store modular, to provide the design flexibility for both high transaction processing and high data transfer applications, is leading to sophisticated disk arrays where the use of redundant drives addresses the challenges of reliability, availability, and fault tolerance. Both disk and tape storage are realized by the use of magnetic recording technology. A small disk drive may contain 100 to 500 million bytes, while an automatic library-type tape subsystem will hold many terabytes of data. And technical developments now under way will materially extend these figures.

Magnetic recording storage has been generally characterized by rapid progress, achieved by evolutionary advances rather than dramatic innovation. The key breakthrough identified with the application of digital magnetic recording to the computer field is the air-bearing head.

Otherwise, advances in the magnetic recording art have largely emanated from increasingly higher precision and quality in materials, components and sophistication in mechanical and electronic packaging. No technology that might challenge the position of magnetic recording now appears in sight. Thus, an increasing effort will continue to be placed on magnetic recording and its functional integration into data storage devices.

1.1 MAGNETIC RECORDING

Magnetic recording has come into popular, general use for the recording of information only since World War II, but its invention, by the Danish engineer Valdemar Poulson, actually dates back to 1898. A magnetic recording apparatus, which used steel wire for its storage medium, was publicly demonstrated for the first time at the Paris Exposition in 1900. The recording and reproduction of sound was the initial application of magnetic recording. Despite the promise of the new technique at that time, the recorded signals could be heard only by using earphones, and sound quality was poor. Consequently, interest in magnetic recording gradually lapsed until about 1925, when the emerging possibilities of electronic amplifiers stimulated an increase in activity.

An enormous improvement in the quality of audio magnetic recording was realized in the early 1930s with the combined development of the magnetic oxide coating and the ring-type magnetic head, a device suited for recording on a surface. It was not until 1941, however, when the added innovations of superior recording techniques were combined with improved heads and media, that magnetic recording could compete with other sound-recording systems. The development of the art of magnetic recording then began to receive the vastly expanded support that was to assure its rapid growth and acceptance.

The activities that heralded the definitive introduction of the application of magnetic recording to digital data storage were initiated in 1947. This work was instigated in response to the needs of the fledgling electronic digital computer field, at this time just entering an explosive growth stage. Up until this time auxiliary storage needs were met by punched cards and paper tape. Digital magnetic recording has acquired and maintained a preeminent status for nonvolatile data storage, and the growth and use of digital magnetic recording parallel the dramatic growth of data processing.

Magnetic recording is based on the interaction between a magnetic storage medium and a magnetic head (transducer), in relative motion with respect to one another. Figure 1.2a illustrates the basic head–medium arrangement in the magnetic recording process and Figure 1.2b the nature of the recorded magnetization. The magnetic head magnetizes the magnetic material traversing through a small region immediately adjacent when recording (or writing). The head provides an induced voltage on readback, reflecting the rate of change of magnetization recorded along this magnetic path.

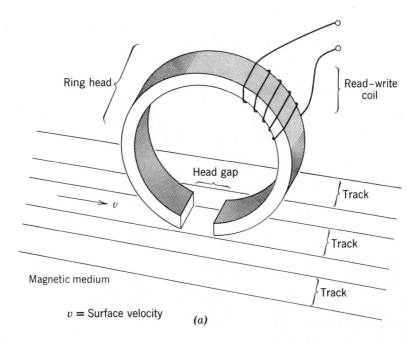

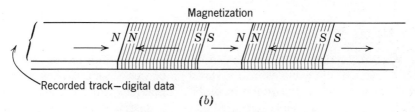

FIGURE 1.2 Magnetic recording.

Magnetic recording depends on the following characteristics of certain fer-romagnetic and ferrimagnetic materials. The storage layer must be capable of retaining a sequence of permanent magnetic states, which are directly related to the applied magnetizing field. The recorded pattern is thus stable and can be erased or modified only through rerecording. On the other hand, the trans-ducer (or magnetic head) is a device that has the basic functions of providing a confined and intense magnetizing field at the storage surface (writing), and during reading (or reproduction) essentially a magnetic flux shunting path for surface flux arising from a magnetized state of the recording medium. Both these functions dictate the need for a linear, relatively high-permeability mag-netic path (one that will retain little if any magnetization on the removal of the magnetizing source) with a short nonmagnetic section located adjacent to the magnetic surface so that the magnetic head device can couple with the storage medium through the fringing field region of the gap. For writing, a high saturation flux density is desired, whereas on reading a high permeability is wanted. Thus, an inductive magnetic head is basically a magnetically soft core possessing a gap and wound with a coil.

The path generated along the recording surface by the magnetic head is called a track. A track is therefore parallel to the direction of relative motion. The output signal from an inductive head is proportional to the rate of change of flux linking the magnetic head, and hence to the track width. Mechanical considerations have resulted in the relative motion being obtained almost exclusively by moving the surface. Surface area storage is achieved by recording tracks of information parallel to one another as indicated. Parallel tracks can be recorded by using a single head and an actuator to position the head normal to the track direction or moving a ganged set of heads both to reduce head travel as well as gain the possibility of reading and writing in parallel to improve data rate. In digital magnetic recording, where the interest is in data storage, a factor frequently of primary importance is the information density per unit area of storage surface. The storage density per unit surface area is the product of the linear density per unit track length times the track density per unit distance normal to the direction of relative motion. The two components of storage density are interrelated; as noted, an increase in track density will cause a reduction in available readback flux, which will reduce the signal-to-noise ratio at the operating linear density.

1.1.1 Modes of Recording

Three primary modes of recording can be defined, based on the direction of surface magnetization relative to the direction of track motion. These modes are: (1) longitudinal or horizontal recording, (2) perpendicular or vertical recording, and (3) transverse recording. Figure 1.3 illustrates these three modes of recording and their associated magnetic head configurations. In longitudinal recording, the principal direction of magnetization is in the plane of the surface and parallel to the direction of surface motion. In perpendicular recording, the principal orientation of the magnetization is normal to the plane of the surface. In transverse recording, the storage medium is magnetized in the plane of its surface but normal to the direction of motion between the head and surface.

Longitudinal recording is almost universally used because of certain inherent advantages. A major objective in magnetic recording is to achieve high resolution, that is, a minimum magnetic coupling zone along a track between the head and surface. A ring head with a narrow gap oriented normal to the direction of relative motion best meets this criterion. Qualitatively, it can be seen that a ring head tends to produce a more confined field than a probe head. An illustration of the form of magnetic head-to-surface coupling obtained with a ring head is given in Figure 1.4, which shows the gap field with its surrounding

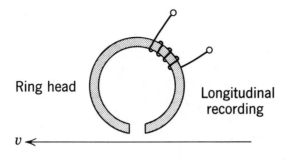

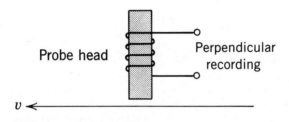

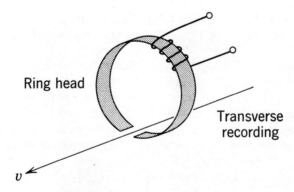

FIGURE 1.3 Modes of recording.

fringing field flux. Several geometrical parameters fundamental to the recording process are also indicated and illustrated. The gap fringing field, in particular the field that occurs in the magnetic recording medium, is the specific region of the magnetic head field of actual utility and interest. However, in the last few years major attention has been given to perpendicular recording. The primary reason is that as recording dimensions become smaller the transition width (the distance on the medium between opposite directions of saturation that occurs when the direction of write current is reversed) becomes a more important factor. This transition tends to spread due to the demagnetizing

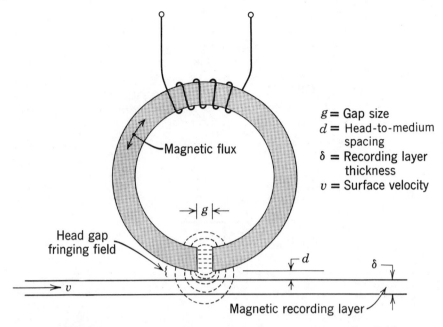

FIGURE 1.4 Ring head structure, showing magnetic coupling field.

field created by the magnetization reversal itself. The narrower the transition, the larger this demagnetizing field. The nature of magnetization reversals with a perpendicular orientation is more favorable to smaller demagnetization effects. This apparent advantage with respect to "self-demagnetization" would be expected to show up at only very small head-to-medium separations, where the spread of the fringing field is much less and the possibility to create very narrow transitions exists. Even then, head design and other issues can outweigh this projected advantage. This has been the case so far and continuing advances in the longitudinal mode of recording indicate its dominant position is still secure.

1.1.2 Magnetic Recording of Digital Information

The storage and retrieval of digital data involves the handling of discrete (or quantized) units of information, whereas in other applications of magnetic recording (e.g., conventional sound and television recording) the goal, until recently, had been to record and later reproduce as faithful a replica as possible of some continuous input signal waveform. Now, with sophisticated error correction capabilities for digital data, all advanced recording is based on digital techniques.

A binary phenomenon is exploited for the recording of digital data. This technique provides for the greatest reliability, as it maximizes the discrimination between recorded medium states, there only being two, for a given signal-to-noise ratio. Further, the recording process involves a saturation phenomenon, shown in Figure 1.5a. This gives rise to two well-defined and more easily reproducible magnetic conditions, of particular consequence when a requirement for "direct overwrite" exists, as in hard disk drives. This property arises from the hysteresis exhibited by the magnetic medium (B–H loop Figure 1.5b). This hysteretic behavior is of course responsible for the "storage" capability of magnetic recording. The two binary symbols can be associated with the two directions of in-plane magnetization, or more commonly with the existence or absence of transitions at clock periods set by the data rate on writing. The two states of "saturation" can readily be established in terms of the direction of the write current in the head coil. The writing current has one magnitude and two possible directions, generally corresponding to positive and negative saturation magnetization of the storage medium, determined by the current level at which further increases in current amplitude do not produce an appreciable increase in output voltage on readback. The actual surface magnetization arises from a very complex and nonlinear magnetization process, and the storage medium state can be inferred only by indirect means. Figure 1.6 shows the input current–output voltage relationship in digital magnetic recording.

The magnetic properties appropriate for a storage medium may be qualitatively enumerated more specifically. (A more detailed treatment of magnetostatics as it relates to magnetic recording is given in Chapter 2). The value of the maximum-energy product of the recording material $(MH)_{max}$ should be large, being a measure of the magnetostatic energy that may be stored in a unit volume of material. The induced voltage from the magnetic head on readback is proportional to M_r, the remanent magnetic state of the magnetic medium magnetization after the applied write field is removed. Hence, a large value for this parameter is normally desired. The coercive force H_c is a measure of the ability of the magnetic medium to hold its magnetism in the presence of demagnetizing fields. The strength of the final demagnetizing field is, however, proportional to the level of medium magnetization. Thus, the magnetization level that remains, M_r, depends on both H_c and M. The coercive force of the medium then needs to be high to limit the reduction in recorded magnetization from the originally saturated magnetization state created by the head field. Therefore, it can be that the output signal will be proportional to H_c rather than to M_s, the saturation magnetic moment of the recording medium. A rectangular hysteresis loop is important, as it causes the region of transition switching to be localized to where the write field equals H_c.

For writing, the magnetic head should have a reasonably high permeability so that essentially all the applied ampere-turns contribute to the gap field; a high saturation flux density, thereby assuring that saturation of the recording medium will occur before the head core itself saturates; and the residual magnetization of the magnetic head core should be quite small, so that there will be no fields that could affect the surface when the head is not energized.

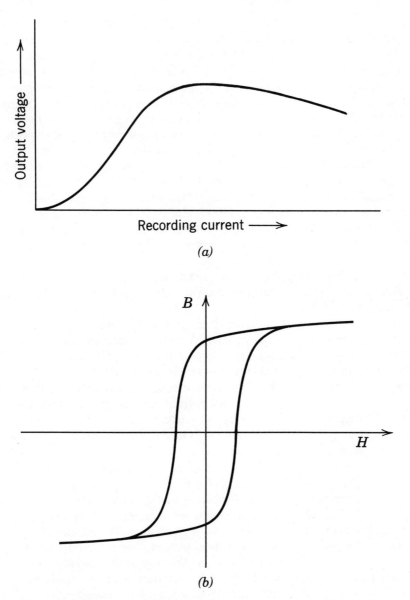

FIGURE 1.5 Magnetic saturation hysteresis phenomena.

The magnetic properties desired for reading include high-frequency response as well as a high permeability.

The inherent differentiation of the recorded magnetization on readback gives a series of alternating voltage pulses, one pulse for each change in direction of surface saturation, for the voltage waveform characterizing digital magnetic recording. The readback of binary information conventionally re-

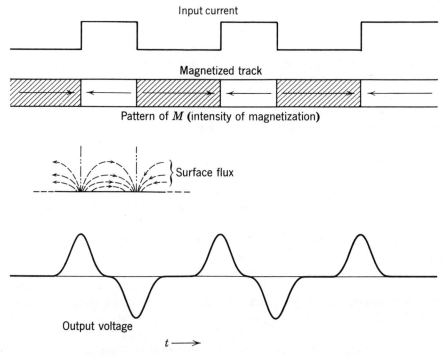

FIGURE 1.6   Input current–output voltage relationship.

quires the capability during each bit period to recognize from an attribute of the recovered waveform the associated bit value. In digital magnetic recording, signal detection techniques receive great attention, particularly where high densities are of interest. Chapter 7, "Digital Recording Techniques," treats this subject in detail. Important aspects of magnetic recording for digital storage are the unlimited reusability of a magnetic storage medium, barring physical damage (this property permits the direct modification of stored information); nonvolatility, that is, the data does not require regeneration for its preservation; and information transfer (reading and writing) occurring directly in the form of electrical signals with obtainable bit rates in the range of tens to hundreds of megabits per second. General advantages of magnetic recording media over other potential storage media include the simplicity of the recording transducer (a magnetic head); the flexibility in mechanical structure possible (for different performance criteria) arising from the ability to place a magnetic layer on almost any supporting surface—in conjunction with the relative simplicity of creating an air bearing for spacing a magnetic head; and considerable ruggedness with respect to handling and environmental conditions. These features of the magnetic recording process contribute enormously to its attractiveness as a storage means. Associated with these attributes is an extreme economy in terms of cost per bit of storage.

1.2 MAGNETIC DATA STORAGE DEVICES

In digital magnetic recording, the bit storage density is principally a function of the spacing and registration tolerances that can be realized between the magnetic storage surface(s) and associated magnetic head(s). Although very large capacities can be realized economically, on-line access times to data are in the range of milliseconds to many seconds (with tape), since this type of storage involves mechanical movement for data access. Access time to a given storage location is variable, depending on the relative position of the desired surface region with respect to the read/write magnetic head at the time of a sector address seek. The ability to obtain a spectrum of mass storage performance specifications through variations in mechanical structure accounts for the extraordinary innovation in this field of application of digital magnetic recording.

The present and potential proliferation of mass storage structures makes a presentation of specific devices of questionable value in developing a perspective for digital magnetic recording. Rather than a discussion of specific hardware, a few generalizations on the nature of structural embodiments of mass storage, reflecting upon the characteristics of the digital magnetic recording of data, will be given here.

Figure 1.7 is a simplified illustration of a disk drive that will serve as a vehicle for presenting the manner in which performance requirements impact design. The disk sectors shown represent addressable locations along the tracks. The maximum data transfer rate is equal to the product of linear bit density times surface velocity. For most disk drives a constant data rate is used, so that the actual linear density will be a function of the track radius. For constant data rate systems the optimum ratio, in terms of maximizing capacity, of inner diameter to outer diameter of the recording band is 1/2. In zone bit recording the data rate increases with radius, for example, being increased at each larger radius where an additional sector can be included on the track. This method takes advantage of available technology to write and read data over the whole recording band at a density close to the maximum possible.

In addition to capacity, access time is of great importance. Access time is composed of a seek time, a latency time, and a data transfer time for a specified block size. As disk drive performance has improved, the overhead time associated with the interface protocols in handling data transfers to the disk has become relatively more significant and this factor is now also being included in speaking of the overall access time. The seek time is the time to reposition the head from one track to another, including the settling time required for the head to be able to write or read. The average seek distance for randomly located data on the disk surface is one-third the maximum (inner diameter of the recording band to outer diameter). For actual applications the average seek distance will be much less than this average owing to the locality associated with data usage. The latency is the time, once the head is on track, for the desired sector to pass by the head so that the sector can be written or

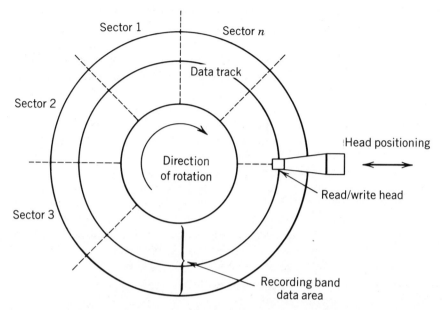

FIGURE 1.7 Elementary digital recording unit (disk).

read. Thus, the average latency time is one-half the time for a revolution of the disk. In addition to these intrinsic delays, there is only one access path to all the data serviced by this head. Accordingly, with frequent read and write or I/O requests to the disk drive, in addition to an inherent access time there will be a delay time due to queuing. The drive response time in servicing requests as seen by the host computer therefore can be much worse than expected from the access time parameter.

Another performance parameter of great interest, although not independent of the choice of capacity and access time, is the data transfer rate. The actual file data transfer rate depends on the disk track formatting (sector, synchronizing bits, address ID, etc.) and location and degree of fragmentation of the file (location of sectors allocated to its storage). There is an instantaneous or maximum data transfer rate associated with reading one sector (or consecutive sectors on a track) and a lower number associated with the transfer of arbitrarily selected files. Systems designers try to optimize storage organization and usage around the random plus sequential capabilities that are inherent in a mechanically accessed disk device. There is a wide time differential between reading the next sector coming up on a track and accessing a sector address chosen at random. These access characteristics make performance highly application-dependent and highlight the desirability of a random–sequential data processing philosophy for mass storage exploitation.

Two distinct application categories often used in characterizing disk systems are transaction-oriented processing systems and large data transfer applications such as image processing. The former puts a high premium on response time (or access rate), while the latter requires a high sustained data transfer rate. Thus, storage systems performance includes much more than the storage hardware capabilities. The use of solid-state memory as a cache (or buffer) for disk devices also provides another reference from which to evaluate disk drive design trade-offs, since a cache offers the opportunity to mask some of the mechanical access limitations from the host computer.

Disk I/O transfers involve both read and write operations. A solid-state cache, by holding many records from the disk locality where transaction activity is occurring, greatly reduces the number of I/O accesses to the disk. The cache then can greatly improve performance. However, for write operations there is a need to record updates to a nonvolatile store to protect against system crashes or power outages. Consequently, unless the cache has a battery backup, disk write I/O transfers still see the mechanical delays associated with disk drive hardware. The advances in sophisticated storage subsystems design should keep the performance of mass storage compatible with the advances in microprocessors and memory and continue the key role played by magnetic data storage in information processing systems.

1.2.1 Technology Objectives

Two critical aims in mass storage technology are to (1) increase storage density and (2) reduce access time. The bit resolution, which sets the linear density, of a magnetic head–magnetic surface combination depends on their proximity. Actual physical contact offers the highest potential recording resolution (or bit density). However, in so-called contact recording (e.g., with magnetic tape) some wear is accepted. This wear is defined in terms of the minimum number of passes guaranteed for the tape and in number of hours of life for the magnetic head. In hard disk drives such limitations are not acceptable and hence an extremely small spacing is sought in which no performance degradation from usage will arise over the life of the product, even with continuous operation. Thus, wear processes must be small enough to satisfy this criterion, and it is customary to refer to recording under such conditions as noncontact recording. Accordingly, the term "contact" in recording is defined more by measurable wear than "zero" spacing. In disk recording, spacings are already below 0.2 microns, which is much less than the wavelength of visible light!

The other factor in setting storage density is the track density. The track density is influenced by both the capabilities of the servo system to maintain head-to-track registration and the signal-to-noise ratio obtainable as we go to narrower and narrower track (and head) widths. The readback signal amplitude is proportional to head width; there are four major noise sources, the medium, the head, preamplifier electronics, and adjacent track interference due to head-track misregistration. Two approaches being explored that represent significant departures from present practice are (1) the development of a magnetoresistive (MR) head that offers higher signal output than the conventional inductive head at higher densities and (2) the use of head structures that permit wide write and narrow read as a means to reduce sensitivity to head registration problems. The second was an approach commonly used years ago but which was abandoned with increasing areal densities due to the difficulties of aligning the head elements needed. Track density is a function of "signal-to-noise" issues that involve not only the head–medium magnetics but the limitations imposed by off-track capabilities and track misregistration on writing and reading in general.

1.2.2 The Beginning

The work that ushered in mass data storage was firmly established by 1947. This activity was associated and concurrent with the explosive "takeoff" of the digital computer field at that time. Since then, progress has paralleled the rapidly expanding growth of data processing. Early work was oriented to the scientific computer market. The initial mass memory device developed was the digital magnetic tape transport, to provide both auxiliary "backup" storage to main memory and buffering between the computer and low-speed electromechanical equipment in large-scale systems. In this latter application, tape served as an intermediate medium to permit better matching of the high data transfer rate of a computer to its low-speed printers, card equipment, and so on. The later emergence of commercial data processing brought a wider variety of functional usages and mass storage hardware.

Commercial or business data processing, as it was evolving as a main facet of activity in the computer field in the early 1950s, gave a tremendous impetus to mass storage development and had a major impact on its direction. File storage for records maintenance was the central requirement. The volume of business records certainly justified the introduction of the descriptor "mass."

Magnetic tape was immediately exploited for storing huge files of records. Tape transports inherently are suited for serial access to information, and conventional batch processing procedures (punched card methods) were therefore instituted. The procedure in brief is to sort all requests for file reference into the same order as that in which the basic or master set of records is maintained. Then the master record file tape need be scanned only once (one pass) during the processing run. However, a major percentage of available computer machine time is then needed for such tape processing activity as sorting and collating. For low activity, tape devices are very inefficient. The entire master tape file must be examined no matter how few records are actually referenced. Further, effective file inquiry operations are not possible. The handling of an inquiry involves a momentary interruption of the normal processing to answer an urgent request. To keep head and surface wear down to acceptable rates in contact recording, tape speed is limited, representing a restriction on access time. Tape speed is also restricted by tape handling problems such as

FIGURE 1.8   RAMAC.

acceleration, deceleration, and maintaining close tolerances on velocity when searching for particular records.

The character of much business data processing thus indicated the need for an entirely different type of mass storage. The desirability of storing large volumes of information with any record available rapidly gave stimulus to the development of a mass "random access" storage device. The term "random access" implies that all address locations can be reached in the same time, which is not true of any mechanical means of access. Thus, the term "direct access" came to be used as well as DASD, standing for direct access storage device, implying that the access is more or less directly to the desired record, without the necessity of scanning through all intervening records located between the present address and the desired address (as must be done for tape). A short (average) access time is then necessary, and a high-speed rotating surface provides this feature. The extremely high surface velocity then arising is only tolerable by providing a slight separation or spacing between the magnetic head(s) and moving surface. This spacing must, however, be quite small if the concurrent requirement of high capacity is to be realized. The air-bearing supported head (using an air cushion to control head-to-surface spacing) was the technical innovation that, combined with the above storage concept, brought about this entirely new family of mass storage devices beginning in 1956. By this novel spacing technique, it was possible to develop a high-capacity rotating disk stack, for a head could then closely follow the appreciable fluctuation of large disks (a disk stack permits a high ratio for magnetic surface area per unit volume).

This air-bearing development, concerned with the magnetic head carrier and its suspension, permits a magnetic head effectively to ride on a cushion of air (the boundary layer) carried along by the moving surface. It has been possible by this means not only for the head to "follow" gross surface fluctuation but to maintain itself at an extremely small spacing from the surface. Initially, the air bearing used pressurized air fed out of nozzles in the head carrier, to be soon superseded by the self-acting slider air bearing, which uses the boundary layer of air carried by the moving surface. Here the term "small" implies a spacing in the range of millionths of an inch. There has been a broad extension in the types of storage devices and in the range of performance features available as a consequence of the introduction of the air-bearing principle.

The first disk file (the IBM RAMAC 350) (Figure 1.8) could store 5 million characters with a maximum access time to any record of less than a second. Note that a single head pair (one head unit for the upper disk face and one for the lower) is mechanically positioned to service all the tracks within the disk stack. This design required a large air compressor to supply air to the head. Secondary technical features of significance were the use of self-clocking (deriving bit timing signals from the data itself on readback) and a wide-erase narrow-read/write head unit. This head unit was a special two-element magnetic head structure that included an erase unit that would create erased guardbands (either just in front of or immediately behind the read/write head) so that precise lateral alignment of the read/write head was not required. These design approaches, combined with the use of an air-supported head, provided techniques that compensate for the head-to-track registration tolerances of such a gross mechanical structure, and therefore permit high bit density and high track density, both necessary for a large capacity. The introduction of the "flying" head eliminated the need for an external air supply and made it feasible to place one or more such heads per surface. Then only one head positioning direction was needed and the access time could be immediately reduced by an order of magnitude.

1.2.3 Current Trends

The increase in storage density has been and continues to be the pacing factor in disk and tape technology. Progress in disk storage is most closely linked to lower flying heights using thin film media, new head materials and fabrication methods, and improvements in closed-loop servo systems for track following. The state of the art in flying height has reached 0.2 microns and many advanced studies are being conducted from 0.1 microns to "contact." Thin film and metal-in-gap ferrite heads have greatly increased the coercive force that can be used for the storage medium, with 1000 to 2500 Oersteds now becoming common. And a higher coercive force directly translates into narrower transitions and higher density. Track-following servo systems using single-element inductive read/write heads are now in the range of 1500 to 2500 tracks per inch. These capabilities mean that as we enter the decade of the 1990s the state-of-the art storage density is almost 10^8 bits per square inch.

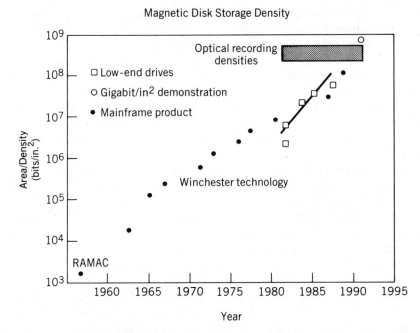

FIGURE 1.9   Density versus time—disk storage.

Looking at the rate of progress over time (Figure 1.9), it can be seen that over 35 years there has been a fairly steady increase in storage density by a factor of 4 to 5 every five years. The more impressive fact, however, is that this rate of advance should continue for at least another decade, leading to products with densities of a gigabit or more per square inch by the year 2000. Many research directions have yet to be exploited. The increase in density has allowed very large capacities to be realized in a small volume. As a consequence, there has been a continuing downsizing in form factor; from 14-inch diameter disks to the current volume leader, the 3.5-inch drive. For low-end applications, 100 to 500 megabytes can be obtained in this size drive, and this in many instances may be more capacity than currently needed. This in turn will make attractive even smaller-diameter disk drive packages. For larger applications, the advantages of multiple paths to the data for throughput and data rate are leading to implementing systems that require gigabytes of disk storage with many small disks. As densities go even higher, this trend will continue. Cost of storage is approaching one dollar per megabyte (OEM). Small-diameter drives are packaging wonders, where, with the emergence of laptop and notebook computers, capacity per unit volume and per watt of power consumption have become key performance measures and battery operation is essential. The standard low-end PC or laptop now includes a 40 to 80 megabyte drive, something undreamed of only a few years ago. Never has the magnetic disk drive industry been growing as rapidly, been able to support such large investments in research and development, been able to put in place such major manufacturing facilities as now. The future looks bright for the industry and, given the ability of users to absorb capacity increases as long as the economics are favorable, this situation should continue.

1.2.4 The Future

In addition to the ongoing progress described above, there are new advances on the horizon that should stimulate further technology advances beyond those being seen today. One is the magnetoresistive head that offers more output at the higher densities than inductive heads and hence a better signal-to-noise ratio. Although the MR head is a read-only element, its film processing features lend to the design of multielement head structures that can again offer such options as "wide-write narrow-read" to compensate for registration tolerances. In the future, higher track densities will require a continuous servo error signal integrated with the data head, such as is achieved with optical storage by pregrooving the substrate. Thus, patterned disks and head devices that include servo elements, or the use of optical servo components mounted with the head, should bring about track densities approaching the range of 10,000 tracks per inch. Another focus in the future will be on "contact" recording using very lightly loaded heads. In time it may be feasible to implement online direct access storage devices this way as the understanding of materials and wear phenomena advances and the future requirements for data storage systems evolve. Even without this step, as spacings approach the range of 0.05 microns, linear densities well above 100,000 bits per inch will be realized. Signal detection techniques will move toward pattern matching concepts where multibit waveforms will be interpreted, providing another avenue to obtain density gains. Sophisticated error correction and detection techniques represent yet another opportunity for further progress that has yet to be fully explored. Hence digital magnetic recording still has a large untapped potential in further meeting the storage needs being generated by new applications becoming possible through computer advances, remarkable progress being made in semiconductor technology, new system architectures, and programming. Accordingly, all signs point to digital magnetic recording remaining the predominant means for mass storage well into the next century with storage densities exceeding 10^9 bits per square inch.

1.3 ALTERNATIVE TECHNOLOGIES

While digital magnetic recording holds a dominant role in meeting the needs of data storage, there is no lack of effort directed to alternative technological approaches that are believed able to challenge or displace this "moving target." One that was aggressively pursued before being abandoned was magnetic bubbles. The two most active alternatives at this time are magneto-optical recording and various versions of high-density semiconductor-type memory.

Solid-state memory is advancing very rapidly, with 4 megabit chips becoming available as we move into the 1990s. As long as magnetic recording technology continues to move at an approximately similar rate to semiconductors, its advantages in cost per bit will be maintained. Therefore, with the growth in storage demand exceeding technology progress, disk and tape storage will always find an important role in mass storage due to economic considerations.

Optical recording disks offer high density and removability. The major problem facing the technology has been to achieve erasability (rewrite) in order to match the update capability provided by magnetic recording. In recent years significant progress has been in magneto-optic materials and such optical drives are now being made commercially available with up to a gigabyte or more of storage on a disk. However, in this period magnetic disk drives have advanced to where they can offer the same or greater capacity with far lower cost and far better access and data rate performance. This arises both from the favorable mechanical characteristics of magnetic disk implementations as well as the huge market size and manufacturing volumes of magnetic recording devices. However, optical disk devices do offer removable storage of very high capacity which is not available in magnetic recording except in the form of magnetic tape. Consequently, the real opportunity for the emergence of optical storage would appear to be those applications in which magnetic tape today is considered the mainstream approach or in new applications where no technology is established and optics can capitalize on the access advantages arising from a removable disk format. Since magnetic tape is also progressing rapidly, primarily driven by the field of consumer electronics (the VCR, camcorder, digital audiotape, etc.), optical recording faces a difficult challenge. Whether optical recording can secure more than a niche market is a question yet to be answered.

1.4 SUMMARY

Digital magnetic recording is unique as an application for magnetic recording, both in the scope and character of the recording conditions under which it is applied. The performance demanded in digital magnetic recording is extreme, for each bit of information is an important entity in its own right and the desired maximum storage capacities and minimum access times seemingly have no bound. (There will always be additional data of value to incorporate within an information processing system if economically feasible.) Particular attention is given in this book to provide a conceptual and basic physical understanding of this form of data storage that has become so vital and critical to the advances in information processing systems. Most on-line transaction-oriented applications, such as airline reservation systems, would not be conceivable without the capabilities offered by the hard disk drive. Thus, the primary focus will be on digital magnetic recording applied to disk, although the principles and analysis are equally valid for all embodiments of the technology for data storage.

The book will provide a basic background in the magnetic theory related to magnetic recording and then cover the recording process, reading and writing, the head and media components, the magnetic recording channel, and coding and error correction techniques relevant to this form of data storage. The basic considerations that set both linear and track densities are a key focus of the development.

REFERENCES

Pioneer Work

1. "IBM Magnetic Tape Reader and Recorder," W. S. Buslik, *Proceedings of the Eastern Joint Computer Conference*, New York, December 10–12, 1952, pp. 86–90.
2. "Notched-Disk Memory," J. Rabinow, *Electr. Eng.*, Vol. 71, pp. 745–749, August 1952.
3. "Photographic Techniques for Information Storage," G. W. King, G. W. Brown, and L. N. Ridenour, *Proc. IRE*, Vol. 41, pp. 1421–1428, October 1953.
4. "Air Floating, a New Principle in Magnetic Recording of Information," G. E. Hanen, *Comput. Autom.*, Vol. 2, pp. 23–25, November 1953.
5. "Engineering Design of a Magnetic-Disk Random-Access Memory," T. Noyes and W. E. Dickinson, *Proceedings of the Western Joint Computer Conference*, San Francisco, February 7–9, 1956, pp. 42–44.
6. "Datafile—A New Tool for Extensive File Storage," D. N. MacDonald, *Proceedings of the Eastern Joint Computer Conference*, New York, December 10–12, 1956, pp. 124–127.
7. "The Random-Access Memory Accounting Machine, System Organization," M. L. Lesser and J. W. Haanstra, *IBM J. Res. Dev.*, Vol. 1, pp. 62–71, January 1957.
8. "Addressing for Random-Access Storage," W. W. Peterson, *IBM J. Res. Dev.*, Vol. 1, pp. 130–146, April 1957.
9. "A High Track Density Servo Access System for Magnetic Recording Disk Storage," A. S. Hoagland, *IBM J. Res. Dev.*, Vol. 5, pp. 287–296, October 1961.

Other Material

1. *Digital Magnetic Recording*, A. S. Hoagland, Wiley, New York, 1963 (reprinted 1983), 154 pp.
2. *The Complete Handbook of Magnetic Recording*, F. Jorgenson, TAB Books, Blue Ridge Summit, PA, 1988, 740 pp.
3. *Computer Storage Systems and Technology*, R. E. Matick, Wiley, New York, 1977, 667 pp.
4. *Inside the IBM PC*, P. Norton, Prentice-Hall, Englewood Cliffs, NJ, 1983, 302 pp.

5. *Digital Computers' Memory Storage*, D. D. Majumder and J. Das, Wiley, New York, 1984.

6. "Information Storage Technology—A Look to the Future," A. S. Hoagland, *Computer (IEEE)*, pp. 60–67, July 1985.

7. "A Quarter Century of Disk File Innovation," J. Harker et al., *IBM Jour. Res. Devel.*, Vol. 25, No. 5, pp. 701–710, September 1981. (This special issue also contains papers on disk file manufacturing and the original diskette drive.)

CHAPTER 2

PRINCIPLES OF MAGNETICS

This chapter presents a review of the principles of magnetics, oriented to the fundamentals relevant to a satisfactory understanding of the digital magnetic recording process. Primary emphasis is given to concepts and mathematical tools useful in dealing with macroscopic magnetic phenomena. A brief treatment of the physical basis for ferromagnetic behavior is included, serving to relate the internal structure of magnetic materials to their external properties.

While magnetic phenomena are generally highly nonlinear, many problems are tractable to conventional mathematical formulation, where piecewise linearity is assumed. The principles presented in this chapter have been extremely valuable, in both a qualitative and a quantitative sense, in yielding a theoretical base for digital magnetic recording. This success is due both to careful analysis of the nature of the problem and to recognition of various ranges within which a valid mathematical model can be constructed. It is as important to be aware of the inherent limitations of the concepts and mathematical relations developed, as well as of their fundamental meaning and significance.

This chapter attempts to organize and present a set of concepts and relations providing a coherent treatment of the subject, rather than to cover only those aspects explicitly introduced in the subsequent chapters. Magnetic fields involve vector quantities, and some familiarity with vector notation and analysis is assumed in the material to follow.

2.1 HISTORICAL BACKGROUND

Before Oersted's discovery in 1820 that an electric current would affect a magnetic needle, magnetism as a branch of physical science was completely independent of the theory of electricity. Following this discovery, Ampere quickly investigated, both experimentally and mathematically, the mutual forces between currents and showed (1825) that a current in a circuit is equivalent to a "magnetic shell" with strength determined by the current. He considered that a "magnet" gives rise to an external magnetic field produced by circulating electrical currents within the molecules of the material. This concept, though not immediately accepted because there was no way to prove or disprove it, stood the test of time and was elaborated upon only by the advent of electron theory.

We shall find it most advantageous to approach the subject of magnetics in terms of its association with current flow. Ampere's law gives the relation governing the force that one current-carrying conductor will exert on another and serves as the basis for the definition of a magnetic field. A current element is a vector, that is, it possesses both magnitude and direction, and therefore the force equation involves vector quantities. Equations are derived in the SI system of units. Values of field quantities are occasionally given in the cgs–emu system of units which has historically been the standard used in magnetic recording. Boldface type is used to distinguish a vector quantity from a scalar quantity.

The force on a differential length of conductor, $d\mathbf{l}_1$, carrying a current i_1, is

$$dF = i_1\, d\mathbf{l}_1 \times \mathbf{B} \tag{2.1}$$

where $\mathbf{B}$ is defined in terms of this force and is called the magnetic flux density or magnetic induction. $\mathbf{B}$ is a field related to the current in a second length of conductor by the following equation:

$$d\mathbf{B} = \frac{\mu_0}{4\pi}\frac{i_2\, d\mathbf{l}_2 \times \mathbf{r}}{r^3} \tag{2.2}$$

The vector distance from the current element $i_2\, d\mathbf{l}_2$ to the point at which $d\mathbf{B}$ is to be determined is $\mathbf{r}$. μ_0 is a constant defined as the permeability of free space. The vectors given by both these equations are the result of a vector or cross-product operation, symbolized by $\times$, and accordingly are perpendicular to the plane described by the component vectors of the product (Figure 2.1). The total field arising from a complete current loop is obtained by integration, summing up the contributions from the differential current elements.

For example, equation (2.2) may be readily applied to calculate the field produced at the center of a circular current loop. In this instance, r is equal to a, the radius of the loop; $d\mathbf{l}$ and $\mathbf{r}$ are mutually perpendicular, so that their

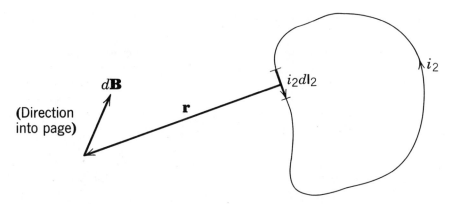

FIGURE 2.1 Incremental field arising from a current element.

cross product is merely $a\,dl$ and all the differential contributions $d\mathbf{B}$ are parallel (and hence directly additive).

For a sector $d\theta$ of a circle $dl = a\,d\theta$ (where θ is in radians)

$$d\mathbf{B} = \frac{\mu_0 i}{4\pi}\frac{(a\,d\theta)}{a^2}\mathbf{a_n} \tag{2.3}$$

where $\mathbf{a_n}$ is a unit vector perpendicular to the plane of the current loop. Integrating to find $\mathbf{B}$ gives

$$\mathbf{B} = \mathbf{a_n}\frac{\mu_0 i}{4\pi a}\int_0^{2\pi} d\theta = \frac{\mu_0 i}{2a}\mathbf{a_n} \tag{2.4}$$

The above phenomena are concerned with static or quasistatic currents. In 1829, Joseph Henry, while experimenting with an electromagnet, noticed the spark that occurred when the circuit was broken, and he was led to the discovery of self-induction. The same phenomenon was independently discovered by Michael Faraday, who was the first to publish results. These discoveries led to the formulation of the law governing the relation between induced voltage and the rate of change of flux linkages, usually known as Faraday's law of induction. This relation can be written as follows:

$$e = \frac{-N\,d\Phi}{dt} \tag{2.5}$$

where Φ is the total flux linking the circuit, which can be directly determined from the flux density $\mathbf{B}$. N is equal to the number of turns composing the loop or coil. The negative sign is consistent with Lenz's law so that the polarity of the induced voltage would produce currents and fields opposing Φ.

The experimentally derived laws of electricity and magnetism were formulated and combined systematically in mathematical equations by James Clerk Maxwell, whose famous treatise was published in 1873.

2.2 MAGNETIC FIELD RELATIONS

We can accommodate magnetic materials in the extensions of the theory given by considering them to give rise to magnetic fields through microscopic "magnetization" currents within their internal structure. This latter concept is consistent with the absence of free magnetic charge in nature. However, since we cannot actually measure such currents, it is necessary to define magnetic properties in terms of the resulting magnetic field arising from the presence of magnetic media.

Current flow is continuous, or more generally, the current density is everywhere solenoidal. Then from the form of the expression for **B** in equation (2.2) we can express this field vector as follows:

$$\mathbf{B} = \nabla \times \mathbf{A} \tag{2.6}$$

where **A** is called the magnetic vector potential. Since the divergence of the curl of a vector is identically zero, we can write

$$\nabla \cdot \mathbf{B} = 0 \tag{2.7}$$

This equation expresses a differential relation for the field vector **B**. The symbol $\nabla\cdot$ denotes "the divergence of." The symbol ∇ is a vector derivative operator, and the dot indicates a scalar or dot product. This equation is another way of stating that the flux density is everywhere continuous, there being no sources or sinks for **B**.

Gauss's theorem (for generalized vector fields) gives

$$\int_v \nabla \cdot \mathbf{B}\, dv = \oint_s \mathbf{B} \cdot d\mathbf{s} \tag{2.8}$$

Here, v indicates a volume, and s indicates the enclosing surface. Considering the divergence of any vector as a density of outward flux flow from a point for that vector, the total flux emanating from a closed region must be obtained by integrating the divergence throughout the volume. Thus,

$$\oint_s \mathbf{B} \cdot d\mathbf{s} = 0 \tag{2.9}$$

This integral can be interpreted as expressing the fact that the net magnetic flux flowing through a closed surface is zero. In addition, since **B** is to be defined only in terms of current sources, based on equation (2.2),

$$\nabla \times \mathbf{B} = \mu_0 \mathbf{j} \tag{2.10}$$

where $\nabla \times \mathbf{B}$ is the curl of **B**, and **j** is the current density at a given point. The integral form of this relation is

$$\oint \mathbf{B} \cdot d\mathbf{l} = \mu_0 I \qquad\qquad \text{Stokes} \tag{2.11}$$

or, the line integral of **B** around any closed path is equal to μ_0 times the *total* current enclosed.

This latter expression, for example, permits ready calculation of the field at a distance r from an infinitely long straight wire carrying a current I. Selecting a circular path at a distance r from the wire, we have (symmetry indicating that $\mathbf{B} = B_\phi$ and is only a function of r)

$$\oint \mathbf{B} \cdot d\mathbf{l} = \int_0^{2\pi} B(r) r \, d\phi = B \cdot 2\pi r = \mu_0 I \tag{2.12}$$

or

$$B = \frac{\mu_0 I}{2\pi r} \tag{2.13}$$

where $B = B_\phi$, encircling the wire.

In a magnetic medium the current density **j** may arise from two contributing sources, that is,

$$\nabla \times \mathbf{B} = \mu_0 (\mathbf{j}_t + \mathbf{j}_m) \tag{2.14}$$

where $\mathbf{j}_t$ is a measurable (or true) conduction current density and $\mathbf{j}_m$ is a so-called magnetization current density accounting for the presence of the magnetic medium. We can set

$$\mathbf{j}_m = \nabla \times \mathbf{M} \tag{2.15}$$

where **M** is defined as the magnetic moment per unit volume or intensity of magnetization of the material. It should be recalled that the basic experimental quantity measured in determining the presence of magnetism in an object is torque exerted on the magnetic dipole moment of the object by a uniform external field. Rewriting equation (2.14) we have

$$\nabla \times (\mathbf{B} - \mu_0 \mathbf{M}) = \mu_0 \mathbf{j}_t \tag{2.16}$$

Let us now define a new magnetic field vector **H** as follows:

$$\mathbf{H} = \frac{1}{\mu_0} (\mathbf{B} - \mu_0 \mathbf{M}) \tag{2.17}$$

or

$$\mathbf{B} = \mu_0 (\mathbf{H} + \mathbf{M}) \tag{2.18}$$

then

$$\nabla \times \mathbf{H} = \mathbf{j}_t \tag{2.19}$$

We have by this means defined a magnetic field quantity (H = magnetic field intensity) whose curl or circulation density is dependent only on the true currents in the system. The integral form of equation (2.19) is

Stokes

$$\oint \mathbf{H} \cdot d\mathbf{l} = I \tag{2.20}$$

By the approach taken here, it is seen that **B** is taken to be the fundamental magnetic field vector and **H** is a derived quantity. This procedure is more in accord with the true nature of magnetic field sources, although one can also start with **H** as the basic magnetic field quantity. The latter perspective results if magnetic fields are postulated starting from the premise of the existence of magnetic poles or charges, drawing a correspondence with the electrostatic field. It will be found mathematically convenient to use both of these magnetic field vectors as basic concepts with which to deal with the diverse problems encountered in applied magnetics. Again, they are distinguished by the fact that the circulation density of the **H** field arises from true currents, and that of the **B** field arises from true currents plus magnetization currents. Since the postulated magnetization currents exist only within magnetic media (to account for their magnetic behavior), the vectors **B** and **H** only differ essentially within magnetic regions. If we take the divergence of both sides of equation (2.18) we have

$$\nabla \cdot \mathbf{H} = -\nabla \cdot \mathbf{M} \tag{2.21}$$

since, as already shown,

$$\nabla \cdot \mathbf{B} = 0 \tag{2.22}$$

Thus, a magnetic field intensity vector **H** can be thought of as arising from magnetic charge source density ρ_m where

$$\rho_m = -\nabla \cdot \mathbf{M} \tag{2.23}$$

in addition to any field originating from current sources. One unit of this equivalent magnetic charge density is usually known as a magnetic pole. In terms of this definition, a magnetic pole has no physical justification, other than that the mathematical description of the field **H** from magnetic material is then formally the same as that for the electrical field due to electrical charges.

In terms of this definition of magnetic charge density, **H** may be expressed as

$$\mathbf{H} = \frac{1}{4\pi} \int_v \frac{\rho_m \, dv \, \mathbf{r}}{|r|^3} \tag{2.24}$$

In the absence of current sources,

$$\nabla \times \mathbf{H} = 0 \tag{2.25}$$

This condition implies that the magnetic field intensity can be derived from a scalar magnetic potential function.

Thus, we can set

$$\mathbf{H} = -\nabla \phi_m \tag{2.26}$$

where ϕ_m is a scalar. This latter fact is extremely important, since it is far easier to deal with scalar quantities. When **H** is expressed as the gradient of a scalar,

$$\int_a^b \mathbf{H} \cdot d\mathbf{l} = \int_a^b d\phi_m = \phi_m(b) - \phi_m(a) \tag{2.27}$$

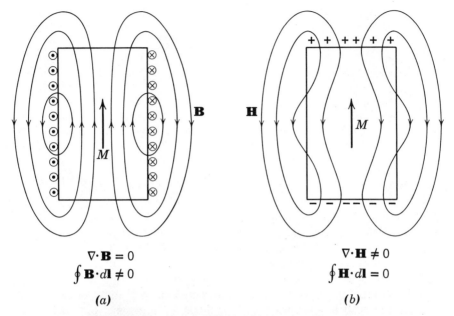

$\nabla\cdot\mathbf{B} = 0$ $\nabla\cdot\mathbf{H} \neq 0$

$\oint\mathbf{B}\cdot d\mathbf{l} \neq 0$ $\oint\mathbf{H}\cdot d\mathbf{l} = 0$

(a)   (b)

FIGURE 2.2   **B** and **H** fields of a permanent magnet.

Therefore, a line integral is only a function of the potential difference between its end points and independent of the path. For a closed path,

$$\oint \mathbf{H} \cdot d\mathbf{l} = 0 \tag{2.28}$$

Recall that we are considering only **H** fields originating from magnetized materials. To illustrate the relation between the magnetic field vectors, we shall consider qualitatively the fields associated with a circular cylinder (Figure 2.2) homogeneously magnetized in the direction of its axis. We will assume **M** to be independent of external fields. From equation (2.14),

$$\nabla \times \mathbf{B} = \mu_0 \nabla \times \mathbf{M} \tag{2.29}$$

because $\mathbf{j_t} = 0$.

The curl of **M** is zero except on the curved surface of the cylinder where the magnetization **M** changes discontinuously from **M** to zero. All internal magnetization currents cancel, and the hypothetical surface currents are the only effective magnetization current sources. Further, the divergence of **M** is equal to zero except on the two end faces, where on one end there is a surface divergence of amount $+M$ and on the other end $-M$.

B, the magnetic flux density, can then be viewed as arising from an equivalent solenoid, which can be thought of as being wound on the cylindrical surface of the magnet. The lines of force thus resulting are shown in Figure 2.2a. On the other hand, **H** can be considered as arising from two layers of

TABLE 2.1   Magnetic Units

Name	Quantity	Units
Magnetic induction	B	Tesla
Magnetization	M	Ampere/meter
Magnetic field intensity	H	Ampere/meter
Magnetic volume charge density	ρ_m	Ampere/(meter)^2
Scalar magnetic potential	ϕ_m	Ampere
Permeability of free space	μ_o	Henry/meter

magnetic charge located on the faces of the magnet, as illustrated in Figure 2.2b. These two pictures represent equivalent means of representing the same physical situation, and depending on the objective, one may be preferable to the other. Below each figure are given the basic vector relations establishing the nature of each field. We know from equation (2.18) that B/μ_0 and H are identical outside of the region where M exists, but they differ by M inside the magnet. In fact, B and H are actually opposite in direction within the magnet, which is obvious from the fact that the line integral of H must be zero about any closed path. It is seen that the H field *inside* the magnet opposes M (its own source) and for this reason is referred to as a demagnetizing field.

2.2.1 Units

The International System of Units (SI) is in common use by engineers and scientists in industry and universities. Magnetic quantities and their SI units are summarized in Table 2.1.

The cgs–emu system of units is used to describe magnetic materials and has had widespread use in magnetic recording. In the cgs–emu system, not only the units but also the form of the basic equations differ from the SI counterparts. For example, the cgs–emu form of equation (2.18) is

$$B = H + 4\pi M \tag{2.30}$$

Note that an emu is the electromagnetic unit of magnetic moment. In the cgs–emu system, the permeability of free space is unity. In this book, developments are carried out in the SI system, and conversions to or from cgs–emu units are made using Table 2.2.

TABLE 2.2   Centimeter-Gram-Second (cgs) and SI Equivalents

Quantity	CGS–EMU Units	SI Equivalent
B	G	10^{-4} T
H	Oe	79.6 A/m
M	emu/(cm)^3	1 kA/m

2.2.2 Magnetic Permeability

Thus far, we have considered the case where the intensity of magnetization **M** is a given function of position, as in an ideal permanent magnet. Let us next examine the situation in which we have an ideally permeable medium, that is, a medium that has no magnetic moment in the absence of external currents and that gives rise to a magnetic moment per unit volume proportional to the field **H** produced by the external currents. The field equations that will consistently apply are

$$\nabla \cdot \mathbf{B} = 0 \tag{2.31}$$

$$\oint \mathbf{H} \cdot d\mathbf{l} = I \tag{2.32}$$

For such a linear medium as postulated, we can set

$$\mathbf{M} = \chi_m \mathbf{H} \tag{2.33}$$

where χ_m is called the magnetic susceptibility. Then, setting $\mu = \chi_m + 1$ and using equation (2.18), we have

$$\mathbf{B} = \mu \mu_0 \mathbf{H} \tag{2.34}$$

where μ is the relative permeability of the magnetic material.

At the interface between two such linear media, the boundary conditions for B and H may be shown to be (in the absence of surface currents)

$$B_2 = B_1; \quad \mu_2 H_2 = \mu_1 H_1 \quad \text{(normal components)} \tag{2.35}$$

$$H_2 = H_1; \quad B_2/\mu_2 = B_1/\mu_1 \quad \text{(tangential components)} \tag{2.36}$$

In general, M and H have a very complex nonlinear relationship, and therefore this simple concept of permeability will have meaning only over specified narrow operating ranges.

2.2.3 Equivalence, Magnetic Shell–Current Loop

A useful relation in formulating many problems in magnetics is the equivalence between a current loop and a magnetic shell. A magnetic shell is a surface possessing a uniform magnetic dipole distribution. The dipole density is simply the magnetic moment per unit area. This equivalence in actuality amounts to no more than a restatement of the fact that a magnetized region is equivalent to a current distribution of density

$$\mathbf{j}_m = \nabla \times \mathbf{M} \tag{2.37}$$

and supports Ampere's interpretation of magnetism in terms of infinitesimal circulating currents.

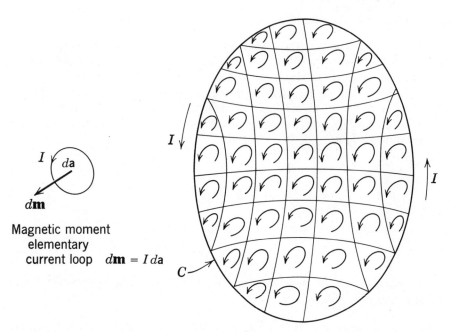

Magnetic moment
elementary
current loop $d\mathbf{m} = I\,d\mathbf{a}$

FIGURE 2.3   Resolution of current loop C into a network of elementary current loops.

It can be shown [1] that the magnetic moment of an infinitesimal current loop is equal to

$$d\mathbf{m} = I\,d\mathbf{a} \tag{2.38}$$

where $d\mathbf{m}$ is the magnetic moment, I the current, and $d\mathbf{a}$ the infinitesimal plane area of the loop. The vector $d\mathbf{a}$ (and hence $d\mathbf{m}$) is normal to this plane. The elementary moment depends on the current and area enclosed by the circuit, not on its particular form. (Note that $d\mathbf{m} = \mathbf{M}\,dv$ for a differential volume of magnetic material.)

Any circuit contour can be resolved into a system of elementary currents. Consider a network of intersecting lines on some surface spanning the current contour C (Figure 2.3). Imagine that about the contour of each elementary area there is a current I equal in magnitude to the current in C. The magnetic field produced by this network of currents is everywhere identical with that of a dipole distribution over the spanning surface. The dipole density, or moment per unit area, of the equivalent surface distribution is constant and equal to

$$\tau = \frac{dm}{da} = I \tag{2.39}$$

Another perspective from which to draw this analogy is through consideration of the scalar magnetic potential of a magnetic shell and a current loop. (A single-valued scalar magnetic potential cannot be used if line integrals are considered that encircle current-carrying regions.)

For a magnetic shell it can be shown [1] that

$$\phi_m(x,y,z) = \frac{\tau}{4\pi}\Omega \tag{2.40}$$

where again τ is the dipole density and Ω is the solid angle subtended by the shell at the point (x,y,z). For a current loop,

$$\phi_m(x,y,z) = \frac{I}{4\pi}\Omega \tag{2.41}$$

where I is the current in the loop and Ω is established by the loop contour.
Since

$$d\phi_m = \frac{\tau}{4\pi}d\Omega \tag{2.42}$$

the discontinuity in the magnetic scalar potential ϕ_m across the selected dipole surface spanning the loop is

$$\phi_m^+ - \phi_m^- = \tau \tag{2.43}$$

corresponding to the change in solid angle of 4π. This result from the magnetic shell analogy correlates with the previously derived relation for the line integral of the magnetic field **H**.
Recall that

$$\oint \mathbf{H} \cdot d\mathbf{l} = I \tag{2.44}$$

about any closed path linking the current loop, and this result must also obtain from the equivalent magnetic shell.

Note carefully that the equivalent magnetic shell could be any arbitrary surface spanning the current contour. Consequently, it serves as a mathematical convenience rather than a representation of a physical identity.

2.3 MAGNETIC FIELDS USING THE CONCEPT OF MAGNETIC CHARGE

The concept of magnetic charge arising from the divergence of magnetization is very useful in calculating magnetic fields in situations that often arise in magnetic recording. The most common of these are image fields, demagnetizing fields, and head fields. Magnetic charge is a source of magnetic field **H** in exact analogy to electric charge as a source of electric field **E**.

2.3.1 Image Fields

Although free magnetic charge does not exist, we can use the concept as long as we remember that the magnetic charge distribution is equal to $-\nabla \cdot \mathbf{M}$ and **M** is defined in terms of magnetic moment per unit volume. Thus, since the net charge in a given volume must equal zero, there will be limitations on the form of $\nabla \cdot \mathbf{M}$. Image magnetic fields occur when a magnetic charge is near a material that has a relatively high permeability. Consider the problem depicted

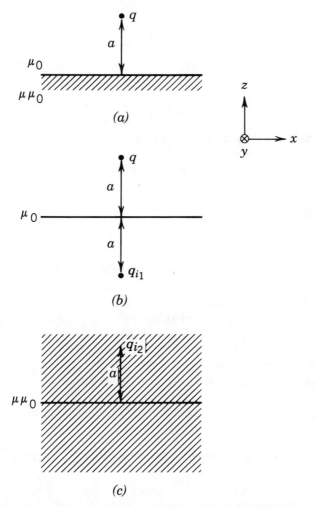

FIGURE 2.4 Image fields. (*a*) Point charge above a magnetic material. (*b*) Image charge added for calculating field above magnetic material. (*c*) Image charge for finding field within magnetic material.

in Figure 2.4*a*. A point charge q is located distance a above a semi-infinite block of magnetic material with permeability μ. The problem is to find the field everywhere in space, satisfying the boundary conditions that normal **B** and tangential **H** are continuous at the material boundary $z = 0$. By breaking this problem into two simpler ones using image charges, a solution for the field can be found.

Figure 2.4*b* shows the geometry for finding the field in the region $z > 0$. The entire space is homogeneous with permeability μ_0, and an image charge is introduced at distance a below the surface $z = 0$. The geometry for $z < 0$ is in Figure 2.4c. This time, the entire space has relative permeability μ, and a second image charge is located at distance a above surface $z = 0$. If the image charges are chosen to be

$$q_{i1} = -\frac{\mu - 1}{\mu + 1}q \qquad (2.45)$$

and

$$q_{i2} = 2\frac{\mu}{\mu + 1}q \qquad (2.46)$$

the boundary conditions are satisfied, and the magnetic potential is given by

$$\phi_m = \frac{1}{4\pi} \left(\frac{q}{[x^2 + y^2 + (z - a)^2]^{1/2}} + \frac{q_{i1}}{[x^2 + y^2 + (z + a)^2]^{1/2}} \right), \qquad z \geq 0$$

$$(2.47)$$

$$\phi_m = \frac{1}{4\pi} \left(\frac{q_{i2}}{[x^2 + y^2 + (z - a)^2]^{1/2}} \right), \qquad z \leq 0 \qquad (2.48)$$

Note that in the limit as μ goes to infinity, the image charge of Figure 2.4b is equal and opposite in sign to charge q and the **H** field solution is exactly analogous to the electric field solution for a point electric charge above a perfect conductor. In this sense, a very high permeability magnetic material is analogous to a perfect electrical conductor. It must be remembered, however, that the magnetic charges on the surface of the magnetic material are bound charges arising from the divergence of magnetization. They are not free to move about on the surface as electric charges do on perfect conductors.

2.3.2 Demagnetizing Fields

The divergence of magnetization at a boundary surface of a uniformly magnetized body produces surface charges given by $\mathbf{M} \cdot \mathbf{n}$. $\mathbf{n}$ is a unit vector normal to and directed outward from the enclosing surface. These surface charges cause **H** fields that oppose the magnetization and hence are called demagnetizing fields. Consider the uniformly magnetized sphere shown in Figure 2.5. The magnetic charge density on the surface is given by

$$\sigma_m = M \cos\theta \qquad (2.49)$$

The resulting demagnetizing field is uniform and in the negative z direction, opposing the magnetization.

$$H_{dz} = -M/3 \qquad (2.50)$$

For uniform demagnetizing fields, the field is proportional to the magnetization and may be expressed as

$$H_d = -N_d M \qquad (2.51)$$

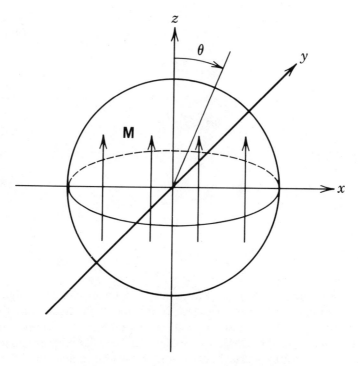

FIGURE 2.5   Uniformly magnetized sphere.

where N_d is defined as the demagnetizing factor. Uniform demagnetizing fields occur only in bodies that are ellipsoidal in shape, spheres and infinitely long cylinders being special cases of ellipsoids. For the general ellipsoid, there are three demagnetizing factors, one for each of three mutually perpendicular axes. From geometrical considerations, the sum of the demagnetizing factors is equal to unity.

$$N_x + N_y + N_z = 1 \tag{2.52}$$

From equation (2.50) and the symmetry of a sphere, we see that demagnetizing factors for a sphere satisfy (2.52).

For nonellipsoidal shapes, the demagnetizing fields are nonuniform, and often cannot be exactly calculated. For many practical applications, an appropriate approach is to approximate the shape by an ellipsoid. For a long rod $N_x = 0$ ($N_y, N_z = 0.5$), while for a flat plate $N_x = 1.0$ ($N_y, N_z = 0$).

2.3.3 Fields at Magnetic Circuit Air Gaps

A useful approach for obtaining fringing fields of magnetic gaps is to represent the magnetic charge distribution on the inner gap faces by sheets of uniform charge density. The field at any point in space produced by a differential element of charge may be easily expressed and then integrated over the charge

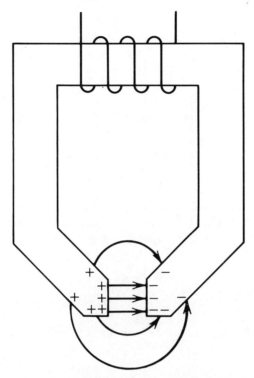

FIGURE 2.6 Recording head showing field lines and magnetic charge in gap region.

sheets to obtain the total resultant field. The field calculated in this manner is often a good approximation to the values found using the more exact methods described in the next section.

As an example, consider the two-dimensional ring head structure of Figure 2.6. The magnetic charge shown on the pole faces may be approximated by two sheets of equal and opposite uniform charge density **M** located on the gap surfaces, as shown in Figure 2.7. Recall that for a uniformly magnetized body the surface charge density σ_m is equal to $\mathbf{M} \cdot \mathbf{n}$. The differential field $d\mathbf{H}+$ produced by a differential element of positive charge located on the gap surface is given by

$$d\mathbf{H}+ = \frac{1}{2\pi} \frac{\sigma_m \, dy' \mathbf{r}}{|\mathbf{r}|^2} \qquad (2.53)$$

which for coordinates $x' = -g/2$, y' can be broken into components

$$dH_x+ = \frac{1}{2\pi} \frac{\sigma_m \, dy'(x+g/2)}{(x+g/2)^2 + (y-y')^2} \qquad (2.54)$$

$$dH_y+ = \frac{1}{2\pi} \frac{\sigma_m \, dy'(y-y')}{(x+g/2)^2 + (y-y')^2} \qquad (2.55)$$

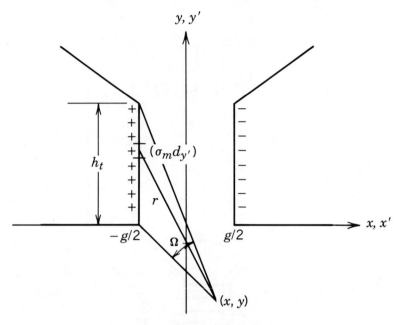

FIGURE 2.7 Approximation of gap charge by uniform charge sheets.

Integrating over the throat height h_t gives for the field components

$$H_x+ = \frac{\sigma_m}{2\pi}\left[\tan^{-1}\frac{x+g/2}{y} - \tan^{-1}\frac{x+g/2}{y-h_t}\right] \tag{2.56}$$

$$H_y+ = \frac{\sigma_m}{4\pi}\ln\frac{y^2+(x+g/2)^2}{(y-h_t)^2+(x+g/2)^2} \tag{2.57}$$

The longitudinal field component has a simple geometrical interpretation. Noting that y is negative, we may write (2.56) as $H_x = \sigma_m\Omega/2\pi$, where Ω is the angle subtended by the charge sheet as shown. Adding the contribution from the negative charge on the gap face at $x' = g/2$ gives the total field

$$H_x = \frac{\sigma_m}{2\pi}\left[\tan^{-1}\frac{x+g/2}{y} - \tan^{-1}\frac{x-g/2}{y} - \tan^{-1}\frac{x+g/2}{y-h_t} + \tan^{-1}\frac{x-g/2}{y-h_t}\right] \tag{2.58}$$

$$H_y = \frac{\sigma_m}{4\pi}\ln\frac{[y^2+(x+g/2)^2][(y-h_t)^2+(x-g/2)^2]}{[y^2+(x-g/2)^2][(y-h_t)^2+(x+g/2)^2]} \tag{2.59}$$

These closed-form expressions are readily evaluated in spite of their complexity. In the limit of very long throat height, the geometrical interpretation gives H_x proportional to the angle at (x,y) subtended by the gap corners.

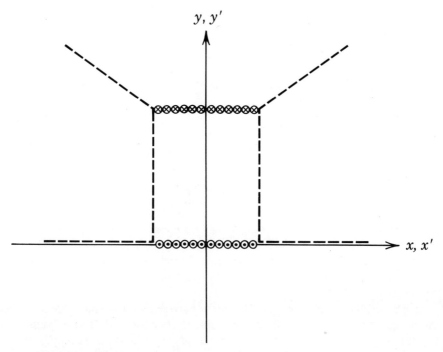

FIGURE 2.8 Solenoid equivalent of charge sheets for producing head fields.

Note that the field produced by the two charge sheets is exactly the same as that produced by a solenoid positioned in the gap as shown in Figure 2.8. This result follows from the magnetic shell equivalence relationship. The charge sheet approach is applicable to other simple geometries such as a probe head for use in perpendicular recording.

2.4 MAGNETIC FIELD BOUNDARY VALUE PROBLEMS

Magnetic recording behavior depends very significantly on the distribution of magnetic fields in space. In all but a very few idealized geometries, closed-form expressions for the field are unobtainable. In general, the engineer must rely upon other techniques for predicting the spatial distribution of a magnetic field. Some of the most useful techniques are graphical mapping, analog methods of field plotting, and numerical calculation using difference equations or finite element techniques. This section will briefly sketch the basics of these approaches. The extremely small physical dimensions of the typical region of concern in magnetic recording make it difficult to set up convenient instrumentation for measuring fields directly. Therefore, it is necessary to place great emphasis and reliance on these modeling techniques. Depending on circumstances, each may have particular advantages.

Since our interest in magnetic field configurations is concerned primarily with current free regions, where

$$\nabla \times \mathbf{H} = 0 \qquad (2.60)$$

we can then write $\mathbf{H}$ as the gradient of a scalar, that is,

$$\mathbf{H} = -\nabla \phi_m \qquad (2.61)$$

In all regions where

$$\nabla \cdot \mathbf{H} = -\nabla \cdot \mathbf{M} = 0 \qquad (2.62)$$

then

$$\nabla^2 \phi_m = 0 \qquad (2.63)$$

The latter equation is known as Laplace's equation. The negative divergence of $\mathbf{M}$, which is equal to the magnetic charge density, will be zero in all media where the permeability is constant. Thus, we can obtain the magnetic field in free space through solution of Laplace's equation and in those magnetic media where it is valid to approximate the ratio of $\mathbf{B}$ to $\mathbf{H}$ by a constant.

The boundary conditions on $\mathbf{H}$ and $\mathbf{B}$ between two magnetic regions of different constant permeabilities have already been stated. These boundary conditions provide the means to match the magnetic field across the interface between two magnetic media. For a magnetic region of sufficiently high permeability, μ can be assumed infinite and a magnetic field emerging into free space will be normal to the bounding surface. In this case, the surface boundary will be an equipotential line of the scalar magnetic potential function.

All points of a magnetic field having the same potential may be thought of as connected by an equipotential surface. The magnetic field vector must be perpendicular to these surfaces at every point. This follows from the relation

$$\int_a^b \mathbf{H} \cdot d\mathbf{l} = \phi_m(b) - \phi_m(a) \qquad (2.64)$$

If we take the line integral along an equipotential, and remember that by definition $\phi_m(b) = \phi_m(a)$ on the equipotential irrespective of the separation between point b and point a, we see that the integral is zero independent of the path along the equipotential surface. Consequently, the component of $\mathbf{H}$ along the equipotential is zero and $\mathbf{H}$ is normal to the equipotential surface.

It is particularly convenient to work directly with magnetic potentials, not only because they are scalar functions but because, in general, the boundary conditions will be identified in terms of a potential. Especially for regions where the relative permeability can be considered infinite (the permeability of air being 1), the boundary surface directly defines a potential line.

For a two-dimensional field, a graphical representation of equipotential and field lines must divide the plane into curvilinear rectangles, where the field and potential lines are orthogonal. This concept corresponds to tubes of con-

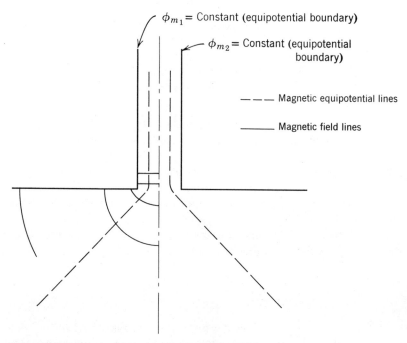

$\phi_{m_1}=$ Constant (equipotential boundary)

$\phi_{m_2}=$ Constant (equipotential boundary)

— — — Magnetic equipotential lines

———— Magnetic field lines

FIGURE 2.9   Graphical development of a magnetic field configuration.

stant flux defined by streamlines intersected by equal intervals of equipotential lines. The usual procedure is to divide the space between known potential lines (boundaries) into a certain number of equal intervals through subdividing equipotential lines. Then field lines are generally inserted in an attempt to establish a net of curvilinear squares, although the requirement of meeting orthogonality is placed first. See Figure 2.9 for such an attempt. Successive revisions using this procedure will lead to an improved field plot [2]. Although the accuracy of this method is not high, it can provide useful insight and serve as a starting point for more elaborate methods.

Analog methods of determining magnetic fields are based on the fact that in a conducting medium of constant resistivity the voltage distribution must satisfy Laplace's equation. Further, electrical conductors, since they do not support a significant potential gradient in comparison with resistive media such as electrolytes, or resistive paper, provide an excellent means to represent equipotential boundaries. Therefore, it is relatively easy to make an electrical analog of many magnetic structures. The advantage of this approach is the ease of plotting potential lines with a voltage probe as well as simplicity of forming scale models of greatly increased size to facilitate instrumentation.

After the potential plot is made, the magnetic field can be determined from

$$\mathbf{H} = -\nabla \phi_m \qquad (2.65)$$

or

$$H_x = \frac{-\partial \phi_m}{\partial x} \tag{2.66}$$

and

$$H_y = \frac{-\partial \phi_m}{\partial y} \tag{2.67}$$

for a two-dimensional field under investigation. Fortunately, in magnetic recording a two-dimensional model of the magnetic structure is usually applicable.

Laplace's and Poisson's equations can also be solved by numerical methods. High-speed, inexpensive computers and applications software now make this technique readily available. A mesh of points is established, and after the boundary conditions, current sources, and material properties are entered, an iterative process is used to adjust the inner potentials until an acceptable level of stability or equilibrium is reached. For a two-dimensional case,

$$\nabla^2 \phi_m = \frac{\partial^2 \phi_m}{\partial x^2} + \frac{\partial^2 \phi_m}{\partial y^2} \tag{2.68}$$

Using finite differences, consider the mesh point in Figure 2.10.

Let $\Delta x = \Delta y = 1$, and approximate derivatives by difference operators. Then

$$\nabla^2 \phi_m = \{[\phi_m(c) - \phi_m(P)] - [\phi_m(P) - \phi_m(a)]\}$$

$$+ \{[\phi_m(d) - \phi_m(P)] - [\phi_m(P) - \phi_m(b)]\} = 0 \tag{2.69}$$

or

$$\phi_m(P) = \frac{[\phi_m(a) + \phi_m(b) + \phi_m(c) + \phi_m(d)]}{4} \tag{2.70}$$

The latter equation states that the potential of any point is equal to the average value of the potentials on its "boundary." Successive iterations over such a mesh is a convergent process. The fineness of the net of points chosen must be commensurate with the actual accuracy required, since the amount of calculation goes up rapidly as greater field detail is sought.

In the finite element method, the solution region is divided by a mesh into small regions, or elements, usually triangular in shape. The potential in each element is expanded in terms of its node potentials by interpolation polynomials. The total energy in the system is then obtained and minimized to give a set of equations from which the node potentials can be solved. Appropriate operations or "postprocessing" on the solution potentials give field plots and other useful design parameters. For more information on the use of numerical methods in magnetic field calculations, see references [4] and [5].

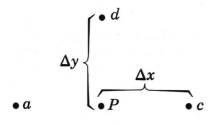

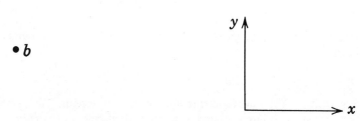

FIGURE 2.10   Mesh point and surrounding neighbors.

2.5 MAGNETIC ENERGY

To calculate the magnetic energy in a system consisting of current-carrying conductors and magnetic media, we can proceed as follows:

$$U_m = \int_0^t ei\,dt \qquad (2.71)$$

where ei is the instantaneous power supplied to the system. Using Faraday's law and taking the circuit sign convention for positive power flowing into the system, the emf e is

$$e = \frac{N\,d\Phi}{dt} = \frac{d\Lambda}{dt} \qquad (2.72)$$

where Λ represents flux linkages $N\Phi$. Now the flux linkages within the system arise only from the source current under the assumption that $\mu(x,y,z)$ is not a function of **H**. Further, with this restriction we can set

$$\Lambda = Li \qquad (2.73)$$

where inductance L is a constant of proportionality.

Then

$$U_m = \int i\,d\Lambda = \int Li\,di \qquad (2.74)$$

or

$$U_m = \frac{1}{2}LI^2 = \frac{\Lambda I}{2} \qquad (2.75)$$

where I is the steady-state value of the current.

2.5.1 Self- and Mutual Induction

The concepts of self- and mutual induction in magnetically coupled systems may be defined from magnetic energy considerations. If we assume that the flux density **B** is everywhere proportional to the magnetic field strength, that is,

$$\mathbf{B} = \mu\mu_0\mathbf{H} \tag{2.76}$$

then

$$U_m = \frac{1}{2}\sum_{k=1}^{n} i_k \Lambda_k \tag{2.77}$$

where U_m = the energy of the field (associated with the current sources i_k). Further,

$$\Lambda_k = N \int_{s_k} \mathbf{B} \cdot d\mathbf{s} \tag{2.78}$$

that is, Λ_k is the magnetic flux linking the kth circuit. The symbol s_k signifies that this surface integral applies to the kth circuit.

The permeability μ may be a function of position but is not to vary with **H** at a given point. The vector **B** is uniquely defined by the currents $i_1,...,i_n$ and because of the stipulation that μ should be independent of **H**, the contributions of the individual currents to **B** are directly proportional to their respective magnitudes.

Accordingly, we can write

$$\Lambda_h = L_{h1}i_1 + L_{h2}i_2 + \cdots + L_{hn}i_n \tag{2.79}$$

Clearly, L_{hk} is a geometrical factor depending on the spatial field distribution. L_{kk} is called the self-inductance of the kth circuit, and L_{hk} is called the mutual inductance between the two circuits h and k. Now

$$L_{hk} \propto \frac{\partial \Lambda_h}{\partial i_k} \tag{2.80}$$

and from equation (2.75)

$$\Lambda_h \propto \frac{\partial U_m}{\partial i_h} \tag{2.81}$$

so that

$$L_{hk} \propto \frac{\partial^2 U_m}{\partial i_k \partial i_h} \tag{2.82}$$

Since in this relation it is immaterial in what order the subscripts appear, it follows that

$$L_{hk} = L_{kh} \tag{2.83}$$

which is an example of the principle of reciprocity.

This latter identity is very important because it permits the magnetic coupling between two circuits to be visualized in terms of the current in one and the flux linking the other or vice versa. In either case, for the same unit current in one circuit there will be the identical number of flux linkages with the

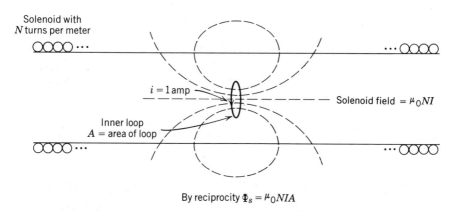

By reciprocity $\Phi_s = \mu_0 NIA$

Φ_s = Flux linking solenoid due to current flow in inner loop

FIGURE 2.11   Magnetic coupling between solenoid and enclosed loop.

second circuit, irrespective of the complexity of the circuit configuration. It is apparent in Figure 2.11 that it would be much easier to determine the flux linking the outer coil, caused by a current through the inner loop, by using relation (2.83). In this instance the reverse problem is readily amenable to solution, since the flux density through the small inner coil, produced by current flowing through the large solenoid, is essentially uniform over and normal to its cross section, quite the contrary of the situation pertaining in Figure 2.11.

2.6 MAGNETIC CIRCUITS

To obtain or sense a given magnetic flux in magnetic recording, specially shaped head structures of ferromagnetic or ferrimagnetic material are used almost exclusively. Suitable assumptions often make possible a simplification of an inherent field problem to a much simpler one involving a circuit concept. Again, in magnetic recording we are concerned only with a quasistationary state. Under these conditions, when the general three-dimensional magnetics problem can be reduced to a one-dimensional model for a particular analysis, we have a so-called magnetic circuit problem.

The concept of a magnetic circuit is based on the fact that magnetic flux tends to confine itself to the high-permeability paths of a region, similar to the manner in which current flow chooses high conductivity paths in an electric circuit. In contrast to conductive electric circuits, the typical ferromagnetic circuit is characteristically nonlinear.

In another important respect, the magnetic circuit differs markedly from its simple electrical equivalent. The conductivity of copper, as an example of an electrical conductor, is on the order of 10^{20} times that of a surrounding insulator material such as air or mica. In contrast, magnetic properties of materials do not vary over nearly such a wide range. Ordinarily, a high-permeability substance will only have a relative permeability of 10^2 to 10^4 times that of air. This condition makes flux leakage a phenomenon of major significance in magnetic circuits. Engineering applications of magnetic materials must particularly recognize and account for the behavior of leakage flux to relate performance to design properly.

Now consider Figure 2.12, which shows a coil on an elementary magnetic toroid consisting of two sections, each with a constant but different permeability. This magnetic structure will be converted to a lumped parameter magnetic circuit to establish formally the basis and nature of the analogy to an electrical circuit.

For μ_1 and μ_2, both quite large, the magnetic flux density vector **B** within the toroid will be essentially parallel to the surface of this ring. Now

$$\Phi = \int \mathbf{B} \cdot d\mathbf{s} \tag{2.84}$$

and for the uniform flux within the core we then have

$$\Phi = BA \tag{2.85}$$

where A is the cross-sectional area of the magnetic path. Since B is everywhere normal to A, the vector symbolism is not necessary (again recall that the magnetic circuit represents a one-dimensional simplification of the field problem). As

$$\nabla \cdot \mathbf{B} = 0 \tag{2.86}$$

the lines of flux are continuous so that Φ can be seen analogous to a current flowing around a circuit loop. Thus,

$$B_1 = B_2 \tag{2.87}$$

or

$$\mu_1 H_1 = \mu_2 H_2 \tag{2.88}$$

H and B are parallel, and their ratio is given by the permeability constants. Therefore, if we take the line integral

$$\oint \mathbf{H} \cdot \mathbf{dl} \tag{2.89}$$

around the path of the magnetic ring, we obtain

$$H_1 l_1 + H_2 l_2 = Ni \tag{2.90}$$

where l_1 = path length corresponding to μ_1,

$\quad\quad l_2$ = path length corresponding to μ_2, and

$\quad\quad i$ = coil current (the line integral is equal to the total current encircled).

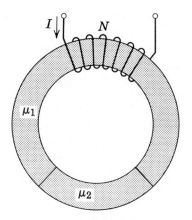
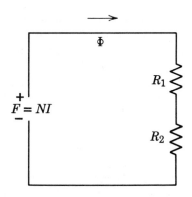

FIGURE 2.12 Equivalent magnetic circuit for toroid.

Defining $F = Ni$ as the magnetomotive force applied to the magnetic ring, we can express the last equation in the following form:

$$F_1 + F_2 = F \tag{2.91}$$

Then, magnetomotive force (dimensionally Ampere-turns) is analogous to electromotive force (Volts), and magnetic flux (Webers) is analogous to current (Amperes). The equivalence to an electric circuit may now be completed by defining

$$R = F/\Phi \tag{2.92}$$

where R is the reluctance of a given branch of the magnetic circuit. For example,

$$R_1 = \frac{F_1}{\Phi} = \frac{H_1 l_1}{BA} = \frac{l_1}{\mu_1 \mu_0 A} \tag{2.93}$$

since

$$B = \mu_1 \mu_0 H_1 \tag{2.94}$$

Equation (2.93) serves also to define reluctance in terms of the parameters of the magnetic circuit. Since reluctance is the ratio of magnetomotive force to flux, it is analogous to resistance in an electrical network. It is now possible to draw the equivalent circuit as given in Figure 2.12 and use this in solving for the magnetic behavior of the toroid. This same analogy can be directly applied to more complicated series-parallel branches in a magnetic structure.

Two points should be noted. First, in general, μ will not be a constant and hence the reluctance of the magnetic branches will be nonlinear functions. When it is essential to treat the reluctance as nonlinear, graphical or numerical techniques may be used to solve the nonlinear magnetic circuit equations.

Second, even in such a simple example as above, one should anticipate the existence of flux leakage. In fact, for the ring of Figure 2.12 it is only through the presence of leakage flux that we can derive a "magnetic circuit." To clarify this point, assume that $\mu_1 = \mu_2$. The magnetic field intensity H is then uniform around the toroid. In the absence of the magnetic ring, the line integral of H around the same path must still yield Ni. However, in the latter case, H is not uniform along the path, and the major contribution to the integral occurs on the section of the path lying inside of the coil. Thus, the magnetic field within the coil is actually reduced by the presence of the magnetic ring. This phenomenon can occur only by the existence of a demagnetizing field arising from equivalent magnetic poles on the surface of the toroid. These magnetic surface charges, of course, give rise to a flux outside the magnetic structure. This phenomenon exists independently of the permeability of the ring.

Because the greater part of the magnetic flux is bounded within the one-dimensional magnetic circuit, the magnetic energy is readily calculated using the approach of equation (2.71):

$$U_m = \int_0^t ei\,dt = \int_0^\Phi Ni\,d\Phi \tag{2.95}$$

For a homogeneous magnetic circuit with volume $V = Al$,

$$\Phi = BA \tag{2.96}$$

and

$$i = \frac{Hl}{N} \tag{2.97}$$

Substituting,

$$U_m = V \int H\,dB = V u_m \tag{2.98}$$

where u_m is the magnetic energy change per unit volume associated with a change of state in B.

$$u_m = \int H\,dB \tag{2.99}$$

The energy calculation is readily extended to magnetic circuits made up of several homogeneous regions.

2.7 EDDY CURRENTS IN MAGNETIC MEDIA

Whenever the magnetic flux in a medium is changing, an electric field appears within the medium as a result of the time variation of flux.

Restating Faraday's law, equation (2.5), with the aid of equation (2.84) and the definition of electromotive force e, we obtain

$$e = \oint \mathbf{E} \cdot d\mathbf{l} = \frac{-\partial}{\partial t}\left[\int_s \mathbf{B} \cdot d\mathbf{s}\right] \tag{2.100}$$

where $\mathbf{E}$ is the electric field intensity.

The differential expression of the above vector field equation is

$$\nabla \times \mathbf{E} = \frac{-\partial \mathbf{B}}{\partial t} \tag{2.101}$$

When the medium is a conductor, currents are set up by this induced electro-motive force. These currents are called eddy currents. Their presence results in an energy loss in the material, the energy being absorbed from the source that sets up the time-varying field and being dissipated as heat in the medium.

Since the permeability of ferromagnetic materials is relatively large, the effects of eddy currents on the flux carried and power loss may be appreciable, as shown below. By Lenz's law, these internal currents tend to oppose any change in flux, and thus their effect is to reduce the flux density at progressively greater distances from the surface. This phenomenon of flux and current concentration at the surface is known as "skin effect." Skin effect is important even in nonmagnetic conductors, and is treated extensively in reference [2]. We shall limit ourselves here to a brief development of the equation governing the behavior of the flux density B as a function of frequency for the one-dimensional problem. This situation is often adequate for describing a magnetic head core, and the results lead to understanding of losses and impedance effects in magnetic heads. Within a conducting material, current density

$$\mathbf{j}_t = \sigma \mathbf{E} \tag{2.102}$$

where σ is the conductivity of the material. Now substituting $\sigma \mathbf{E}$ into equation (2.19) and assuming the material has a constant permeability, we can write

$$\nabla \times \left(\frac{\mathbf{B}}{\mu\mu_0} \right) = \sigma \mathbf{E} \tag{2.103}$$

Taking the curl of both sides of this equation and using the vector identity

$$\nabla \times \nabla \times \mathbf{B} = \nabla(\nabla \cdot \mathbf{B}) - \nabla^2 \mathbf{B} \tag{2.104}$$

and equation (2.101), we obtain

$$\nabla^2 \mathbf{B} = \mu\mu_0\sigma \nabla \times \mathbf{E} = \mu\mu_0\sigma \frac{\partial \mathbf{B}}{\partial t} \tag{2.105}$$

When $\mathbf{B}$ is a function of only one spatial dimension, the following differential equation gives the dependency of B on frequency f:

$$\frac{d^2 B}{dx^2} = j\omega\mu\mu_0\sigma B \tag{2.106}$$

where angular frequency $\omega = 2\pi f$. In this particular equation, j stands for the imaginary operator of complex variable theory. B is a steady-state sinusoid varying as $e^{j\omega t}$. Equation (2.106) gives the relation between the space and time derivatives of B. Solutions of this equation are subject to the boundary conditions imposed by the physical shapes under investigation. As an example, consider a semi-infinite material extending infinitely in the x direction with the boundary in the $x = 0$ plane. For a magnetic field with a z component only, imposing boundary conditions on solutions of (2.106) gives

$$B_z = B_0 e^{-(1+j)x/\delta} \tag{2.107}$$

where the skin depth δ is

$$\delta = \frac{1}{\sqrt{\pi f \mu_0 \sigma}} \tag{2.108}$$

From (2.107) we see that the field strength falls to $1/e$ of its value at the surface for a value of x equal to the skin depth. To examine the eddy current power-loss relationships, consider a small circular cross section of radius r oriented normal to the direction of a sinusoidally time-varying flux density in a cylindrical magnetic material. Then

$$2\pi r E = \pi r^2 j\omega B \tag{2.109}$$

The eddy current power loss in a unit length is obtained by integrating σE^2 over the cross section of the material. For a flux density uniform over the cross section

$$P_e \propto \sigma(\omega B)^2 \tag{2.110}$$

where P_e is the eddy current loss.

Thus, P_e is proportional to the square of the rate of change of flux density and inversely dependent upon the resistivity. Since the induced voltage in a coil encircling the magnetic path is proportional to dB/dt, it can be deduced that

$$P_e \propto e^2 \tag{2.111}$$

where e is the open circuit coil voltage. This relation holds, even when B is not uniform within the coil.

2.8 FERROMAGNETIC MATERIALS

Ferromagnetic behavior on a macroscopic scale may be understood through the nature of the magnetic domain substructure. An actual ferromagnetic specimen is composed of a number of small regions called domains, within each of which the atomic magnetic moments are held in parallel alignment. For this reason the domain represents a saturated region of magnetization. The directions of magnetization of different domains need not be parallel. The net magnetization of the magnetic specimen represents the integrated effect of these elemental domains. Domain structure always has its origin in the possibility of lowering the energy of a system by going from a uniformly saturated configuration with high magnetic energy to a domain configuration with a lower energy. The domain structure is a natural consequence of the various major contributions to the total energy—exchange, anisotropy, and magnetic—of a ferromagnetic body. The interplay of these factors will be briefly sketched, for

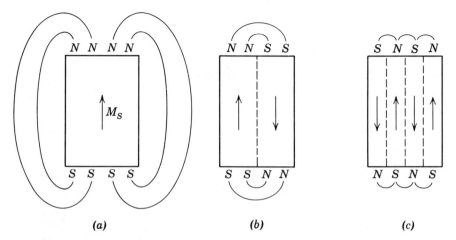

FIGURE 2.13   Domain behavior—magnetostatic energy.

their relative influences establish the magnetic behavior of a ferromagnetic material. Further, in digital magnetic recording the recording of individually saturated magnetic cells is the means by which information bits are stored; the concepts and phenomena of domain behavior are therefore also instructive from the viewpoint of understanding digital magnetic recording.

The anisotropy energy tends to make the magnetization of a domain align itself along certain crystallographic axes. The axes thus favored are known as preferred axes, or directions of easy magnetization. A considerably larger amount of energy is generally required to saturate a specimen along an arbitrary axis than along one of the preferred axes. The nonpreferred axes represent directions of "hard" magnetization. For example, in iron, which is cubic, the preferred axes are the cube edges. The origin of domains may be understood by considering Figure 2.13, which shows several magnetization patterns of a sample with no externally applied field. In Figure 2.13a we have a saturated configuration, consisting of a single domain, which may be considered to lie along an axis of easy magnetization. To find the energy of this pattern, we need an expression for the magnetostatic energy.

The magnetostatic energy density of a permanent magnet in a uniform external field is

$$u_m = -\mathbf{M_s} \cdot \mathbf{B} \tag{2.112}$$

where $\mathbf{M_s}$ denotes the permanent magnetization. This relation may be seen by considering a small magnet of moment $\mathbf{m}$ in a magnetic field $\mathbf{B}$ (Figure 2.14). The torque on the magnet is

$$\mathbf{m} \times \mathbf{B} \tag{2.113}$$

and the potential energy associated with its orientation can then be shown to be

$$U_m = -\mathbf{m} \cdot \mathbf{B} \tag{2.114}$$

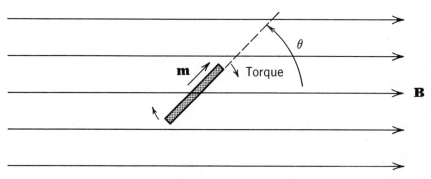

FIGURE 2.14   Torque on a magnet in an external field.

with

$$T(\text{torque}) = \frac{\partial U_m}{\partial \theta} \tag{2.115}$$

Therefore, the energy is a minimum when the magnet is parallel to the field, and work is required to rotate it antiparallel to the external field. The external field B is equal to $\mu_0 H$. When the field is not external but arises from the magnetization itself, the magnetostatic energy density can be expressed as

$$u_m = -\frac{\mu_0}{2}\mathbf{M_s} \cdot \mathbf{H} \tag{2.116}$$

where $\mathbf{H}$ is the demagnetizing field due to $\mathbf{M_s}$. The factor 1/2 arises since equation (2.112) when applied to self-energy would effectively count each unit dipole in the assembly comprising the magnetic region once as a field source and once as a magnet in the field. The factor 1/2 has been encountered previously in our discussion on self- and mutual induction. Since we have seen it is frequently possible to express the demagnetizing field in terms of a demagnetizing factor N_d:

$$H = -N_d M$$

the energy density can then also be expressed in the form

$$u_m = \frac{\mu_0}{2} N_d M_s^2 \tag{2.117}$$

For the patterns of Figure 2.13, the H field of the energy expression is the demagnetizing field produced by the magnetic charge at the ends of the domains. It can be seen that the domain configuration of Figure 2.13b has a demagnetizing field that is reduced and more localized to the ends of the sample than that in Figure 2.13a. This reduction in the H field results in a magnetic energy for pattern b that is approximately half that of the single domain structure of a. The subdivision process may be carried further, as in Figure 2.13c. Here, the magnetic energy is roughly one-quarter of that associated with the single domain. Another way to view the situation is to recognize that each subdivision changes the geometrical shape of the magnetized domains in a manner that reduces their demagnetizing factor.

The subdivision will continue, being energetically more favorable, until the energy required to establish an additional domain wall, the boundary separating two oppositely magnetized domains, is greater than the reduction in magnetic energy consequent on finer subdivision.

Quantum-mechanical exchange forces favor parallel orientation of atomic magnetic moments, which arise primarily from electron spins. These forces are nonmagnetic in origin and account for the saturation magnetization condition within a domain that gives rise to ferromagnetic behavior in materials. Because the magnetization is antiparallel on opposite sides of the domain boundary, there will be energy associated with the formation of a domain wall. The domain wall width is determined by the minimization of the sum of exchange energy and anisotropy energy. A wide wall will allow a gradual reorientation of the spin moments, reducing the exchange energy. Within the wall, the directions of magnetization must necessarily reorient through a nonpreferred axis of magnetization, thus contributing anisotropy energy which is smaller for a narrower wall. The trade-off between these two effects gives a domain wall width that minimizes the sum of the energies.

The interaction of the various energy terms will generally give rise to very complex domain patterns. An unmagnetized magnetic specimen hence consists of a somewhat randomly oriented set of domains, in a pattern that has zero average magnetization and minimizes the total energy.

In addition to ferromagnetic materials, ferrimagnetics also have wide application in magnetic recording. Magnetically, ferrimagnetics behave very similarly to ferromagnetics, and the treatment of the magnetization process in this section applies equally well to the two classes of materials. The distinction is that in ferromagnetic materials, such as iron, quantum-mechanical exchange forces favor parallel spin alignments of neighboring atoms to produce a magnetic moment. In ferrimagnetic materials, on the other hand, spin alignments alternate up or down for atoms in the crystal, but because of the different elements making up the compound, there is a net magnetic moment. Ferrites are the most common ferrimagnetic materials, and they find wide application as magnetically soft materials, such as Mn–Zn ferrite heads, and hard materials, such as barium ferrite particulate media.

2.8.1 The Magnetization Process

Multidomain Samples

The increase in magnetization of a sample in an externally applied field takes place by two independent processes: a growth of the domains favorably oriented with respect to the applied field at the expense of the unfavorably oriented domains; and rotation of the directions of magnetization toward the direction of the field. Figure 2.15 illustrates these two methods by which the resultant magnetization may change. In weak fields, magnetization changes usually proceed by domain boundary displacements. In stronger fields, a rotation of the direction of magnetization of the domain occurs. Figure 2.15 also shows

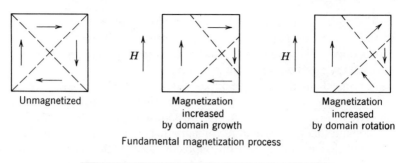

Fundamental magnetization process

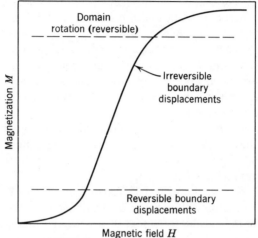

Typical magnetization curve

FIGURE 2.15   The magnetization process.

a typical magnetization curve, designating the regions in which each process is dominant.

For weak fields, the boundary displacements are reversible. That is, a wall may be viewed as moving within one of a number of potential energy wells. When the applied field causes a local energy peak (threshold) on an energy versus boundary position curve to be overcome, an irreversible boundary displacement occurs. On the scale of Figure 2.15, that portion of the curve for irreversible boundary displacements appears smooth. On a much smaller scale, the magnetization exhibits sharp discontinuities, or Barkhausen jumps, when local energy thresholds are exceeded. The crystal structure, purity, and so on, of the magnetic material have a pronounced influence on the magnetization process and make the physical theory very complex.

If the magnetic material is cycled by an alternating magnetic field sufficiently strong to saturate the sample, we get the familiar hysteresis loop of Figure 2.16. The various conventional magnetic material parameters: the coercive force or coercivity H_c, the remanent induction B_r, and the saturation flux density B_s, are defined by means of this diagram. Further, various perme-

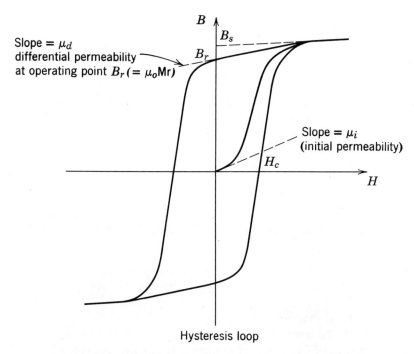

Hysteresis loop

FIGURE 2.16 *B–H* cyclic characteristic: ferromagnetic material.

ability factors are given. For hard magnetic materials, used for digital storage media, the loop should be open and rectangular. On the other hand, soft magnetic materials, used in magnetic heads and magnetic shields, perform better with closed, low coercive force loops.

The hysteresis loss per cycle per unit volume is equal to the area enclosed by the hysteresis loop, obtained by integrating

$$U_m = \int H \, dB \qquad (2.118)$$

over a complete cycle. This hysteresis loss represents a conversion of input energy into heat within the magnetic specimen and is a result of the irreversible nature of the magnetization process.

Since

$$\mathbf{B} = \mu_0[\mathbf{H} + \mathbf{M}] \qquad (2.119)$$

B will still increase proportionally to the applied field *H* even after saturation is reached. This will be true only for the magnetic material within the exciting coil however, for with saturation the magnetic circuit becomes highly nonlinear. More importantly, the conventional magnetization curve and hysteresis loop are based on all the magnetic field vectors being parallel. This condition is often not met in the magnetic recording process. The highly nonlinear, multivalued magnetic characteristics of the materials exploited in digital magnetic

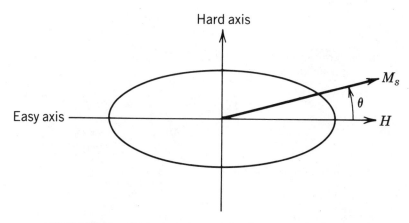

FIGURE 2.17   Single-domain particle aligned with applied field.

recording place great demands on insight and engineering approximations to secure useful and "pseudo-optimal" design criteria.

Single-Domain Behavior

When a sample becomes small enough, it is no longer energetically favorable for domain walls to form. This is because the magnetostatic energy in a uniform field is proportional to the volume of the sample, while the domain wall energy varies with cross-sectional area. As particle size decreases, the surface-to-volume ratio increases rapidly (proportional to $1/r$ for a sphere). The critical dimension, below which single-domain behavior occurs, is on the order of a domain wall width. For gamma ferric oxide, a material widely used as a particulate storage medium, the domain wall width is approximately 0.2 microns. Below this size, the particles are single domains.

The magnetization process for single-domain samples (particles) occurs through rotation of the magnetization in an applied field. The angle of rotation away from the easy axis minimizes the sum of the anisotropy energy and the magnetic potential energy in the applied field. Figure 2.17 shows a single-domain particle with its easy axis aligned with an applied field H. The magnetization is rotated at an angle θ with respect to the easy axis. Note that it is the magnetization that rotates, not the particle.

The anisotropy energy U_a is given by

$$U_a = K \sin^2 \theta \tag{2.120}$$

where K is a uniaxial anisotropy constant, which may include effects of shape, stress, and crystalline anisotropies. For very acicular (needlelike) particles, shape anisotropy dominates behavior and the easy axis will lie along the long axis of the particle. Such particles are commonly used in magnetic recording, since the particles can, through physical and magnetic means, be oriented both in the plane of the medium and in a desired direction, giving a maximum

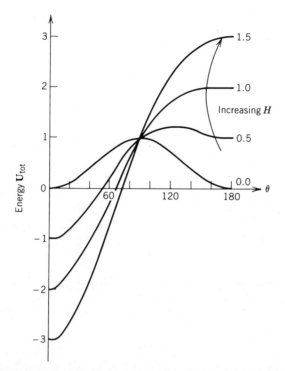

FIGURE 2.18 Total particle energy as a function of magnetization angle θ for several values of applied field H.

of magnetization parallel to the longitudinal axis along which the field of the magnetic head is oriented. The potential energy is, from equation (2.114),

$$U_m = -\mu_0 H m \cos\theta \tag{2.121}$$

where m is the particle moment. Figure 2.18 shows the total energy, $U_a + U_m$, plotted versus θ for various values of applied field. At zero applied field, there are two distinct energy minima, or wells, at $\theta = 0°$ and $180°$, corresponding to two stable states of magnetization along the easy axis as expected. As H is increased in a positive sense, the well at $0°$ becomes depressed and steeper, while that at $180°$ is elevated and shallower. At a critical field H_{crit}, the energy minimum at $180°$ becomes a maximum, and magnetization oriented opposite to the applied field is an unstable state.

The value for H_{crit} may be found by setting the second derivative of the total energy equal to zero and solving for the applied field:

$$\frac{d^2 U_{tot}}{d\theta^2} = -2K\cos\theta + \mu_0 H m\cos\theta = 0 \tag{2.122}$$

from which

$$H_{crit} = \frac{2K}{\mu_0 m} \tag{2.123}$$

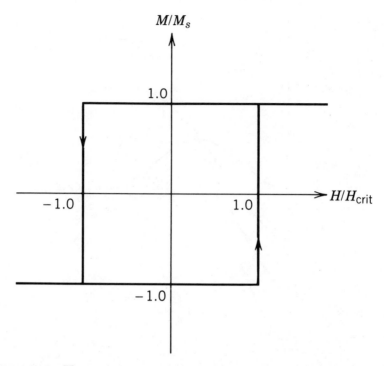

FIGURE 2.19   Hysteresis loop for single-domain particle aligned with applied field.

The magnetization process is summarized in the hysteresis loop of Figure 2.19. The loop is perfectly square with a coercive force equal to H_{crit}. This analysis is readily extended to arbitrary angles of applied field with respect to the easy axis. Stoner and Wohlfarth [10] solved this problem in detail and derived hysteresis loops for assemblies of particles with random orientation of easy axes. Their work has been fundamental to the understanding of the magnetic recording process in particulate media.

REFERENCES

1. *The Physics of Electricity and Magnetism*, W. T. Scott, Wiley, New York, 2nd Edition, 1966.
2. *Fields and Waves in Communications Electronics*, S. Ramo, J. R. Whinnery, and T. Van Duzer, Wiley, New York, 1967.
3. *Foundations of Electromagnetic Theory*, J. R. Reitz, F. J. Milford, and R. W. Christy, Addison-Wesley, Reading, MA, 3rd Edition, 1979.
4. *Finite Elements for Electrical Engineers*, R. P. Silvester and R. L. Ferrari, Cambridge University Press, Cambridge, 1983.
5. "Survey of Numerical Methods in Field Calculations," T. Tortschanoff, *IEEE Trans. Magn.*, MAG-20, pp. 1912–1917, 1984.

6. *Physical Theory of Ferromagnetic Domains*, C. Kittel, Bell Telephone System Monograph 1709, Bell Laboratories, 1949.

7. *Ferromagnetism*, R. M. Bozorth, Van Nostrand, New York, 1951.

8. *Introduction to Solid State Physics*, C. Kittel, Wiley, New York, 2nd Edition, 1956.

9. *Introduction to Magnetic Materials*, B. D. Cullity, Addison-Wesley, Reading, MA, 1972.

10. *"A Mechanism of Magnetic Hysteresis in Heterogeneous Alloys,"* E. C. Stoner and E. P. Wohlfarth, *Phil. Trans. Roy. Soc. Ser. A*, Vol. 240, pp. 599–642, 1948.

CHAPTER 3

THEORY OF THE DIGITAL MAGNETIC RECORDING PROCESS: READING

In digital magnetic recording data is handled in a *binary* symbolism. The use of binary sequences makes the theory of digital magnetic recording more analogous to time domain analysis, in contrast to traditional analog magnetic recording theory, which primarily focuses on frequency or wavelength response. Consequently, digital magnetic recording is most properly and effectively treated as a distinctive subject in itself. The step function output response of a magnetic recording system (a voltage pulse for a steplike change in write current) is the most *fundamental* descriptive characterization for the digital magnetic recording channel.

The purpose of this chapter is to develop a useful theory and associated set of mathematical models specifically suited to digital magnetic recording. We want particularly to formulate the issues in a manner that will give insight into the basic nature of the magnetic recording process and from which valid engineering design criteria may be readily derived. For this reason the emphasis will be on concepts and explicit mathematical relations rather than on quantitative data. Digital magnetic recording performance will be clearly related to the basic parameters of the recording operation.

Figure 3.1 shows a generalized block diagram, indicating the overall input–output transfer function block diagram in magnetic recording. The magnetic recording process consists of two distinct operations, writing and reading. The relative motion of the storage medium provides the means by which signals in time are preserved in space, as Figure 3.1 indicates. At some arbitrary later period of time, the written information can be scanned and the stored signal recovered as a waveform in time. The relative velocity v represents the scale factor that relates the time and space domains in the recording process. There-

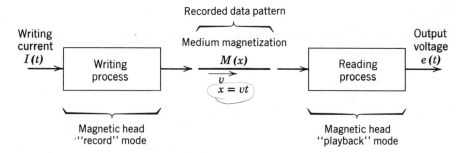

FIGURE 3.1 Magnetic recording process.

fore, it is possible to separate time-dependent factors from spatially dependent factors in analyzing overall magnetic recording performance. The source of the signal energy from the head is the spindle motor providing the relative motion between medium and head.

This chapter is devoted to the magnetic head–magnetic medium interaction phenomena as related to the read process in digital magnetic recording, while the next chapter treats the write process. Great attention will be given to the issue of head–medium magnetic coupling in digital recording processes, since it intrinsically establishes the storage density potential.

The theory of magnetic recording can be based on quasimagnetostatic field theory. For any given recording frequency, the ratio of the recorded wavelength to the associated free space electromagnetic wavelength, for the same frequency, is given by v/c, where c is the velocity of light. Magnetic recording is concerned with spatial dimensions (e.g., the head-to-medium spacing) less than or of the order of the shortest recorded wavelength. Therefore, we can neglect retardation phenomena and deal simply with quasistatic field relations. There may still be, of course, a measurable time lag produced by eddy currents associated with flux changes impressed on a magnetic head (Chapter 5) as well as the conventional time-dependent behavior arising from the electrical characteristics of the transducer that must be considered.

Recording of binary signals generally dictates using two opposite senses of medium saturation to define the two distinct magnetization states required. In saturation recording, the write current can be chosen large enough in a well-designed system to assure consistent reproducibility of two medium states, independent of the previous history of the recorded magnetization. Thus, saturation recording is assumed in the subsequent discussions, although this assumption is not essential to the bulk of the exposition. The read process has been selected to be studied first, as this will provide a better introductory perspective of the magnetic recording process. Elegance and rigor are not ends in themselves and, where warranted, will be subordinated to the twin objectives of clarity of comprehension and utility of results.

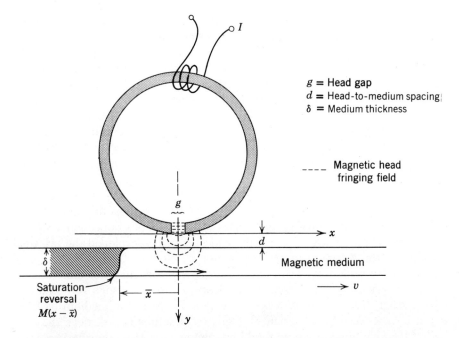

FIGURE 3.2   Magnetic ring head and medium, longitudinal recording.

3.1 PRINCIPLE OF RECIPROCITY

The write process dictates a high saturation flux density in order to write on high-coercivity media. On reading, it is the magnetic field from the recorded magnetization pattern that gives rise to flux in the magnetic head. The resulting magnetic head flux density is quite small, especially in comparison to the saturation flux density of the head material. Moreover, we are concerned here with a very high permeability magnetic core that includes a nonmagnetic gap structure. The head gap is a linear magnetic element that essentially dominates and linearizes the magnetic behavior of the magnetic head path (i.e., the ratio of flux to applied current is equal to a constant). Therefore, it is a valid approximation to assume that the magnetic head will act as a linear component on readback. Further, in view of the high relative permeability of the *magnetic head* in comparison to its surroundings, we can consider its permeability infinite. In digital magnetic recording, with every region of a track magnetized to saturation, the relative permeability of the magnetic storage medium can be considered as closely equal to one. The magnetic medium with its recorded magnetization distribution then appears as a "frozen" magnetic field source.

Under the conditions given, the principle of reciprocity can be very effectively applied to determine the magnetic coupling between the recording medium and the magnetic head on readback. Figure 3.2 illustrates the conventional ring head with a generalized picture of the magnetic field distribution setup along the recording medium when the *read coil* is energized. If only one coil is used for both writing and reading, then this coil is referred to as the read coil in what follows. Under the assumption of infinite permeability, the magnetic head boundaries are magnetic equipotentials, and it is clear that it is very much easier to determine the fringing magnetic field of the gap than to ascertain the flux from a given magnetization pattern that passes through the coil on the head core. Since the head gap g is much less than the head width W, the magnetic field pattern is effectively two-dimensional, as shown. Note that the magnetics of contact recording may be viewed as a special case of noncontact recording, corresponding to setting the parameter d equal to zero. Knowing the magnetic head field distribution $\mathbf{H}(x)$ due to 1 ampere-turn through the read coil, the flux Φ, through an arbitrary cross section of the magnetic recording medium caused by NI ampere-turns through the read coil, can be calculated. $\mathbf{H}(x)$ also varies with y and this dependency will be introduced as appropriate, but for the concepts being developed the principal focus is on the direction of relative motion x. Now the reciprocity theorem states that the same number of ampere-turns NI, encircling this cross section of the recording medium, excites the identical flux Φ through the read coil on the magnetic head. If we were to replace the magnetic medium by a set of current sources of appropriate strength, the resulting flux through the read coil of the head could then be found by summing the flux contributions from all these currents, determined in this manner.

With medium motion, the magnetization pattern $\mathbf{M}$ is continually moving relative to the head. Therefore, $\mathbf{M} = \mathbf{M}(x - \bar{x})$ where $\bar{x} = vt$. The variable $(x - \bar{x})$ establishes the gap centerline of the stationary magnetic head as the frame of reference for $\mathbf{M}$. Then t (or $\bar{x}$) equal to zero corresponds to the defined magnetization pattern being directly centered under the magnetic head. The head fringing field $\mathbf{H}(x)$ is of course fixed with respect to the x axis. Note that with time, t, the pattern is scanned from right to left or in the negative x direction.

Let the head-gap fringing field magnitude be considered normalized to a unit magnetomotive force. That is, $\mathbf{H}$ is defined for $NI = 1$, where N is the number of turns on the read coil. The fringing field of the magnetic head coupling with the medium is composed of two magnetic field components, H_x and H_y. Thus, 1 ampere-turn through the read coil would excite in an element of the magnetic medium of width W and thickness dy a differential flux

$$d\Phi_x = \mu_0 H_x W \, dy \qquad (3.1)$$

where the subscript x denotes the x-directed components. According to the reciprocity theorem, 1 ampere-turn around the element $W \, dy$ would excite the same flux in the head read coil.

If the medium is actually magnetized with a horizontal component of magnetization $M_x(x - \bar{x})$, the magnetic moment of an element of length dx and cross section $W \, dy$ forms a magnetic shell that is equivalent to a current of magnitude equal to

$$M_x(x - \overline{x})dx \tag{3.2}$$

encircling the element $W\,dy$. This equivalent current represents the factor to be applied to equation (3.1) to adjust the latter to the actual level of the medium magnetization. The total flux through the read coil of the magnetic head caused by M_x is then obtained by integration of the differential flux contributions, arising from this magnetized pattern along the track, and is equal to

$$\Phi_x(\overline{x}) = \mu_0 W \int_{y=d}^{d+\delta} \int_{x=-\infty}^{+\infty} M_x(x - \overline{x}, y) H_x(x, y) dx\, dy \tag{3.3}$$

where δ is the thickness of the recording medium and d the spacing of the medium from the magnetic head (Figure 3.2). Φ_x is a function of $\overline{x}$, since the flux linking the read coil at any instant of time will depend on the corresponding location of the magnetization pattern relative to the position of the magnetic head.

In a similar manner,

$$d\Phi_y = \mu_0 H_y W\, dx \tag{3.4}$$

where we now deal with a cross section in the plane of the medium, since $d\Phi_y$ is by definition normal to the recording medium. Similarly, with a perpendicular component of magnetization M_y, the resulting magnetic moment of an element of length dy is equivalent to a current equal to

$$M_y(x - \overline{x})dy \tag{3.5}$$

encircling the element $W\,dx$.

Thus, the flux linking the read coil produced by a recorded magnetization component M_y is

$$\Phi_y(\overline{x}) = \mu_0 W \int_{y=d}^{d+\delta} \int_{x=-\infty}^{+\infty} M_y(x - \overline{x}, y) H_y(x, y) dx\, dy \tag{3.6}$$

Or, in general,

$$\Phi(\overline{x}) = \mu_0 W \int_{y=d}^{d+\delta} \int_{x=-\infty}^{+\infty} \mathbf{M}(x - \overline{x}, y) \cdot \mathbf{H}(x, y) dx\, dy \tag{3.7}$$

where we take the *dot* product of the two vectors. It should be noted that the two flux contributions, arising respectively from M_x and M_y, being scalar quantities, are linearly superimposed. Where only one component of magnetization exists, the behavior on reading depends *only* on the nature of the corresponding component of the magnetic head fringing field. Equations (3.3) and (3.6) represent extremely powerful tools in the analysis of the digital magnetic recording process, for they provide an effective means to deal with discontinuous and nonperiodic magnetization patterns characteristic of digital recording. $\mathbf{H}$ is proportional to NI and in the above equation $\mathbf{H}$ has been normalized to 1 ampere-turn and its actual units are (H/NI) or meters^{-1}.

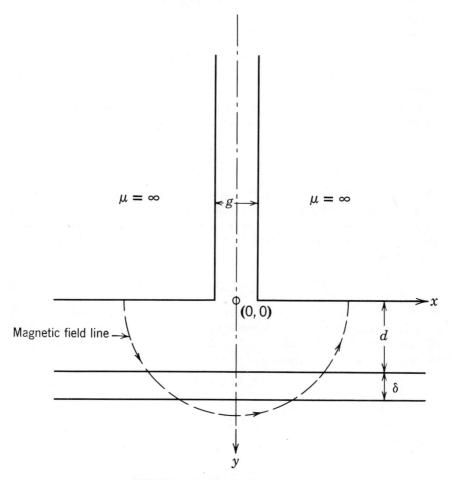

FIGURE 3.3   Idealized ring head.

3.2 IDEALIZED RING HEAD

An idealized ring head is shown in Figure 3.3. The pole faces in this structure are parallel to the recording medium, and they are assumed to extend to infinity. The gap or throat height also extends to infinity in the $-y$ direction. Again, the permeability of the magnetic head core is assumed to be infinite. This convenient model is usually a valid representation for many magnetic heads, and therefore results obtained using it are of wide general interest. In particular, it permits analytical means to be applied to calculate the relative influence of the various spatial parameters encountered in the magnetic recording process.

A precise analytic solution of this idealized ring-head fringing field is not obtainable in explicit form, and the equations involved are quite complicated, even though the geometry is simple. An analytical expression (Karlqvist [2]) has been obtained for the fringing field component $H_x(x,y)$ of this idealized ring head by assuming a linear magnetic potential variation across the gap at the plane $y = 0$ (Figure 3.3). This expression gives a very close approximation to the fringing field except very near the gap region for example, distances from the pole faces much less than the gap length [8]. The horizontal fringing field component is of primary importance, since, in writing with a ring head on a medium with an in-plane easy axis, longitudinal magnetization is predominant. Often, further simplifications are made, depending on the ratio of y/g to obtain expressions for the fringing field components. Their applicability is justified because: (1) only relatively coarse control can be exercised in magnetic recording technology over the precision, stability, and reproducibility of the geometric dimensions in the head–medium interface; and (2) the possibilities for precise instrumentation and, consequently, detailed experimental confirmation of theory are severely limited. Engineering design, of course, must strike a proper balance between useful theory and practice.

By viewing the idealized head fringing field as arising from equal and opposite sheets of magnetic charge density on the inner gap surfaces (an approach discussed in Chapter 2), a visual way to see and express the fringing field equations is possible. These fields can be expressed and estimated in terms of the subtended angle and distances from a field point to the pole face corners, and H_g, the deep gap field, as shown in Figure 3.4.

$$H_x(x,y) = \frac{H_g \Omega}{2\pi} = \frac{H_g(\theta_1 - \theta_2)}{2\pi} \tag{3.8}$$

or

$$H_x(x,y) = \frac{H_g}{2\pi}\left[\tan^{-1}\left(\frac{x+g/2}{y}\right) - \tan^{-1}\left(\frac{x-g/2}{y}\right)\right] \tag{3.9}$$

and

$$H_y(x,y) = \frac{H_g}{2\pi}\ln\left(\frac{R_2}{R_1}\right) = \frac{H_g}{4\pi}\ln\left[\frac{(x+g/2)^2 + y^2}{(x-g/2)^2 + y^2}\right] \tag{3.10}$$

To agree with the Karlqvist equations, which are based on a magnetic potential approach, it is necessary to multiply them by a factor of 2, making $H(0,0) = H_x(0,0) = H_g$.

For a magnetic head with an infinite permeability, we have

$$H_g g = NI \tag{3.11}$$

The maximum horizontal field intensity for a given value of y will occur along the plane $x = 0$. The equation giving the dependency of $H_x|_{\max}$ upon $y(y > 0)$ is then

$$H_x(0,y) = \frac{2NI}{\pi g}\tan^{-1}\left(\frac{g/2}{y}\right) \tag{3.12}$$

For $y \gg g/2$, this equation can be simplified to

$$H_x(0,y) = \frac{NI}{\pi y} \tag{3.13}$$

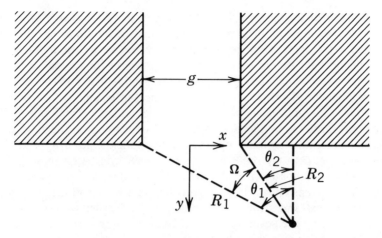

FIGURE 3.4 H_x and H_y in terms of angle and distances.

For the plane $y = 0$, normalizing H_g by NI,

$$H_x(x,0) = \begin{cases} 0 & |x| > g/2 \\ 1/g & |x| < g/2 \end{cases}$$

(3.14)

This result corresponds to the pole faces being constant potentials and, of course, just represents a check with the basic assumptions upon which equation (3.8) was derived.

Also, we note above that at large values of y, the value of the fringing field along the gap center drops off inversely with spacing. A region where we can obtain a simplified formulation of $H_x(x)$ is for values of spacing y for which $y > g$. Whereas this relation can be obtained by mathematical manipulations by using equation (3.8), it is much more instructive to deduce the form of H_x by a geometrical consideration of the field of Figure 3.3, under the condition that g approaches zero. Then the magnetic equipotential lines, subdividing the region between the external pole faces, become radial. The magnetic field lines are then semicircles and also lines of constant magnetic field strength. Thus, using the line integral equation relating H to the magnetic potential difference,

$$H = \frac{NI}{\pi r}$$

(3.15)

where $r^2 = x^2 + y^2$.

We then have

$$H_x = H\frac{y}{r} = \frac{NI}{\pi}\left(\frac{y}{x^2 + y^2}\right)$$

(3.16)

and with the definitions of the x- and y-coordinate axes:

$$H_y = -H_x\frac{x}{y}$$

(3.17)

Note that for a given value of y, H_x has a Lorentzian shape. This equation for H_x, completely valid for $y \gg g$, is identical with the field that would be obtained from a "filamentary" wire current source placed at the gap origin $x = y = 0$ in place of the idealized ring head. For obvious reasons these particular fringing field expressions are frequently referred to as the "far field" equations of a magnetic head.

In the expressions above, the parameter g no longer appears. This is consistent with our initial assumption that g is negligible compared to the other spatial dimensions. Even for y only somewhat larger than g, these expressions are good approximations and thus represent particularly simple and useful analytical models for purposes of mathematical analyses of magnetic recording behavior.

3.3 STEP FUNCTION CHANGE IN MAGNETIZATION

The signal we obtain on readback is a voltage, proportional to the time derivative of flux through the read coil. We are especially interested in the waveform of the voltage pulse produced for a step function change in magnetization, since any pattern of magnetization changes made up of alternations between two discrete states can be resolved into a unique series of step functions. Then the output voltage for a given binary input signal can be synthesized from a single standard waveform response. In this section we will obtain and characterize the behavior of this waveform with respect to head–medium geometry. Therefore, we shall first extend equation (3.3) to obtain a general expression for the read coil voltage.

Since

$$e_x(vt) = e_x(\overline{x}) = vN\frac{d\Phi_x}{d\overline{x}} \tag{3.18}$$

we can write

$$e_x(\overline{x}) = \mu_0 W v N \int_d^{d+\delta} \int_{-\infty}^{+\infty} \frac{\partial M_x(x-\overline{x},y)}{\partial \overline{x}} H_x(x,y)\,dx\,dy \tag{3.19}$$

We express e_x as a function of $\overline{x}$, since the output voltage is inherently related to a distance measure rather than absolute time. As $\overline{x} = vt$, v is a scale factor for the output voltage both in time (pulse width) and in amplitude, as indicated by equation (3.18). The integral in equation (3.19) is a superposition or convolution integral, and thus H_x can be thought of as a "weighting" function. It is a measure of the sensitivity of the coupling between head and magnetization of the medium and is often referred to as the "head sensitivity function."

Let us now consider the case where $M_y = 0$ and we have a step function change in horizontal magnetization M_x from $-M_r$ to $+M_r$ throughout the recording medium (see Figure 3.2, for example). We will not initially place any restraints on the spatial parameters, d, δ, and g.

Now for the problem under consideration,

$$\frac{\partial M_x(x - \overline{x})}{\partial x} \equiv -M_x'(x - \overline{x}) = -2M_r\,\delta(x - \overline{x}) \tag{3.20}$$

where $\delta(x - \overline{x})$ is the unit impulse or delta function (area = 1). Then, substituting in equation (3.19), we find

$$e(\overline{x}) = e_x(\overline{x}) \propto \int_d^{d+\delta} H_x(\overline{x}, y)\,dy \tag{3.21}$$

the various constants being omitted to give maximum focus on perhaps the most significant relation in digital (or pulse) magnetic recording. Equation (3.21) provides a direct means of predicting the shape of the output pulse from a step change in magnetization, knowing the coupling fringing field of the magnetic head. This expression is applicable to any magnetic head structure, although an estimate for H_x is essential. H_x may be determined analytically, graphically, numerically, or experimentally, depending on the suitability of a given method for the complexity of the problem. If there were also a perpendicular component of magnetization present, its output voltage contribution would depend in a similar manner on H_y and directly add algebraically to the above signal.

For $\delta/d \to 0$,

$$e(\overline{x}) \propto \delta H_x(\overline{x}, d) \tag{3.22}$$

Equation (3.22) states that if the ratio δ/d is small, the output voltage waveform in time from a steplike horizontal magnetization reversal will resemble the static field distribution of the head H_x at a distance d from the head and the pulse amplitude will be proportional to the medium thickness δ. For a step function change in M_y, we have

$$e(\overline{x}) \propto \delta H_y(\overline{x}, d) \tag{3.23}$$

If the recorded magnetization has a component out of the plane, then the output signal will be the sum of the contributions for the two magnetization components. Since the orientation of the write field on the trailing leg, where the transition is written, lies at a large angle with respect to the medium (see Figure 3.3), a significant perpendicular component of magnetization may be recorded, particularly if the medium is somewhat isotropic. Given the axes shown, we see that in this case the magnetization will be oriented either with $+M_x$ combined with the $-M_y$ component or with both directions reversed, that is, the magnetization vector will lie in either the first or third quadrants. As expected, the maximum coupling at a given location arises when the magnetization is parallel to the direction of the fringing field at that point. The resulting pulse is asymmetrical, since no matter how the magnetization is aligned, H_x is an even function and H_y is an odd function. Again, returning to the case where $d > g$, we can use equation (3.16) as follows:

$$H_x \propto \frac{y}{r^2} = \frac{y}{x^2 + y^2} \tag{3.24}$$

and therefore

$$e(\bar{x}) \propto \int_d^{d+\delta} \frac{y\,dy}{\bar{x}^2 + y^2} = \ln \left[\frac{\bar{x}^2 + (d+\delta)^2}{\bar{x}^2 + d^2} \right] \qquad (3.25)$$

The peak value for this pulse occurs at $\bar{x} = 0$:

$$e_{pk} \propto 2\ln \frac{d+\delta}{d} \qquad (3.26)$$

An important parameter of any readback pulse is PW_{50}, defined as the width of the pulse at its half-amplitude points. Let x_{50} be the value of x at which the pulse amplitude is equal to half the peak value. Substituting into (3.25) we have

$$\ln \frac{d+\delta}{d} = \ln \frac{x_{50}^2 + (d+\delta)^2}{x_{50}^2 + d^2} \qquad (3.27)$$

Solving for x_{50}, and noting that

$$PW_{50} = 2x_{50}$$

we get

$$PW_{50} = 2[d(d+\delta)]^{1/2} \qquad (3.28)$$

The term

$$[d(d+\delta)]^{1/2}$$

is the geometric mean spacing of the medium from the head. This distance is a natural choice in defining an "effective" spacing for the medium, as it provides a bias toward the top surface where the magnetic coupling is stronger. A reasonably thin medium (that is uniformly magnetized) can be represented by a magnetization thickness factor proportional to $M_r\delta$ at a spacing y' where $y' = [d(d+\delta)]^{1/2}$. In order to include the gap length we use the Karlqvist expression to recalculate the value of x_{50}. A PW_{50} that then includes all the geometrical parameters will be twice this distance.

We can rewrite equation (3.9) by using the tangent identity

$$\tan(A - B) = \frac{\tan A - \tan B}{1 - \tan A \tan B} \qquad (3.29)$$

Where we define

$$A = \tan^{-1}[(x + g/2)/y'] \qquad \text{or} \qquad \tan A = (x + g/2)/y'$$
$$B = \tan^{-1}[(x - g/2)/y'] \qquad \text{or} \qquad \tan B = (x - g/2)/y'$$

we can then express the equation for H_x in the following form:

$$\tan[H_x(x,y')\pi/H_g] = \left[\frac{g y'}{y'^2 - x^2 + (g/2)^2} \right] \qquad (3.30)$$

But previously we found

$$H_x(0, y')\pi/H_g = 2\tan^{-1}(g/2y')$$

and therefore setting $H_x(x_{50}, y')$ equal to one-half this value, we require

$$\tan[H_x(x_{50}, y')\pi/H_g] = g/2y'$$

Thus, at $x = x_{50}$

$$\frac{g}{2y'} = \left[\frac{g y'}{y'^2 - x_{50}^2 + (g/2)^2}\right] \tag{3.31}$$

Solving this equation for x_{50}, we get

$$x_{50} = [(g/2)^2 + y'^2]^{1/2}$$

Therefore, the earlier expression for PW_{50} can be now modified to include all three geometrical parameters:

$$PW_{50} = 2\left[(g/2)^2 + d(d + \delta)\right]^{1/2}$$

or, as more commonly written,

$$PW_{50} = \sqrt{g^2 + 4d(d + \delta)} \tag{3.32}$$

In Chapter 4 we will see how this expression can be further modified to account for an arctangent approximation to a recorded transition.

For spacings larger than the gap length and with a thin medium, we can use the series approximation

$$\ln(1 + u) \approx u$$

in (3.25) to obtain

$$e(\bar{x}) \propto \frac{\delta/d}{1 + (\bar{x}/d)^2} \tag{3.33}$$

This expression very directly shows the manner in which the spatial parameters affect both the output pulse amplitude and pulse shape when the head-to-medium spacing is the dominant parameter.

Furthermore,

$$\frac{e(\bar{x})}{e(0)} = \frac{1}{1 + (\bar{x}/d)^2} \tag{3.34}$$

where $e(0) = e_{\text{peak}}$. If we measure the pulse width at the points where the relative amplitude of the pulse is down to 10 percent of its peak value, we find

$$|(\bar{x}/d)| = 3.0 \tag{3.35}$$

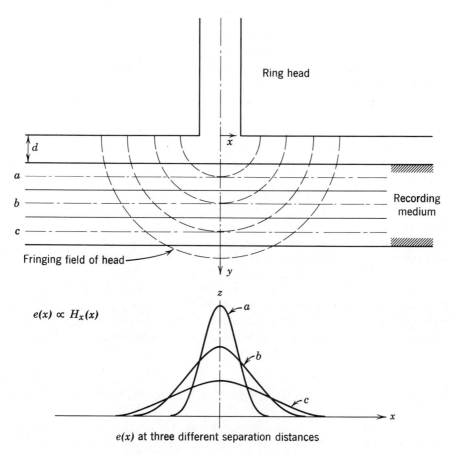

$e(x)$ at three different separation distances

FIGURE 3.5 Step response output signals.

or the pulse width PW_{10} is equal to six times the head-to-medium spacing. The pulse shape is Lorentzian.

Figure 3.5 illustrates the character of output signal that would be obtained from a step change in horizontal magnetization along a differential recording layer, when located at progressively larger distances from the head. The waveforms are identical with the fringing field component H_x at these same spacings. For the overall recording medium indicated, the net output pulse may be approximated to a fair degree by the linear addition of the component signals produced by the three strata shown. The further a given stratum is from the magnetic head, the smaller its corresponding output signal amplitude and the broader its pulse width. For highest pulse resolution, a very thin medium is hence required, unless it is practicable to use nonsaturation recording techniques which can confine the magnetized layer to the upper section of the medium. In either case, increasing pulse resolution by reducing the thickness of the magnetized layer means the acceptance of an appreciable reduction in the isolated pulse amplitude. The reduction in thickness as an approach to improvement in pulse resolution, of course, will be only important when there results a significant decrease in the effective spacing y'.

Figure 3.6 gives curves of H_x and H_y for the idealized ring head. It is seen that the output signal from a step change in perpendicular magnetization will be a dipulse. Any significant degree of perpendicular magnetization will result in pulse distortion because of the nature of this contribution to the total output signal. Figure 3.6 also shows the pulse asymmetry that results when both components of magnetization are present. Note that when the transition passes by the trailing leg (where it was recorded), **M** and **H** tend to be more parallel than when the transition is going by the leading leg, and from reciprocity we see that the output signal is consequently greater. The difference in response between e_x and e_y provides a means to determine the general character of the medium magnetization. It is found that with ring heads, used in conjunction with media oriented in-plane, it is generally adequate to assume that the resultant magnetization is entirely horizontal. Thus, great attention is given in the design of the magnetic head configuration to narrow the H_x coupling function of the recording system. This type of improvement is directly translated into a higher pulse resolution. In addition to gap length and magnetic pole widths, factors such as the contouring of pole tips, coil location, and so on, can contribute significantly to the shape of the head sensitivity function and consequently to the readback pulse.

3.4 FINITE TRANSITION WIDTH IN THE MAGNETIZATION REVERSAL

In practice we would not expect to record true step changes in magnetization. Here we shall consider how the output pulse is modified if the change in magnetization from $-M_r$ to $+M_r$ occurs over a distance x_1 in a uniform manner, that is, M is a ramp function. Again, we consider the case of a thin medium and assume $H_x(x)$ does not vary throughout the medium thickness.

We see from Figure 3.7

$$
\begin{aligned}
M_x' &= 0 & x &\leq \overline{x} \\
M_x' &= \frac{2M_r}{x_1} & \overline{x} &\leq x \leq \overline{x} + x_1 \\
M_x' &= 0 & x &\geq \overline{x} + x_1
\end{aligned}
\tag{3.36}
$$

Substituting into equation (3.19), we obtain

$$
e(\overline{x}) \propto \frac{\displaystyle\int_{\overline{x}}^{\overline{x}+x_1} H_x(x)\,dx}{x_1}
\tag{3.37}
$$

This expression is seen to agree with our earlier analysis, as $x_1 \to 0$. Equation (3.37) may be interpreted as follows. $e(\overline{x})$ is obtained by averaging H_x over the distance x_1 for all values of $\overline{x}$. The finite transition width x_1 has the

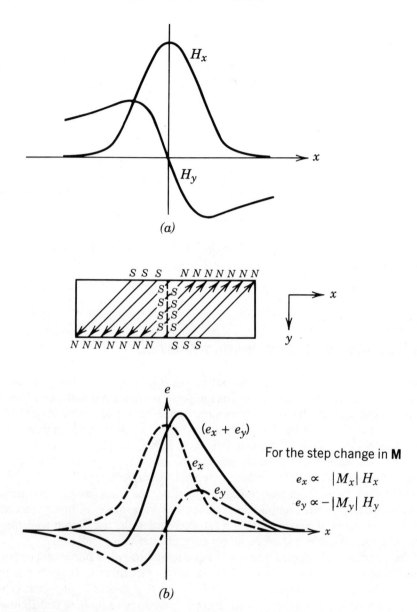

FIGURE 3.6 Output signal when both components of magnetization are present.

effect of reducing the signal peak and increasing the pulse width. To a first-order approximation, the pulse width will be increased by the amount x_1 over that obtained from a step change in magnetization, and the pulse amplitude will be reduced to the average of the pulse peak signal over the distance x_1. Normally, x_1 is considerably less than the spread of H_x along the track, and

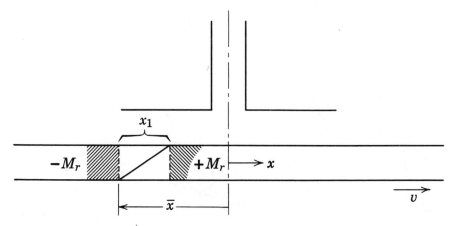

FIGURE 3.7 Model for finite width of magnetization reversal.

therefore the step function approximation for a magnetization change can often prove adequate.

3.5 VOLTAGE WAVEFORM CHARACTERISTICS

The basic signal characteristic is an output pulse for a step change in horizontal magnetization. The peak of the voltage pulse is coincident with the passage of the magnetization change, or transition, by the center of the head gap. The pulse duration is given by the time required for the transition to traverse the horizontal fringing field of the magnetic head gap. Changing the speed of relative motion will proportionately change the pulse amplitude and inversely change the pulse width. Since a step reversal in saturation represents the maximum change in medium magnetization possible, the associated output pulse gives the peak readback amplitude obtainable. Furthermore, in binary recording the two states of magnetization must alternate; thus, the output waveform from a recorded pattern must be a sequence of alternating pulses.

The principles developed here apply equally well to either horizontal or perpendicular magnetization. To predict recording performance, it is absolutely essential to have an adequate picture of the reading head fringing field. The relation between the magnetic head structure and its fringing field distribution will be further addressed in Chapter 5. Frequently, the idealized ring head serves as an adequate model for initial design analysis.

Another fundamental property of the fringing field H_x (or the output voltage pulse) may be seen by reference to Figure 3.8, which shows two pole pieces of infinite permeability material with a magnetic potential drop of 1 ampere-turn between them. Shown by dotted line is an integration path from one pole piece of a magnetic head to the other. We have seen that the line integral $\int \mathbf{H} \cdot d\mathbf{l} = 1$ (the potential difference) for any path chosen. As the path

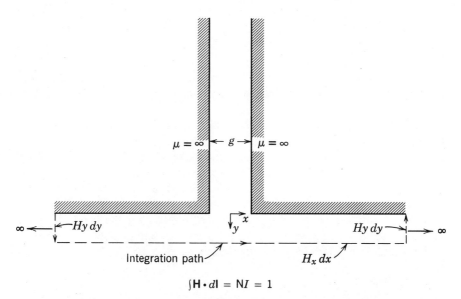

$$\int \mathbf{H} \cdot d\mathbf{l} = NI = 1$$

FIGURE 3.8 Selected path of line integral of fringing field.

shown is modified and the vertical path segments move further away from the gap, their contribution to the integral becomes very small. In the limit,

$$\int_{-\infty}^{+\infty} H_x \, dx = 1.0 \tag{3.38}$$

This is an exceedingly useful relation, since we already have derived an equation for the amplitude of $H_x(0, y)$. We are able to state a great deal about the general nature of the H_x fringing field without any real computation. We know that (1) the integral from $-\infty$ to $+\infty$ of the function $H_x(x)$ is constant, independent of the value of y taken for the integration path; (2) we have a relation for $H_x|_{max}$ versus y; and (3) H_x is symmetrical about $x = 0$ for a symmetrical head structure. These conclusions will also apply directly to the output pulse. That is,

$$\int_{-\infty}^{+\infty} e(\bar{x}) \, d\bar{x} \propto \int_{-\infty}^{+\infty} H_x(x) \, dx \tag{3.39}$$

or the voltage pulse area is essentially independent of spacing. Further, in the time domain

$$e(t) = N \frac{d\Phi}{dt}$$

thus

$$\int_{-\infty}^{+\infty} e \, dt = N \int_{-\Phi_r}^{+\Phi_r} d\Phi = 2N\Phi_r \tag{3.40}$$

Also

$$\Phi_r \propto M_r \delta$$

so that

$$\int_{-\infty}^{+\infty} e\,dt \propto 2NM_r\delta \qquad (3.41)$$

Geometrical scaling is an important design concept. For example, with a ring head with broad pole faces, if we reduce both g and d by a factor of 2 (δ being quite small), the resulting fringing field function is identical, since we have merely scaled both axes by a factor of $1/2$. Accordingly, in this instance, the output pulse width would be halved. As the pulse area does not change, as we have seen above, we could expect the pulse amplitude to double, which is necessary to preserve the integral relation given above. The reason so much emphasis is placed on the reduction of dimensions becomes evident from the consequences of geometrically scaling down the coupling fringing field.

In practice, the inductance and distributed capacity of the head influence the basic readback pulse shape set by the head–medium magnetic coupling of head and medium. The electrical characteristics of magnetic heads and their impedance are subjects included in Chapter 5.

3.5.1 Three-Dimensional Factors

Even though a two-dimensional model is valid for the fringing field along the track as $W \gg g$, there will exist some degree of magnetic coupling between head and medium in the transverse direction at the edges of the head, leading to side writing and reading. Normally, this will be a small effect. A track profile can be obtained by writing a track and then scanning the head transversely while reading back and measuring the signal output. If the read/write head width defines exactly the recorded track width, then a triangular waveform will result. The maximum occurs when the head is at the recorded track center and the amplitude goes to zero linearly with distance off center, reaching zero when the head has been moved a distance to either side equal to its own width. The head or track width can then be defined as the distance between the half-amplitude points. A departure from this ideal track profile is an indication that side fringing effects are occurring.

A simple way to visualize and estimate these side fringing fields to gain an idea of their significance will be outlined (for simplicity a thin medium is assumed and we let $y' = d$).

As shown earlier,

$$H_x(0,d) = \frac{H_g}{\pi} 2\tan^{-1}(g/2d) \qquad (3.42)$$

On writing, in order to assure saturation we would normally set

$$H_x(0,d) \geq 2H_c$$

Now let us consider the $H_x(z)$ field of the head for $x = y = 0$, where z is the distance along the outward normal from one side of the head. The magnetic surfaces of an idealized ring head, when viewed from either side, appear similar to that of the pole faces when viewed from the medium, except that in this latter case the poles extended in both the $\pm z$ directions to infinity. When the head is similarly viewed from the side, the poles extend to infinity only in the $-y$ direction. Thus, the H_x component at the side effectively arises from an equivalent head only "half" as wide. Based on symmetry arguments, H_x at $x = 0$, $y = 0$, $z = d$ will be one-half its value at $x = 0$, $y = d$, there being no variation with z in this latter case (since we are referencing the normal x, y fringing field of an ideal head). Choosing $y = 0$ gives the maximum value for the H_x side fringing field and provides an approximate answer without much difficulty. Moreover, we can view the side fringing magnetic coupling as decreasing with distance from the side of the head in the same manner as the useful fringing field decreases with spacing. The attenuation factor in both cases is set by the same gap and hence gap length.

Side-writing

We immediately conclude that at a distance of $z = d$ the maximum side-writing field in the x direction H_x is approximately H_c for the condition taken above, i.e., $H_x(0, d) = 2H_c$. The distance from the sides of the head over which the write field may influence the recorded state of the medium is on the order of the spacing. However, with a relatively large gap the write field does not drop off very rapidly with distance and consequently the side fringing fields can have an effect over greater distances, depending on the magnitude of the current chosen to assure saturation. The "low resolution" characteristic of the side fringing fields in the lateral direction because they couple with a medium that extends indefinitely in the z direction—can product erasure effects on the track edges even with magnetic field intensities less than H_c. This is totally unlike that in the y direction, where the magnetic coupling occurs only over a distance δ.

Side-reading

The side fringing fields also determine the sensitivity to side-reading. Again, estimates can be made by relating the side fields to the actual head sensitivity function along the track. However, on reading, the side signal contribution must be compared to the full track width signal, and if W is much greater than the extent of this side coupling, this side-reading effect will be small. Further, since short-wavelength response drops rapidly with distance, most of the signal contribution from side-reading will be in the longer-wavelength or low-frequency range.

3.6 WAVELENGTH RESPONSE AND SINE WAVE MAGNETIZATION

The wavelength response of a recording system corresponds to the frequency response of an electrical circuit, but here wavelength, measured in terms of distance along the recording medium, is the fundamental parameter rather than frequency. The geometry of the recording head–medium region is the crucial aspect in magnetic recording. The associated frequency response is determined by the relative velocity between the head and medium.

To develop the wavelength response we use the Fourier transform, relating distance x and wave number k where the variable $k = 2\pi/\lambda$. Note that k is inversely proportional to the wavelength λ and thus the frequency will be directly proportional to k, that is, $f = v/\lambda = vk/2\pi$.

The following are Fourier transform pairs for a function $f(x)$ and its derivatives:

$$
\begin{array}{ll}
f(x) & F(k) \\
f'(x) & jkF(k) \\
f''(x) & -k^2 F(k)
\end{array}
$$

We can express the magnetic potential in the recording region, created by the magnetic head for our two-dimensional case as follows, using Laplace's equation:

$$\left[\frac{\partial^2}{\partial x^2} + \frac{\partial^2}{\partial y^2} \right] \phi_m(x,y) = 0 \tag{3.43}$$

Taking the transform of $\phi_m(x,y)$ with respect to x, we get

$$\left[-k^2 + \frac{\partial^2}{\partial y^2} \right] \phi_m(k,y) = 0 \tag{3.44}$$

A solution to this second-order differential equation is

$$\phi_m(k,y) = \phi_m(k,0)e^{-ky} \tag{3.45}$$

Now since $\mathbf{H} = -\nabla \phi_m$, we have for the fringing field wavelength dependence the following expressions for the Fourier transforms of the field components:

$$H_x(k,y) = -jk\,\phi_m(k,0)e^{-ky} \tag{3.46}$$

$$H_y(k,y) = k\,\phi_m(k,0)e^{-ky} \tag{3.47}$$

We note the exponential attenuation of the field with y, the distance normal to the direction of x, or in this case with distance from the magnetic head pole faces. The field components can be rewritten in terms of the transform of the H_x field along the pole face boundary, $y = 0$.

$$H_x(k,0) = -jk\,\phi_m(k,0) \tag{3.48}$$

and thus

$$H_x(k,y) = H_x(k,0)e^{-ky} \tag{3.49}$$

$$H_y(k,y) = jH_x(k,0)e^{-ky} = jH_x(k,y) \tag{3.50}$$

That is, we can express the H field transforms at any point in terms of the H_x field transform along the pole face boundary plane, $y = 0$. Note that the H_x and H_y transforms have the same magnitude, but are 90° out of phase with each other at all wave numbers. This is the condition for a Hilbert transform pair and H_y is the Hilbert transform of H_x.

For those cases where we can determine or assume $H_x(x,0)$ (or equivalently, the magnetic potential along the head plane, $y = 0$), we can explicitly obtain the wavelength dependency factors.

For example, for the Karlqvist head, where the value for $H_x(x,0)$ normalized to NI takes the form

$$H_x = \begin{cases} 0 & |x| > g/2 \\ 1/g & |x| < g/2 \end{cases} \tag{3.51}$$

we can take the Fourier transform to get

$$H_x(k,0) = \frac{\sin(kg/2)}{(kg/2)}$$

and thus the transform of the horizontal head fringing field becomes

$$H_x(k,y) = \frac{\sin(kg/2)}{(kg/2)} e^{-ky} \tag{3.52}$$

When considering longitudinal magnetization, the output flux, as seen previously, can be expressed as follows for a medium thin enough that we can ignore any variation of H or M with medium thickness:

$$\Phi_x(\overline{x}) = \mu_0 W \delta \int_{-\infty}^{+\infty} M_x(x - \overline{x}) H_x(x) \, dx \tag{3.53}$$

where $\overline{x}$ is the x-coordinate location of the recorded magnetization pattern with respect to the gap center of the magnetic head at a given time.

Now in this form, $\Phi_x(\overline{x})$ is expressed in the standard form of a superposition or convolution integral where $H_x(x)$ corresponds to the impulse response function. However, instead of $M(\overline{x} - x)$ as in the standard convolution formula, we have $M(x - \overline{x})$. Therefore, here the system input signal is $M_x(-x)$. The reason is that we defined $M_x(x)$ in terms of the x coordinate and the medium is moving in this direction. Hence, in terms of time, the actual magnetization pattern the head "sees" is $M_x(-x)$.

This superposition integral is extremely useful in determining the output when the magnetization $M_x(x)$ is not a simple mathematical function. When we write the Fourier-transformed convolution integral in transfer function form, we get the product $H_x(k)M_x(k)$, where $M_x(k)$ is the Fourier transform of $M_x(-x)$. When $M_x(x)$ is an even function, $M(x) = M(-x)$, and they have the same transform, $M(k)$. For all functions $M_x(x)$, the magnitudes $|M_x(k)|$ of the Fourier transforms of $M_x(x)$ and $M_x(-x)$ are identical.

We can then apply linear system theory and write (dropping the subscript x, which is hereafter to be understood)

$$\Phi(k) \propto M(k) H(k) \tag{3.54}$$

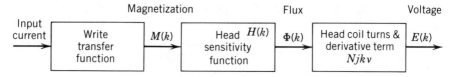

FIGURE 3.9   Recording process transfer function block diagram.

where $\Phi(k)$ is the Fourier transform of the head flux $\Phi_x(\overline{x})$. The angular frequency $\omega = kv$. For time domain analysis or synthesis (as, for example, in equalizer design), we make the substitution $k \rightarrow j\omega$ in the above transfer functions.

The transfer function perspective is suggestive of the time–frequency relations in linear circuit theory, and from this point of view, the recording operation can be represented in block diagram form as shown in Figure 3.9. From the communications viewpoint, it is noted that since the limits of the integral in equation (3.53) extend from minus infinity to plus infinity, this expression is not restricted to physically realizable "filters" of the electrical network variety. Since we have been defining $H(x)$ for $-\infty < x < +\infty$, and since in our analogy $\overline{x}$ (or x) corresponds to "time," we see that our impulse response transfer function provides an anticipatory output. This behavior does not violate causality; the reading head is simply picking up flux from the magnetization pattern at negative values of time, that is, before the coordinate reference origin of the defined magnetization pattern reaches the gap center.

From this background the conventional magnetic recording wavelength response dependency on spatial parameters can now be developed, giving the nature of the wavelength characteristics arising from the recording geometry. For ease of expression the subscripts x and y are dropped, recognizing that H and M can be associated with either component. For a differential recording medium layer dy thick,

$$d\Phi(k) = \mu_0 W M(k) H(k) dy \qquad (3.55)$$

and the differential signal at wave number k, $dE(k)$, is

$$dE(k) = (jk)Nv\, d\Phi(k) \qquad (3.56)$$

where the factor k is associated with the inductive nature of the conventional magnetic head in which the output voltage is proportional to the rate of change of flux through the head coil. We then have, ignoring phase,

$$dE(k) = \mu_0 W N v k M(k) H(k) dy \qquad (3.57)$$

Now with the assumption that the medium is uniformly magnetized throughout its depth and substituting in the above expression,

$$dE(k) = (\mu_0 W N v)k M(k) H(k,0)e^{-ky} dy \qquad (3.58)$$

Then integrating over the medium thickness (depth of recording) δ,

$$E(k) = \mu_0 W N v k M(k) H(k,0) \int_d^{d+\delta} e^{-ky} \, dy \tag{3.59}$$

or

$$E(k) = [\mu_0 W N v][k][M(k)][H(k,0)] \left[\frac{1 - e^{-k\delta}}{k} \right] [e^{-kd}] \tag{3.60}$$

Consider the role of each bracketed term in the above expression. The first is an amplitude scaling factor, the k factor accounts for the differentiating nature of the inductive head, the third term for the recorded wavelength, the next term for the effect of the gap, the fifth for the influence of the medium thickness, and the last term for the spacing loss factor. The fourth term is associated with the presence of a gap. For the idealized ring head we have seen that $H_x(x,0)$ is a rectangular pulse waveform and we obtain the conventional gap loss function

$$H(k,0) = \frac{\sin(kg/2)}{(kg/2)} \tag{3.61}$$

This expression is the typical aperture resolution factor. $\lambda = g$ corresponds to a point of infinite attenuation (the head flux is identically zero, giving zero output). Points of infinite attenuation also are predicted at all wavelengths that are submultiples of the gap width, that is, $\lambda = g/n$ where n is an integer. A derivation of the gap loss factor under less restrictive assumptions has been made by Westmijze [8], which results principally in an approximately 14 percent increase in the value of the null-point wavelengths, corresponding to an effective gap length larger than the physical gap g.

Let us now consider the thickness factor. For an alternative expression, this term is obtained by including δ in both numerator and denominator and rewriting it as follows:

$$\delta \left[\frac{1 - e^{-k\delta}}{k\delta} \right] \tag{3.62}$$

The bracketed quantity is then dimensionless and frequently referred to as the thickness loss. This comes from the fact that an inductive head signal is proportional to the rate of change of flux and therefore could be expected to provide an output signal that increases linearly with frequency (or k), giving a 6 dB per octave rise. The thickness loss term accounts for a falling off of the actual signal from this rate with increasing frequency due to the thickness parameter δ. There actually would be a continuing increase in output at a given frequency with thickness, although, as the expression indicates, the rate will progressively diminish, the larger the value of k. Since k and δ occur together in this "loss term," the output signal will only increase with frequency at 6 dB per octave at low frequencies.

For small values of k this thickness term starts at the value δ. Thus, the output signal will be proportional to both the medium thickness and the wave number, or frequency, which is the second term in the general expression for voltage. As $k\delta$ becomes large, the thickness term is decreasing as $1/k$ and will effectively cancel out the k factor in the voltage expression. Note that at very short wavelengths, the "effective" medium thickness is $1/k$ or $\lambda/2\pi$, clearly a function of the recording wavelength. This dependency on thickness behavior is best understood by recognizing the increasing spacing loss factor associated with each lower differential thickness stratum.

The last term gives the effect of spacing. The importance of spacing on the short-wavelength response is evidenced by the exponential attenuation factor within which the spacing variable appears. The spacing loss falls off very rapidly with d. The loss expressed logarithmically is

$$\approx 55\,d/\lambda \ \text{dB}$$

Accordingly, the signal attenuation due to the separation between head and medium will be 55 dB as the recorded wavelength decreases and approaches the spacing parameter d. To determine the output signal versus frequency f all terms must be included and evaluated with the given geometrical parameters.

The factors describing the influence of the gap, recording medium thickness δ and the spacing between head and medium surface d, occur in separate terms, so that the influence of each individual parameter on signal wavelength response becomes immediately evident. The frequency response of the recording channel is shown in Figure 3.10. The individual contribution of each term is illustrated.

We can also extend the wavelength response approach to side-reading. In developing the equations for side-writing and side-reading, the approach taken showed that the fringing fields on the sides of the head decrease with the transverse distance z in a manner similar to the way the fringing field decreases with spacing or y. Carrying these ideas over into the wavelength domain via the Fourier transform, a term of the form

$$\tfrac{1}{2}e^{-kz}$$

can be used to give the wavelength response for side-reading (again, z is the distance from the head side and $z = 0$ at the edge of the head). Normally, where the head width is large compared to the spacing, the relative influence on the output from reading recorded patterns at the sides of the track will be negligible.

3.7 ALIGNMENT OF GAP AND TRACK

In magnetic recording we have essentially a two-dimensional magnetic fringing field, and each incremental strip of track width couples independently with the corresponding incremental width of the head as it moves by. So far, it has been presumed that the magnetic head gap is perfectly aligned normal to the recording track, so that the recorded magnetization pattern traversing across each differential head width section is identical at every instant. In practice,

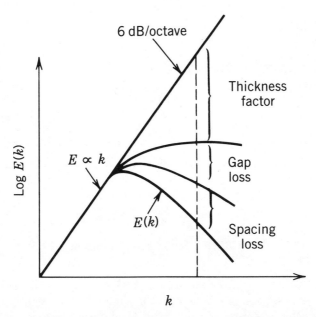

FIGURE 3.10 Frequency response and effects of parameters.

some azimuth misalignment (skew between the alignment of the gap and a recorded transition in the transverse direction) on reading can occur between the recorded pattern and head gap when reading at a later time because of the inability to achieve a mechanically stable recording system. We shall calculate in this section the manner in which azimuth misalignment influences the output signal.

The simplest way to formulate this problem is by regarding the magnetic head as composed of a set of read elements of differential width operating in parallel whose output signals are added together. This viewpoint corresponds to the fact that the net flux (and hence voltage output) of a magnetic head is directly proportional to its width.

Let ψ be the angle between the line of the head gap and a line normal to the recording track, W_R the width of the read head, and W_W the width of the recorded track, as shown in Figure 3.11. We shall consider the problem in its most general form, where W_R can be either less than or greater than W_W.

(1) $W_R < W_W$ $(W_W = W_{W1})$.

For this case, the net flux intercepted by the magnetic head is set by W_R. If $e(\overline{x})$ is the output voltage when $\psi = 0$, then dw/W_R is the fraction of the output voltage contributed by each differential head width dw. For $\psi \neq 0$, the actual output signal $e_a(\overline{x})$ can be written as

$$e_a(\overline{x}) = \int_{-W_R/2}^{W_R/2} e(\overline{x} - x)\frac{dw}{W_R} \qquad (3.63)$$

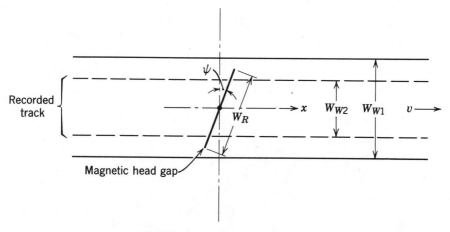

FIGURE 3.11   Azimuth alignment.

where x is replaced by $(\bar{x} - x)$ to reflect the fact that the voltage signal from each differential section is slightly offset in time from that signal contribution arising from the center of the magnetic head (where the x-axis origin has been set). The total "intercept" cross section of the head is $W_R \cos\psi$. We now express the integral only in terms of the x variable by using the relation

$$dw = dx / \sin\psi \tag{3.64}$$

where the corresponding limits in terms of x now become $\pm W_R \sin\psi/2$. Therefore, we get

$$e_a(\bar{x}) = \frac{1}{W_R \sin\psi} \int_{-W_R \sin\psi/2}^{W_R \sin\psi/2} e(\bar{x} - x)\,dx \tag{3.65}$$

It is recognized in this form that the output signal is affected by the misalignment ψ in a manner similar to that caused by a finite magnetization reversal region treated earlier. That is, the output signal is the time-averaged signal obtained with an interval, expressed in distance, of $W_R \sin\psi$. Thus, any azimuth misalignment will result in a spread of the pulse width and a reduction in its amplitude. Moreover, $W_R \sin\psi$ should be small compared to the basic pulse width to avoid a significant loss in resolution. It is apparent that narrow-width heads will be less affected by misalignment.

(2) $W_R > W_W$ ($W_W = W_{W2}$).

In this case, the flux intercepted by the magnetic head is set by W_W. It is only necessary here to replace $W_R \sin\psi$ by $W_W \tan\psi$ in the previous equation. Examination of the previous derivation showed that the limits of integration are set by the x distance over which the head is actively reading. In this case, these limits are controlled by W_W, as seen from the figure. Accordingly, the limits for x will now be $\pm(W_W \tan\psi)/2$, corresponding to the limits of $\pm W_W/2$ for the effective reading "cross section" of the magnetic head. The equation becomes

$$e_a(\overline{x}) = \frac{1}{W_W \tan\psi} \int_{W_W \tan\psi/2}^{W_W \tan\psi/2} e(\overline{x} - x)\,dx \qquad (3.66)$$

To show the correlation of this analysis with the more familiar sine wave theory, let us take as an example

$$W_R > W_W \qquad (3.67)$$

where the head becomes misaligned between write and read and we wish to examine the effect this misalignment may have on the frequency response. For $\psi = 0$,

$$e(\overline{x}) = \cos k\overline{x} \qquad (3.68)$$

Substituting into the equation (3.66), we obtain

$$e_a(\overline{x}) = \left[\frac{1}{W_W \tan\psi} \int_{-W_W \tan\psi/2}^{W_W \tan\psi/2} \cos k x \, dx \right] \cos k\overline{x} \qquad (3.69)$$

or

$$e_a(\overline{x}) \propto \frac{\sin\left(\dfrac{\pi W_W \tan\psi}{\lambda}\right)}{\left(\dfrac{\pi W_W \tan\psi}{\lambda}\right)} \qquad (3.70)$$

A $\sin x/x$ wavelength response results, or a "gap loss" type factor. This feature is capitalized upon in video recording by deliberately skewing in opposite directions alternate recorded tracks (one head is used for the even-numbered tracks and another for the odd-numbered tracks). Thus, on readback any adjacent track signal sensed by a head is attenuated by the above factor. The skew angle is chosen to place this adjacent track pickup attenuation in the appropriate wavelength range. Ideally, a null should be located in the frequency range of greatest concern. The use of such "herringbone" recording allows higher track density with no guardband between adjacent tracks—for the same tracking accuracy. The expression for the null wavelength is

$$\lambda = W_W \tan\psi$$

In disk drives with rotary actuators, the read/write gap will be skewed (from the normal to the direction of track motion), the skew varying as a function of radial position. In this case, however, the gap is at the same skew angle for both reading and writing. If the relative velocity of the head–medium is v and θ is the angle between the gap line and the perpendicular to the direction of track motion, then the relative velocity of a transition across the gap is

$$v \cos\theta$$

and hence the output signal amplitude as a function of θ is

$$e_x(\theta) = e_x(\theta = 0)\cos\theta \qquad (3.71)$$

In addition to this effect on output amplitude, since the transition will take somewhat longer to traverse the gap, the pulse width will be slightly increased.

In digital magnetic recording an understanding of both the pulse and wavelength characteristics is essential. Both approaches provide tools and techniques that are important in recording systems analysis, measurement, and characterization.

REFERENCES

1. "The Reproduction of Magnetically Recorded Signals," R. L. Wallace, Jr., *Bell Syst. Tech. J.*, Vol. 30, pp. 1145–1173, 1951. Reprinted in *Introduction to Magnetic Recording*, R. M. White, Ed., IEEE Press, New York, 1985.
2. "Calculation of the Magnetic Field in the Ferromagnetic Layer of a Magnetic Drum," O. Karlqvist, *Trans. Roy. Inst. Technol., Stockholm*, No. 86, 1954. Reprinted in *Introduction to Magnetic Recording*, R. M. White, Ed., IEEE Press, New York, 1985.
3. "Magnetic Data Recording Theory: Head Design," A. S. Hoagland, *Commun. Electron. (AIEE)*, pp. 506–513, November 1956.
4. "On the Resolving Power in the Process of Magnetic Recording," S. Duinker, *Tijdschrift van het Nederlands Radiogenootschap*, pp. 29–48, January 1957.
5. "The Dependence of Recording Characteristics of Thin Metal Tapes on Their Magnetic Properties and on the Replay Head," B. K. Middleton, *IEEE Trans. Magn.*, MAG-2, pp. 225–229, 1966.
6. "The Replay Signal from a Tape with Magnetization Components Parallel and Normal to Its Plane," B. K. Middleton, *IEEE Trans. Magn.*, MAG-11, pp. 1170–72, 1975.
7. *The Fourier Integral and Its Applications*, A. Papoulis, McGraw-Hill, New York, 1962.
8. "Studies on Magnetic Recording," W. K. Westmijze, *Philips Res. Rep.*, Part II, Vol. 8, No. 3, pp. 161–183, 1953. Reprinted in *Introduction to Magnetic Recording*, R. M. White, Ed., IEEE Press, New York, 1985.
9. "Reciprocity Principles for Magnetic Recording Theory," N. Smith, *IEEE Trans. Magn.*, MAG-23, pp. 1995–2002, 1987.

CHAPTER 4

THEORY OF THE DIGITAL MAGNETIC RECORDING PROCESS: WRITING

In digital magnetic recording, one design goal in writing data is to achieve (as closely as possible) a true step change in saturation magnetization upon switching the direction of writing current. Further, the transition recorded should not be dependent on the current magnetic state of the region being written. For linear behavior on readback, successive changes in writing current should have no effect on the previous transitions just recorded. As the spacing of transitions is set by the relative velocity between head and medium, this latter aspect will be influenced by the data rate as well as the head–medium magnetic interface. In addition to taking cognizance of the saturation transition length, there is the associated question of the density at which such transitions can be recorded. To preserve the integrity of a transition, the surface needs to move some minimum distance before another magnetization change is initiated. This displacement is to move the transition region, which has just been created in the desired sense, out beyond the head magnetizing field range where this recorded transition could be further altered.

While the write process can set limits on the density of saturation reversals, data recording performance is a function of both the writing and readback process. This chapter focuses on the write process and its characterization. Chapter 7 addresses the magnetic recording channel and the overall writing and reading systems associated with digital recording.

4.1 WRITING: THE TRANSITION

No completely accepted analysis relating the magnetization transition length to the recording head geometry, writing current, and magnetic properties of the recording medium has been yet developed, although the Williams–Comstock model [1] analysis is the most widely used. The physics is complicated not only by the highly nonlinear nature of the problem, but also by the fact that the individual magnetic surface regions are actually acted upon by a time-varying vector field as they leave the vicinity of the magnetic head.

The following graphical model is first presented to give an intuitive understanding of the write process as well as to provide guides for initial design in terms of recording system parameters. For explanatory purposes the write field will be considered constant through the recording depth (almost always equal to the medium thickness for a rigid disk).

For a steplike reversal in the magnetizing field, the region of the medium under the trailing leg half of the magnetic head is where the desired transition is actually formed. Shown in Figure 4.1 is a transition created on the trailing leg, centered about the write field contour where $H_x = H_c$. The magnetic medium of the recording track passing by the head gap centerline will traverse the same magnetizing field until the current is again reversed and hence will be similarly saturated. By the graphical procedure illustrated in Figure 4.2 it is possible, where in this example it is assumed the storage medium is designed for in-plane magnetization, to construct a curve of $M_x(x)$ versus x by using only the write field longitudinal component $H_x(x)$. The transition length can be expressed as follows:

$$x(H_2) - x(H_1)$$

where H_2 is the write field that just begins to reverse the direction of remanent magnetization and H_1 the magnetizing field (nearer the gap) that essentially completely reverses the direction of magnetization. However, the graphical approach will give information on the shape of the transition reversal as well. Before application of a current change, the medium is being uniformly saturated in one of two possible directions. Assuming an instantaneous reversal in the head gap magnetic field, the resultant writing field can be graphically projected onto the recording medium magnetization characteristic as shown to yield the resultant variation in $M_x(x)$. Each point in the medium as it passes the trailing leg side of the head gap is exposed to its maximum magnetizing field, tending to set its direction of saturation, at the initial instant of switching. As an elemental volume leaves the trailing leg of the head, it passes through a continuously diminishing longitudinal field. Therefore, a reasonable first-order simplification is to assume that the final transition shape between magnetic saturation states is the same as that created initially. The foregoing procedure then can provide a meaningful first-order approximation to the transition shape.

Several qualitative deductions may be made from this simple model of the writing process. First, the resulting magnetization change is displaced from the gap centerline, as shown in the illustration given in Figure 4.1, by x' (in the direction of surface motion). This displacement will depend on the magnitude of the write current, since H_x is proportional to the write current, and hence slight output pulse time displacements can result from differing

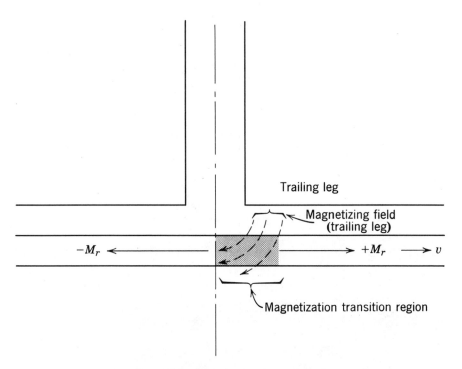

FIGURE 4.1   Idealized ring head: saturation reversal.

levels of write current. Second, the greater the fringing field gradient and/or the more rectangular the magnetic properties of the storage medium, the closer the magnetization transition length will approach a step change. At a given spacing d, the gap is the major factor setting the magnitude of H_x for a fixed number of ampere-turns. Figure 4.3 illustrates H_x curves for different levels of write current and the location of the transition center is shown, based on its occurring at $H = H_c$. By observation it is clear that the spatial rate of change or gradient of the head field at $H_x = H_c$ is a function of the write current. The optimum current value is that which maximizes the head field gradient at the point where $H = H_c$. Increasing the current further will lead to a broader transition and hence a lower readback signal amplitude.

The actual transition length is subject to various definitions. In Figure 4.2, the transition length x_1 is taken as the distance between the 10 to 90 percent points in a magnetization reversal change. Later we will develop an analytical model that uses an arctangent approximation to a transition. With this approximation a single parameter characterizes the transition. Since the output signal is proportional to the rate of change of magnetization, the most meaningful way to define a transition length is in terms of the nature of the derivative of the magnetization reversal (a pulselike function) rather than the magnetization change itself.

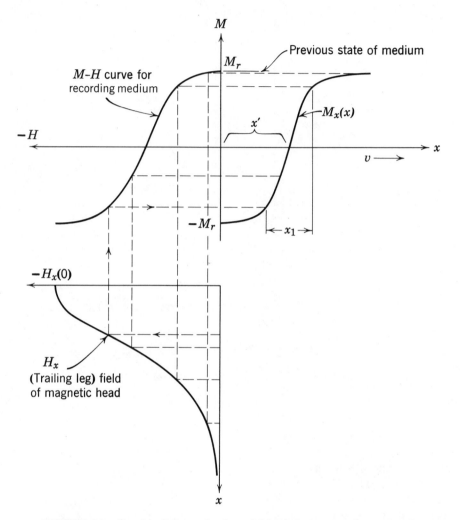

FIGURE 4.2   Graphical determination of $M_x(x)$ for a saturation reversal.

The transition normally will be considerably shorter than the spread of the head sensitivity function. This fact is indicated in Figure 4.2, by comparing the curve of $M(x)$ with that of $H(x)$. This result, of course, is a consequence of the steep nonlinear saturation characteristic of the magnetic storage medium. The shape of the readback output pulse width from a step change in recorded magnetization is the same as that of the sensitivity function H_x (Chapter 3). If the transition length is small compared to the spatial extent of the head sensitivity function, a step function approximation for transitions will suffice.

An additional aspect in writing a transition is that whenever the medium is being recorded, a magnetization reversal may concurrently be created on the

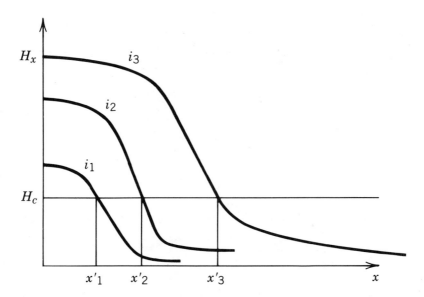

FIGURE 4.3 Write field as function of current.

leading leg side of the magnetic head, depending on the previous state of the medium in this region. With continuous current (NRZ) type recording, every time the write current is reversed a transition will be formed at the trailing leg edge of the gap which will remain recorded. If writing a transition involves the remagnetization of the previous state of the region, a transition also will be temporarily created at the leading edge of the gap. These leading edge magnetization transitions are immediately eradicated as they pass by the gap centerline. However, a demagnetizing field will arise from the "magnetic cell" established during remagnetization in a direction to oppose the applied head field. Thus, the switching location of the desired transition being recorded will occur somewhat closer to the gap center, that is, where the net field acting to reverse the state of magnetization equals H_c. When the region being written is in the same direction as that of the write field, this leading edge transition does not occur and the recorded transition will not be displaced. The result is that timing shifts in readback pulses can arise that are dependent on the previous state of the medium.

A special situation also arises when the write current is turned off, as any transition formed on the leading edge will remain. Moreover, should a pulsed write current be used, the output from a single current pulse will be two voltage pulses displaced in time (by approximately $2x'/v$) and of reverse polarity (since two oppositely directed transitions have been recorded, one under the trailing leg and one under the leading leg). The output signal then appears as a dipulse.

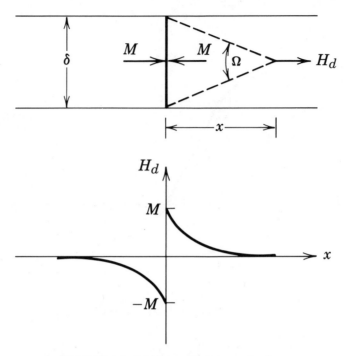

FIGURE 4.4   Medium self-demagnetization.

4.1.1 Media Self-Demagnetization

After the writing and passage of newly recorded information away from the neighborhood of the magnetic head gap, this recorded magnetization will still exist in the presence of its own self-demagnetizing field. Each time a recorded region traverses by the magnetic head, its demagnetizing field is temporarily decreased by the presence of the soft magnetic head core (the effect is larger the smaller the head–medium spacing). In practice, these small effects are reversible, so that the magnetic recorded state is stable.

In digital magnetic recording we deal only with discrete changes in magnetization. Therefore, our principal concern with respect to self-demagnetization is the influence this phenomenon has on the final transition length of a saturation magnetization reversal. We will first look at the minimum transition length that can be supported by the recording medium. An estimate will be made for this medium-determined density limitation using idealized $M - H$ relationships and the medium thickness δ.

To develop a mathematical model, let us start by considering a medium in which an ideal step change in saturation magnetization is hypothesized. Again, the track width is assumed to be infinite, since it is so large compared to the other dimensions involved. Now recalling the expression for a magnetic field arising from a magnetic charge density on a plane (Chapter 2), we can write an expression for the demagnetizing field along the centerplane of the medium as a function of distance from the transition as follows:

$$H_d = -\frac{2M}{\pi}\tan^{-1}\left(\frac{\delta}{2x}\right) \tag{4.1}$$

where x is the distance from this step transition along the track. $2\tan^{-1}(\delta/2x)$ is the angle at x subtended by the transition magnetic charge and is shown in Figure 4.4 as Ω. As H_d is proportional to M, we can identify a demagnetizing factor

$$N_d = -\frac{H_d}{M} = \frac{2}{\pi}\tan^{-1}\left(\frac{\delta}{2x}\right) \tag{4.2}$$

Figure 4.4 shows also shows a plot of H_d versus x about this step transition along the midplane of the medium. We see that $H_{d\,max}$ occurs at the location of the step change $(x = 0)$ and has a value of

$$H_d = -M$$

Our interest will therefore be at this location in terms of establishing criteria. Now the maximum value of H_d must be less than or equal to H_c (otherwise the material would spontaneously switch). Assuming an ideal square loop material, we can draw on this loop a demagnetizing line representing H_d versus M for the location $x = 0$. Note that for this case N_d is independent of δ and equal to -1. The intercept of this line with the M–H loop gives the values of M and H that satisfy the medium and demagnetization constraints.

A "saturation" reversal cannot be sustained at the level M_r if the demagnetizing line intersects the M–H loop where M is less than M_r, as shown in Figure 4.5. For the magnetic material designated M_1 the result of the demagnetizing geometry is such as to reduce the remanent magnetization associated with the transition below M_{r1}. The readback signal is proportional to the magnetization value at the operating point. If the coercive force of this material were increased, the output voltage will be proportional to H_c until $H_c > M_{r1}$. (Recall that $0 \leq N_d \leq 1$.) To obtain a further increase in output signal, it would then be necessary to increase M_r as illustrated by material M_2. Thus, understanding the role of medium demagnetization is essential in assessing the significance of recording media parameters.

Note that away from the transition, the demagnetizing field decreases to zero, so the medium can be completely saturated sufficiently far from the transition. A finite transition can be viewed as a spreading of the magnetic charge concentration created on writing in order to reduce its maximum self-demagnetizing field to less than H_c. In the next section more realistic models will be examined in order to arrive at an expression that will provide quantitative measures of transition length.

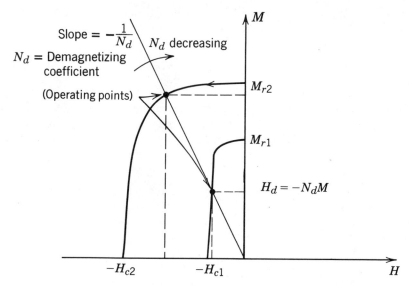

FIGURE 4.5 $M-H$ characteristic and demagnetizing factor.

4.2 TRANSITION MODELS

We have discussed the step function magnetization change and the fact that in many cases it is adequate to the level of understanding needed for performance estimates. A simple modification, the ramp function, gives an insight into the influence of a finite transition length and was discussed in the last chapter. The ramp function approximation can be helpful in making quick sensitivity analyses. Both of these transition approximations suffer by involving functions that do not have continuous derivatives. This limits their use in analytical studies. The arctangent function thus has become widely used as the mathematical approximation for a transition and the basis for analyzing and understanding of the write process. This model by its nature assumes the transition shape is symmetrical. Beyond these approximations, self-consistent calculations of the write process have been developed, although the computer time and expense have limited the use of this approach. In these calculations, finite mesh iterative techniques are employed. $\mathbf{M}(x,y)$ is first calculated using the head field for a given position of the medium relative to the gap; from this $\mathbf{M}(x,y)$, the resultant demagnetizing field is determined and then this field is combined with the applied head field to determine new values for $\mathbf{M}(x,y)$. This process is iterated until a suitable level of convergence is achieved and then the head is incrementally moved relative to the medium and the calculations repeated. This method does not impose any restrictions on the character of the transition shape that is derived.

Again, the most frequently used transition model for digital recording is based on the arctangent function, and much of the theory of the write process has been developed using this approximation. Thus, we will focus on this transition model in our analysis of the write process.

4.2.1 Arctangent Model

For longitudinal (in-plane) magnetization, assumed uniform throughout the medium thickness, the following expression is used to represent a transition:

$$M = \frac{2}{\pi} M_r \tan^{-1}(x/a) \tag{4.3}$$

As discussed earlier, the head width is so much greater than the other dimensions setting the head–medium magnetic coupling that we are able to use a two-dimensional approach. In this expression for M, the variable x refers to the distance along the track measured from the center of the transition. (The parameter x is also used as the distance variable from the head gap centerline but it will be made clear which interpretation is applicable.) Again, the arctangent function is attractive, since its first and second derivatives are continuous, lending to simple mathematical analysis; it is a symmetric function about its center and only one parameter, a, completely characterizes the key information relating to a transition.

Note that this expression approaches asymptotically $-M_r$ as x approaches $-\infty$ and M_r as x approaches $+\infty$. Further, $|M| = M_r/2$ at $x = \pm a$. The derivative of this function is

$$M' = \frac{2}{\pi a} M_r \frac{1}{1 + (x/a)^2} \tag{4.4}$$

Thus, the slope of the function at $x = 0$ is

$$M'(0) = \frac{2M_r}{\pi a} \tag{4.5}$$

Since the distance along the x axis between the intercepts of a straight line through the origin (with this slope) and the $\pm M_r$ asymptotic limits of M is πa, this term is frequently identified as the transition length. This distance corresponds to the distance over which a reversal goes from approximately 20 to 80 percent of its total change. However, the so-called a parameter provides all the information needed (or available) about a transition, owing to the simple functional form assumed. Also, a is the specific factor that shows up in calculations of pulse width and wavelength response. Hence, transition length is usually only thought of in terms of the value of a. One reason the arctangent approximation works well, even though it provides an unrealistic measure for the distance between magnetization directions due to its asymptotic behavior, results from the fact that the output pulse is related to the rate of change of the magnetization (Chapter 3); therefore, the relatively gradual approach of arctangent function to its limits is not really reflected in the associated pulse width behavior.

The volume magnetic charge density of the arctangent transition as defined above is

$$\rho_m = -\frac{dM}{dx} = -\frac{2M_r}{\pi}\frac{a}{(x^2 + a^2)} \tag{4.6}$$

Along the midplane of a thin medium of thickness δ, the field at x produced by a differential element of charge $\rho_m \delta dx'$ located at x' is

$$dH_d = \frac{\rho_m \delta dx'}{2\pi(x - x')} \tag{4.7}$$

Integrating over all of the charge gives

$$H_d = -\frac{M_r a \delta}{\pi^2}\int_{-\infty}^{\infty}\frac{dx'}{(x - x')(x'^2 + a^2)} \tag{4.8}$$

This equation can be integrated by a partial fraction expansion to give

$$H_d = \frac{M_r \delta x}{\pi(x^2 + a^2)} \tag{4.9}$$

and the derivative of this function at the transition center $(x = 0)$ is

$$\frac{dH_d}{dx} = \frac{M_r \delta}{\pi a^2} \tag{4.10}$$

The maximum value of H_d occurs at $x = a$, and setting this maximum value of H_d equal to H_c at $x = a$, we have

$$H_d = H_c = \frac{M_r \delta}{2\pi a} \tag{4.11}$$

or

$$a = \frac{M_r \delta}{2\pi H_c} \tag{4.12}$$

This is the minimum value the parameter a can have as determined only by a consideration of self-demagnetization of the medium and, consequently, is only a function of the medium parameters. Even if we could create a sharper transition, it would not remain after its initial formation on account of demagnetization.

So far we have looked at the generation of a transition in two ways. First, using the head field gradient and the M–H loop of the storage medium and, second, in terms of self-demagnetization alone of an isolated transition in the medium. A more complete understanding can be obtained if we consider the interplay of all these factors together at the time the transition is recorded. This leads to a consideration of the Williams–Comstock model [1], which pro-

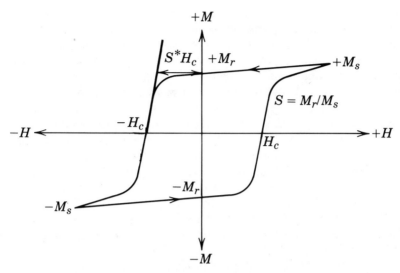

FIGURE 4.6 $M-H$ loop and parameter definitions.

vides an analytic means to determine a, taking into account media characteristics, head field gradient, and demagnetization. A somewhat simplified version of this approach was developed by Middleton [2].

The key assumptions used in the Williams–Comstock model include

- A Karlqvist semi-infinite pole piece head from which the write field magnitude and gradient are determined.
- A hysteresis loop whose vertical sides are characterized by the parameter S^* which is illustrated in Figure 4.6. Figure 4.6 also illustrates other loop parameters that are commonly used in analyzing the recording process. From Figure 4.6 it can be seen that the slope of the $M-H$ loop at $H = -H_c$ is

$$\frac{dM}{dH} = \frac{M_r}{(1-S^*)H_c} \tag{4.13}$$

- An arctangent transition. This assumption provides a fairly simple means to include demagnetization.

The basic approach is to start from the expression for the total derivative of M_x versus x. For this reason the method is often called the slope model. Thus,

$$\frac{dM}{dx} = \frac{dM}{dH}\left(\frac{dH_h}{dx} + \frac{dH_d}{dx}\right) \tag{4.14}$$

where the total field H seen by the medium is the sum of H_h and the demagnetizing field H_d. We will find that with an arctangent assumption we only need solve this expression at one point ($M = 0$), that is, at the location of the transition center, to get a, and since a is the only arctangent parameter, we immediately obtain the expression for the written transition.

Now we can substitute into this equation the respective derivatives. We have already obtained expressions for all terms except the head field gradient at the location of the transition center. For a minimum transition length, the head field gradient should be as large as possible at the location where the transition will be recorded. The location of the transition center will occur where $H_x = H_c$. Thus, if x is now taken as the distance from the head gap center, we need to determine the value of x where the head field gradient will be a maximum under the constraint that $H_x = H_c$ at this point. We then can determine the optimum write current, the value that gives rise to this condition. This calculation is somewhat complicated for the Karlqvist head equation. A simplification is to use the "far field" equations for an ideal head with infinite permeability. This head model will be used here to show the method and later a comparison will be made with the result obtained with a Karlqvist head.

To determine the head field gradient from the far field equations, we take the longitudinal head fringing field component

$$H_h = \frac{NI}{\pi} \frac{d}{x^2 + d^2} \tag{4.15}$$

where d is the spacing, and again the thickness is small compared to the spacing. Then,

$$\frac{dH_h}{dx} = \frac{NId}{\pi} \frac{-2x}{(x^2 + d^2)^2} = H_h \frac{-2x}{x^2 + d^2} \tag{4.16}$$

Substituting H_c for H_h in the above equation, we have

$$\frac{dH_h}{dx} = H_c \frac{-2x}{x^2 + d^2} \tag{4.17}$$

This equation gives the head field gradient as a function of distance from the gap center, under the constraint that $H_h = H_c$.

The field gradient has its maximum value at $x = d$:

$$\frac{dH_h}{dx}(\text{max}) = \frac{-H_c}{d} \tag{4.18}$$

To determine the optimum write current, we set

$$H_h(x = d) = H_c$$

and solve for NI. That is,

$$H_c = \frac{NI}{\pi} \frac{d}{d^2 + d^2}$$

or

$$NI = 2d\pi H_c$$

The write field in the medium at the head gap centerline is

$$H_h(x = 0) = 2H_c$$

while $H_h = H_c$ at $x = d$.

Since the demagnetizing field gradient term contains the parameter a, we are now in a position to solve the "slope expression" for the transition parameter a, where the solution includes the medium M–H characteristic, the write head field gradient, and the medium demagnetizing effect.

The Williams–Comstock model used the Karlqvist head field and took head imaging and remanent coercivity into account. The latter feature involves solving for the transition parameter using the remanent coercivity and then adjusting the result by assuming a relaxation path for the transition to $M = 0$ when the applied field is removed.

Middleton [2] analyzed the slope model with some key simplifications. In addition to using the far field head equations, he assumed that $S^* = 1$, that is, that the medium has a square loop. Then, since

$$\frac{dM}{dH} = \infty$$

to obtain a finite transition length requires that

$$\frac{dH_h}{dx} = -\frac{dH_d}{dx} \tag{4.19}$$

Under these assumptions we can substitute the equations derived previously and have

$$\frac{H_c}{d} = \frac{M_r \delta}{\pi a^2} \tag{4.20}$$

or

$$a = \sqrt{\frac{M_r \delta d}{\pi H_c}} \tag{4.21}$$

If the value of a from the transition parameter calculation, based on the write process, is less than the value of a based on medium self-demagnetization alone, then the self-demagnetization result is taken, that is, the larger of the two values of a will determine the transition parameter for performance analysis of a recording system.

From these analytic approaches we can see that a small value of a requires a high value of H_c, a thin medium, and a small spacing. Note that while the a parameter determined from demagnetization alone varied linearly with

$$\frac{M_r \delta}{\pi H_c}$$

when the writing process is included in the analysis, the transition length varies as the square root of this term. If we set $a = a_m$ to denote the a parameter determined from demagnetization alone and $a = a_h$ to be the value from the write process analysis and equate the two, we have

$$a_m = a_h^2/2d \tag{4.22}$$

Setting $a_m = a_h$,

$$d = a_m \tag{4.23}$$

This is the value of d at which we have the onset (due to the spread of the head field with spacing) of transition broadening due to writing. It is clear that if the actual magnitude of d is greater than the above value, the transition length will be governed by equation (4.21) and reflect the limitations of the write process. In all cases, these models and their results are primarily used as guides in recording design studies.

At very high linear densities and with thin film media, "sawtooth" transitions can arise owing to domain interactions and require a micromagnetic approach to the study of transitions. This topic will be discussed in Chapter 6.

The Arctangent Wavelength Factor

Another useful perspective can be drawn from the wavelength response associated with an arctangent approximation for a transition.

The Fourier transform of the function M [equation (4.3)] is

$$M(k) \propto e^{-ka}/k \tag{4.24}$$

and

$$M'(k) \propto e^{-ka} \tag{4.25}$$

where

$$k = \frac{2\pi}{\lambda}$$

Recall that the output voltage of an inductive magnetic head is proportional to the rate of change of flux or

$$E(k) \propto M'(k) \propto e^{-ka}$$

Now in Chapter 3 we saw that the wavelength dependence of the signal on spacing was given by

$$e^{-kd}$$

and therefore we can combine the spacing and transition a-parameter factors as follows:

$$E(k) \propto e^{-kd}e^{-ka} = e^{-k(d+a)}$$

Thus, we see that d and a have the same form of wavelength response function in the output signal frequency response. As the spacing and a parameter occur together in the form $(d + a)$, in a sense defining a new parameter, the wavelength response behavior arising from the above exponential term cannot be uniquely attributed to either parameter by itself, if there is an uncertainty in the measurement of spacing. One conclusion that can be drawn is that spacing and transition length can be equally detrimental to recording density. Recognize, however, that this picture arises from the assumption of an arctangent transition shape and is meaningful only to the degree that this is a good approximation. As a perspective on the similarity of the influence of d and a, the output pulse from a thin medium at zero spacing from a recorded transition characterized by the parameter a will be identical to the output pulse from a step function transition located at a spacing equal to this value of a.

In Chapter 3 an expression for PW_{50} was derived for an ideal step function transition. To modify this expression to include the effect of an arctan transition, we can now see that it is only necessary to replace d by $d + a$ in that equation. The expression for PW_{50}, including both reading and writing, then becomes

$$PW_{50} = \sqrt{g^2 + 4(d + a)(d + a + \delta)} \qquad (4.26)$$

The reason PW_{50} is so commonly referenced is that the output signal for an all-ones signal (i.e., square wave input current) begins to decrease, due to intersymbol interference, at a transition density (directly related to linear recording density) essentially inversely proportional to the pulse width.

The analysis given of the write process has assumed that the head fringing field is proportional to the write current so that this field directly scales with NI. However, if saturation effects occur in the head, then the actual write field will no longer behave in this manner as the current reaches and then exceeds the saturation value. Saturation in the head often first takes place at the pole tips so that the maximum write field reflects the saturation flux density of the head material (a design goal). A field map, considering the pole faces as equipotentials, will show that the magnetic field intensity is a maximum at the gap corners where the actual field direction will be at 45° with respect to the pole faces. Further increases in write current beyond saturation will tend to increase the "effective" gap length and consequently decrease the head field gradient. The cross section of the head core increases with distance away from the gap inner pole faces owing to the tapered throat. Thus, maximum flux density will first be reached at the gap edges and then, with increasing current, a saturation condition will progressively expand into the core. This topic will be treated further in Chapter 5.

4.3 WRITE PROCESS: OVERWRITE PHENOMENA

As outlined at the beginning of the chapter, the nature of the write process in magnetic recording leads to a number of phenomena that can significantly affect the readback of data.

Peak detection is almost universally used today in digital magnetic recording. Thus, the decision as to whether a bit is a zero or one is decided by whether a pulse peak is detected within the timing window allocated to that bit period. An error in that bit position will result if an intended pulse peak falls outside the window or an unintended pulse peak is detected within the window. The term "bit shift" is used to define the shift of a detected peak relative to the center of its clock window. The importance of pulse timing to reliable detection is the reason we consider here various write phenomena that influence the written location of a transition.

Readback signal timing effects will arise if the saturation current is not sufficiently large to reverse completely the previous state of the medium. For this reason it is typical to set the write current to provide a field at the bottom of the storage film approximately 2.5 times the coercivity of the material. Further, examining our analysis of the write process, it is seen that when the current amplitude is not optimum, in addition to a larger value for the transition parameter a, there will be differences in the location where a transition is located relative to the gap center of the head, which may result in measurable bit shift.

When overwriting an alternating saturation magnetization pattern, the location of the written transition can be modified, depending on the existing state of the medium. For example, writing a square wave on a uniformly saturated medium will lead to a signal pattern where alternate pulses, positive pulses for example, are offset from the center locations between the negative pulses, giving rise to what is called pulse pairing. More generally, this is evidence of nonlinear bit shift on writing. Figure 4.7 provides an illustration of the magnetic pattern factors that are the source of the behavior. If the write field is remagnetizing a dc erased medium, then when the current is reversed, there is created a reverse magnetization cell, including a transition formed on the leading as well as trailing leg of the head. The "demagnetizing field" from the leading edge transition cell will oppose the write head field that set it up. Consequently, the desired transition formed on the trailing leg will occur closer to the gap center, that is, where the head field is greater and the effective (or total) write field becomes equal to the coercive force. This leads to a bit time (measured by the occurrence of the pulse peak) that is "late" in terms of the relative timing of this recorded transition contrasted to when it would be sensed if recorded without the presence of a leading edge transition. A transition written in this manner is often referred to as a late bit or sometimes a hard bit, reflecting the fact that this transition required remagnetizing the medium. When the write field is reversed to create the next transition, no leading edge transition is formed (the medium already being in the desired direction) and hence the trailing leg transition can be considered to be unshifted in location. This transition is usually referred to as an early bit or an easy bit, since no remagnetization is required to create the transition on the trailing leg. Therefore, in writing an all-ones pattern on a dc erased medium, every other pulse has a relative shift with respect to its neighbors and will create a pattern on readback in which adjacent pulses are paired (see Figure 4.7).

If the time periods between successive pulses are T_A and T_B, then

$$T_A - T_B = (T + \Delta) - (T - \Delta) = 2\Delta$$

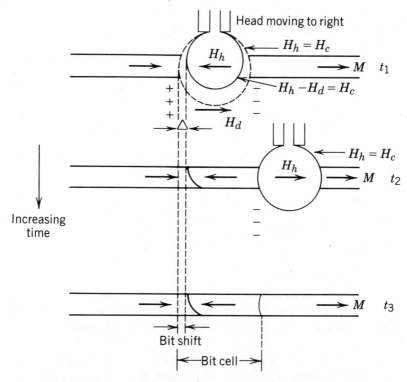

FIGURE 4.7   Nonlinear bit shift due to previous state of medium.

where T is the readback clock period and Δ is the offset of the sensed peaks that are displaced owing to transition shifting. Self-clocking is used on readback (the clock timing is derived from the readback pulses themselves) and thus the averaging of the clock will center windows around the midposition of these offsets. Then

$$T_s = \Delta/2 = \frac{T_A - T_B}{4} \tag{4.27}$$

where T_s is a measure of bit shift from this effect.

While the presence of additional recorded transitions could be also considered, the leading edge transition most commonly is significantly closer to the transition being written at the trailing leg than any other prerecorded transitions and therefore more dominant. This is certainly true when recording at densities where relatively little intersymbol interference occurs, as the head sensitivity function is then much broader than the transition length.

Writing over random data patterns will produce bit timing offsets that, like pulse crowding (or intersymbol interference), cause an increase in the soft error rate for a given clock timing window and hence represent another bit shift source that combines with others to limit achievable density. The read-back channel and soft error rate performance issues are discussed in Chapters 7 and 8.

Another similar overwrite-related issue has to do with the current rise time. If the current rise time is a significant fraction of the bit period, then when writing a transition that involves remagnetization, the transition will not be formed until the write field reversal is almost complete (i.e., from $-H_c$ to $+H_c$). Conversely, when writing a transition that involves switching the head field to align in the same direction as the medium when traversing the head gap, a transition will be established as soon as the write field is reduced relatively little (particularly for a material with S^* close to one), as it is only necessary here to cease remagnetizing the medium. A finite current rise time can therefore create nonlinear bit shifts similar to those that arise from the premagnetized state of the medium when overwriting data. It is difficult to state with assurance the relative importance of these various sources of non-linear bit shift.

At very high linear densities transition shifts can also occur from the previous transition(s) that have already been written. At these densities the previously written transition will be as close or closer to the location on the trailing leg where recording occurs than the leading edge transitions discussed above. The field from the previously written transition will combine with the head field to set the total field which determines the position of the transition just being written. Thus, the H_c coercivity contour is displaced as a a function of the bit sequence being recorded which in turn leads to bit timing displacements. Precompensation is one way to address this type of bit shift since it is directly related to the pattern being recorded.

4.3.1 Overwrite Criterion

The standard method to measure overwrite performance is to record the low frequency all-ones pattern, overwrite this pattern with the high-frequency all-ones pattern, and then measure the ratio of the residual low-frequency amplitude to that prior to overwriting. The measurement is made in this manner since in longitudinal recording, low frequencies are harder to overwrite than high frequencies. Self-demagnetization tends to favor long bit cell lengths for an in-plane magnetic orientation. Disk design usually requires a 26 to 30 dB overwrite ratio for reliable data recording.

Now from the previous discussion it is apparent that writing a high-frequency pattern over a low-frequency pattern will create bit shift variations that on readback will be reflected as additional frequency components. While the amplitude of these shifts may be small, the changes in peak timing can play a major factor in setting readback performance. Overwrite is a very complex and inadequately understood topic and the development below is intended to give some perception of the relation between overwriting data and the write process as it has been discussed here. However, since peak detection focuses on bit shift phenomena, the approach taken is to relate the overwrite measurement to write-induced bit shift. In Chapter 8 we combine the various sources of bit shift in a discussion of channel error rate.

Let OW be the measured overwrite value, which is defined as

$$OW = 20\log(E_{lr}/E_l) \text{ dB} \tag{4.28}$$

where E_{lr}/E_l is the ratio of the residual low-frequency signal compared to the original value, measured after overwriting the low-frequency all-ones pattern with the high-frequency all-ones pattern. With the above definition, OW will be a negative quantity. Or

$$\frac{E_{lr}}{E_l} = 10^{(OW/20)} \tag{4.29}$$

To relate OW, which is a voltage ratio, to a bit shift effect, we take the following approach. After overwriting in the manner above, we express the readback signal in terms of the fundamental sine wave components as follows:

$$e = E_h\cos(\omega_h t) + E_{lr}\cos(\omega_l t + \phi) \tag{4.30}$$

where ω_h corresponds to the high-frequency all-ones pattern and ω_l corresponds to the low-frequency all-ones pattern. The location of the peaks of $e(t)$ can be found by finding the zero crossings of the signal. Now

$$e'(t) = -\omega_h E_h \sin(\omega_h t) - \omega_l E_{lr}\sin(\omega_l t + \phi) \tag{4.31}$$

The peak locations appearing as zero crossings in the differentiated signal will be located near $\omega_h t = 0$ because $E_h \gg E_{lr}$. The relative phase angle corresponding to the worst case shift in these zero crossings will be that value that results in the absolute value of the low-frequency component being a maximum at this location. That is, $\omega_l t + \phi \approx n(\pi/2)$ where $n = 1,3,5,7,\ldots$. Therefore, we can make the following approximations:

$$E_h \sin(\omega_h t) \approx E_h \omega_h t \tag{4.32}$$

and

$$E_{lr}\sin(\omega_l t + \phi) \approx \pm E_{lr} \tag{4.33}$$

Then for $e'(t) = 0$, we have

$$\omega_h(\omega_h E_h T_s) = \omega_l E_{lr} \quad \text{or} \quad T_s = \frac{\omega_l E_{lr}}{\omega_h \omega_h E_h}$$

where T_s represents the worst-case shift in the location of high-frequency peak due to the presence of a residual low-frequency signal.

The self-clocking circuitry will stabilize to sample at a rate corresponding to the average spacing of the peak locations (varying between $-T_s$ and T_s), then

$$T_{ow} = T_s$$

and

$$T_{ow} = \left(\frac{\omega_l}{\omega_h}\right) \frac{1}{\omega_h} \frac{E_{lr}}{E_h} = \left(\frac{\omega_l}{\omega_h}\right) \frac{1}{\omega_h} \frac{E_{lr}}{RE_l} \tag{4.34}$$

where R is the readback resolution defined as

$$R = E_h/E_l$$

T_{ow} is the bit shift in the location of a transition from overwriting the low-frequency pattern with the high-frequency pattern. Moreover, letting v = velocity and with our sine wave approximations,

$$\omega_h = \pi v f c i_{max} \quad \text{and} \quad \omega_l = \pi v f c i_{min}$$

and finally

$$T_{ow} = \left(\frac{f c i_{min}}{f c i_{max}}\right) \frac{1}{\pi v f c i_{max}} \frac{10^{(OW/20)}}{R} \tag{4.35}$$

The bit shift associated with overwrite is seen from this conceptual approach to depend on the encoding scheme (i.e., the ratio of $f c i_{max}$ to $f c i_{min}$), the maximum flux density, the resolution, and the overwrite ratio in dB (the overwrite measurement itself will depend on the above factors as well). The expression clearly reveals why a high overwrite ratio is desired.

We have focused on writing phenomena that can affect transition length as well as transition timing, the latter directly applicable to peak-sensing detection. A general discussion of the magnetic recording channel and error rate issues in later chapters will further address the role of the write process in the overall writing and reading of data.

REFERENCES

1. "An Analytical Model of the Write Process in Digital Magnetic Recording," M. L. Williams and R. L. Comstock, *AIP Conf. Proc.*, Part 1, No. 5, pp. 738–742, 1971. Reprinted in *Introduction to Magnetic Recording*, R. M. White, Ed., IEEE Press, New York, 1985.

2. "A Simplified Model of the Writing Process in Saturation Magnetic Recording," V. A. J. Maller and B. K. Middleton, *Radio Electron. Eng.*, Vol. 44, pp. 281–285, 1974.

3. *Magnetic Recording*, Volume I: *Technology*, C. D. Mee and E. D. Daniel, McGraw-Hill, New York, pp. 58–64, 1987.

4. "Analysis of Saturation Magnetic Recording Based on Arctangent Transitions," R. I. Potter, *J. Appl. Phys.*, Vol. 41, pp. 1647–1651, 1970.

5. "A New Theoretical Approach to Digital Magnetic Recording," R. H. Noyau, B. K. Middleton, J. J. Miles, and E. W. Williams, *IEEE Trans. Magn.*, MAG-24, pp. 1811–1813, 1988.

6. "Self-Consistently Computed Magnetization Patterns in Thin Magnetic Recording Media," R. I. Potter and R. J. Schmulian, *IEEE Trans. Magn.*, MAG-7, pp. 873–880, 1971.

7. "Modeling the Record Process," I. A. Beardsley, *IEEE Trans. Magn.*, MAG-22, pp. 454–460, 1986.

8. "Computer Simulation of Magnetic Recording," I. Tagawa and Y. Nakamura, *J. Magn. Soc. Jpn.*, Vol. 13, Suppl. No. S1, pp. 97–101, 1989.

9. "Effect of Nonzero Write Field Rise Time in Digital Magnetic Recording," J. Fluitman, *IEEE Trans. Magn.*, MAG-12, pp. 218–224, 1976.

10. "A Model for Overwrite Modulation in Longitudinal Recording," R. E. Fayling, T. J. Szczech, and E. F. Wollack, *IEEE Trans. Magn.*, MAG-20, pp. 718–720, 1984.

11. "An Experimental Study of Hard-Transition Peakshifts through the Overwrite Spectra," C. Tsang and Y. Tang, *IEEE Trans. Magn.*, MAG-24, pp. 3087–3089, 1988.

CHAPTER 5

MAGNETIC HEADS

In digital magnetic recording, transducer area resolution is very important for achieving high storage density; hence, understanding of magnetic heads becomes of particular interest. This chapter is concerned with the design considerations associated with magnetic heads. Principal emphasis will be given to those aspects relating to noncontact magnetic disk recording. The magnetic head interaction with the magnetic surface occurs in that region of the gap fringing field intercepted by (or coupled to) the magnetic track and its edges. Therefore, in the treatment of magnetic heads the two spatial parameters d and δ (head-to-surface spacing and surface thickness, respectively), which together define the location of the magnetic medium with respect to the head, must necessarily be included. Surface thickness is thus a common parameter in discussions of both magnetic heads and storage media.

The magnetic and electrical characteristics of magnetic heads are covered here. No attempt is made to document design details or specifications; rather, broad design procedures and guides are given. The work presented builds on the theory developed in the preceding chapters.

5.1 MAGNETIC HEADS—MAGNETIC ASPECTS

As mentioned in Chapter 1, three modes of recording are possible. In practice, longitudinal recording using a ring head is the choice in almost all recording systems. The analyses presented here will emphasize the ring head structure, but the general principles set forth also apply to heads for perpendicular and transverse recording modes. The main objective in head design is to achieve an intense write field with a high field gradient in order to record narrow transitions, and a minimal magnetic spatial coupling between the head and magnetic medium for readback.

Magnetic heads are fabricated from soft magnetic materials. Briefly, we will restate the magnetic properties desired for a magnetic head core: (1) a high saturation flux density to assure saturation of the recording medium on writing; (2) a high initial permeability to maximize the magnetic coupling between read coil and surface on readback; and (3) negligible residual induction so the continued presence of the head, when inoperative, will not affect a previously recorded signal. Further, the frequency response of the head should extend high enough to avoid frequency limitations on performance at high data rates. In practice, high-frequency ferrites or metallic film materials are generally used for core construction.

5.1.1 Gap Fringing Field—General

The importance of the magnetic head gap fringing field has been stressed previously. This field distribution not only magnetizes the surface on writing, but in digital magnetic recording also sets the basic readback pulse shape and magnetic pattern resolution on reading. The configuration of the magnetic pole pieces, in conjunction with the size of the gap, establishes the predominant character of this fringing field. Our frame of reference will be the idealized magnetic ring head which has been illustrated again in Figure 5.1. A magnetic head may be approximated by an idealized ring head if its pole faces and gap throat height are many times greater than the largest parameter among spacing, gap length, and surface thickness. Although the pole faces and throat height of the idealized ring head model extend to infinity, this model serves as an excellent representation of a large number of practical devices.

The gap length g is always much less than the head track width W. This design guideline is the result of practical considerations involved in the head–surface geometry. The gap length is dependent on the head–medium separation. The head output signal is proportional to W, and the greater this head width, the more effectively averaged out are noise signals from minute surface defects. Further, head positioning systems to seek and follow tracks are used, and the tracking tolerances provide additional limitations on the minimum head width and thus track density. Therefore, we typically find gaps on the order of 0.5 or less microns associated with head widths ranging from 10 to 40 times this magnitude. Hence, the gap fringing field can be represented as a two-dimensional magnetic field distribution. Consequently, the magnetic design of a head configuration is effectively a two-dimensional field problem. Side fringing fields can be separately estimated from calculations of the magnetic fields fringing outward from the gap side planes and are minimized by having the surfaces of the head perpendicular to the plane of the recording medium.

As mentioned earlier, in analyzing the idealized ring head we need a means of incorporating the effects of head-to-surface spacing and recording medium

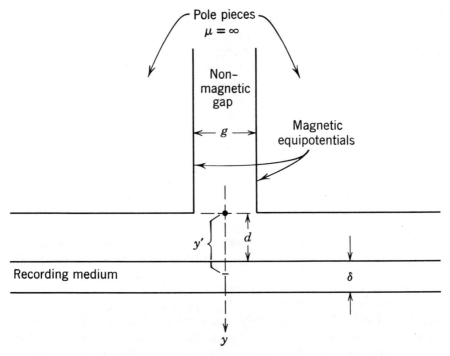

FIGURE 5.1 Idealized ring head geometry.

thickness. In Chapter 3 we showed that the pulse width of the readback signal, when we integrated the contributions throughout the medium thickness, was related to these two parameters as follows:

$$PW_{50} \propto \sqrt{d(d + \delta)}$$

The term $\sqrt{d(d + \delta)}$ is the geometric mean distance between the head pole face and the top and bottom surfaces of the recording medium. For our purposes we will introduce y' to represent this parameter. The head sensitivity function falls off with spacing and thus the incremental signal contributions from the medium strata are greater the nearer the layer is to the head. The way y' is defined automatically provides this type of weighting. The term δ then becomes a multiplier to the coupling function to account for the actual thickness (and hence amount of magnetic material) actually recorded. The magnetic coupling between the head and medium at a given position x from the gap center is then

$$\int_d^{\delta+d} \mathbf{H}(x,y)dy \longrightarrow \delta\mathbf{H}(x,y') \qquad (5.1)$$

where $\mathbf{H}$ is the magnetic head fringing field (Chapter 3). We can correctly consider δ as the recording surface thickness in saturation recording; in non-saturation binary recording, the parameter δ should be viewed as a measure of the effective surface layer penetration of the magnetizing field. The definition of y' will permit a single field distribution $\mathbf{H}(x,y')$ to be used as a "weighted value" approximation for the actual coupling function. This approach has the advantage of permitting analysis to proceed without having to introduce spacing and thickness as qualifiers at each step. Moreover, by using y' the results can be applied to both contact ($d = 0$) and noncontact recording, with no need to distinguish between them. In practice, δ is usually less than or on the same order of magnitude as g and d, and thus $\mathbf{H}(x,y')$ will represent a very good approximation for the coupling field, from which the actual writing and reading behavior of the magnetic recording configuration can be predicted. The objectives in head design for both the functions of reading and writing are compatible in the sense that a narrow magnetic coupling function is desired to achieve a high head field gradient for writing as well as high readback resolution. However, the length of the gap imposes a compromise, since the gap length must be great enough to assure saturation of the recording medium on writing. Again, for in-plane recorded magnetization patterns, the fringing field component of interest is H_x.

Given that high-coercivity media offer the potential for higher density, the head will usually be driven to take advantage of the available saturation flux density of the head material. Therefore, some comments on the saturation features of magnetic heads are in order. The magnetic circuit of the head should be such as to ensure that the location of the maximum flux density occurs at the pole tips. Then the highest value of write field can be obtained, since the first region to reach saturation would be in the front gap region. Thus, the gap cross-sectional area should be less than that of the head core. Further, the gap edges should be well defined. The flux density will be larger at the gap corners than within the gap if they have a very small radius of curvature (evident from a field plot). The intent is to obtain the maximum write field intensity for any given value of current up to the saturation value of the head material. However, it is very important not to go into saturation, for this will result in an "effective" gap greater than the actual gap length and reduce the head field gradient.

5.1.2 Idealized Ring Head

The only head design variable available with an idealized ring head is the gap length g and our only control over the fringing field is through selection of this parameter. We will investigate here the influence of the head gap on the writing and reading performance of the idealized magnetic head.

Gap Size—Writing

The maximum value of the longitudinal fringing (or magnetizing) field exists along the head gap centerline. It was shown in Chapter 3 that the field $H_x(0,y')$ along the gap centerline in the Karlqvist model is given by the expression

$$H_x(0,y') = \frac{H_g}{\pi} \left[2\tan^{-1} \frac{g}{2y'} \right] = \frac{H_g}{\pi} \Omega \qquad (5.2)$$

Ω, again, is the angle subtended at the point, x,y, by lines from the corners of the gap. H_g is the deep gap field, that is, the gap field calculated from the write ampere-turns using a magnetic circuit model of the head. However, this expression requires some clarification. The Karlqvist model of the ideal head assumes the magnetic field of the head along the pole face plane across the gap is the same as the deep gap field, or $H_x(0,0) = H_g$. The magnetic charge head model (two semi-infinite charged sheets) gives $H_x(0,0) = H_g/2$. Other than this factor of 2, both ways of viewing an ideal ring head give identical results, as they should. The measured field at the gap center along the pole faces generally lies between these two values. No difference, of course, results with these two models in the calculation of the fringing fields taken relative to $H_x(0,0)$ but would, of course, if referred to the deep gap field. Given these comments, we will proceed using the above equation. For $y' = g/2$, the maximum fringing field is 50 percent of the gap field. Figure 5.2 is a curve of the ratio of the fringing field $H_x(0,y')$ to the internal gap field as a function of y'/g.

The attenuation of the fringing field with increasing distance from the head is apparent. The choice of a storage medium with a high coercive force, with its advantages for high linear recording density, is limited by the saturation flux density of the magnetic head and the ratio of the write field at the medium to the head gap field, as given by the above equation. While for the ideal head the gap flux density would equal the head core flux density, in practice it will be less, due to a finite permeability and flux leakage. Since in practice the minimum value of y' is often limited by spacing and surface thickness requirements, the dimensionless quantity y'/g establishes a lower limit on the size of the writing gap. For example, if $g = 2y'$, then the maximum horizontal write field at the medium $H_x(0,y')$ is one-half H_g. Furthermore, of course, in order to assure adequate overwrite, $H_x(0,y')$ may be specified as two to three times the medium H_c or, for the case above, the deep gap head field must be four to six times the coercive force of the medium. For a given magnetic core material, there is then a minimum usable gap size in order to meet overwrite requirements. If a single head element is used for both writing and reading, this constraint requires selecting a larger head gap than would be desired from the point of view of reading high-density signals.

Reading—The Magnetic Coupling Function
We are particularly interested in the spread of the fringing field along the x axis, since this sets the resolution of transitions in reading. In this section we study the fringing field distribution in order to determine the pulse width and pulse shape obtained for steplike changes in magnetization.

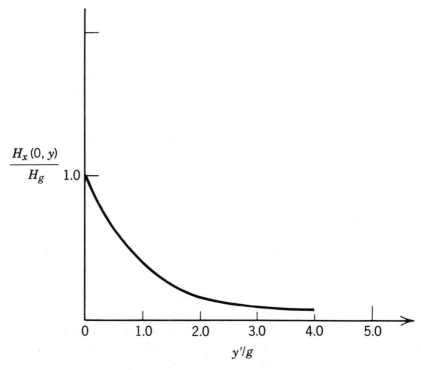

FIGURE 5.2 Attenuation of gap fringing field with spacing.

In longitudinal recording, the surface magnetization is primarily horizontal. For this reason the fringing field component of principal interest is H_x. Although knowledge of H_x will usually provide adequate performance predictability, we shall also examine the nature of H_y. The inclusion of H_y in the analysis will provide a way of analyzing how much perpendicular magnetization could be tolerated before the output signal wave form is adversely affected. From the reciprocity theorem, understanding of the nature of H_y will yield the character of the signal perturbation or distortion arising from a component of perpendicular magnetization.

For purposes of discussion we will divide the gap fringing field region into two zones: $y' \geq g$ and $y' < g$. This division has been made because in the area very near the gap, the fringing field is not amenable to simple analytical formulation, this region being indicated in Figure 5.3a by shading. In the range $y' < g$, reasonable estimates of the fringing field vector components can be established by the Karlqvist expression to provide an insight into the overall nature of the fringing field and consequently the character of the pulse output (except for $y' \ll g$). However, for $y' \geq g$ we can approximate the fringing field closely with a simple analytical expression whose accuracy improves with

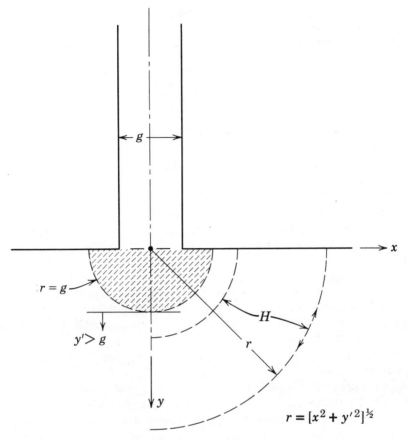

FIGURE 5.3a Fringing field zones.

increasing y'. The resulting expressions are frequently referred to as the magnetic head "far field" equations. We take this case first.

(1) $y' \geq g$.

For the case $y' \geq g$, we approximate the fringing field by a semicircular field distribution (see Figure 5.3a). Thus,

$$|H| \propto \frac{1}{r}$$

where r is the distance from the origin to the point in question. Then, from Chapter 3,

$$\frac{H_x(x,y')}{H_x(0,y')} = \frac{1}{1 + (x/y')^2} \tag{5.3}$$

We see that $H_x(x,y')$ (and thus the output pulse for a narrow transition) has a Lorentzian shape, giving relatively long "tails." For this function, the half-width of the pulse $PW_{50} = 2y'$. And

$$\frac{H_y(x,y')}{H_x(0,y')} = \frac{-x/y'}{1+(x/y')^2} \tag{5.4}$$

We can calculate the points where H_y is maximum or minimum by taking the derivative of the right side of equation (5.4) with respect to x and setting it equal to zero. Doing this we get a minimum at $x = y'$ and maximum at $x = -y'$. Substituting these values of x into equation (5.4) gives a value of 1/2 for the ratio of $H_y \mid_{max}$ to $H_x \mid_{max}$.

In Figure 5.3b are plotted the curves of H_x and H_y as given by equations (5.3) and (5.4). Their amplitudes are normalized by the factor $H_x(0,y')$, and the normalized distance measure is $u = x/y'$. In this form these two curves are a dimensionless representation of the fringing field for $y' \geq g$ and, as such, are applicable for any selected value of y' in this range. This one set of curves then serves for this whole fringing field region. Note how the positive x and y axes are defined. Since the fringing field must go from one pole to the other, with y being positive away from the head, $+H_x$ is always associated with $-H_y$, and $-H_x$ with $+H_y$.

If we define the spread of the horizontal fringing field between its 10 percent relative amplitude points by PW_{10}, then $PW_{10}/y' = 6$. Thus, for a step change in horizontal magnetization, the resulting output voltage pulse will have a pulse width (measured between its 10 percent amplitude points) equal to six times the separation between the magnetic head and the geometric midplane of the recording surface. This distance measure of pulse width is converted into time by dividing by the surface velocity v.

The $H_y(u)$ curve of Figure 5.3b shows the nature of the readback signal component for a recorded step change in perpendicular magnetization. The deleterious influence of a significant perpendicular magnetization component upon bit resolution is readily apparent from the slow drop-off of H_y with increasing u. In addition, an appreciable component of perpendicular magnetization in a step change would make the output pulse highly asymmetric, since the total signal is obtained by directly adding the x and y field components shown, with their relative amplitudes weighted according to the magnitude of their respective medium magnetization components.

To determine a bound on the ratio of perpendicular-to-horizontal recorded magnetization that can be tolerated before a noticeable decrease in the pulse resolution is seen, we can require that the peak amplitude of the signal component contributed by M_y be no greater than 10 percent of the peak signal due to M_x. Using the far field equations,

$$H_y \mid_{max} = H_x \mid_{max} /2$$

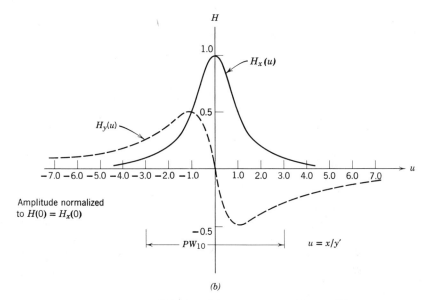

FIGURE 5.3b Fringing field components H_x and H_y.

Now

$$e \propto \mathbf{M} \cdot \mathbf{H} \propto M_x H_x + M_y H_y \tag{5.5}$$

Then it is necessary that

$$M_y \leq 0.2 M_x$$

M is a vector and

$$|\mathbf{M}|^2 = M_x^2 + M_y^2$$

where the maximum value of **M** is given by the remanent magnetization intensity M_r of the medium. Thus, for $M_y = 0.2 M_x$, the *peak amplitude* of the primary signal component e_x will only be decreased by approximately 4 percent. The output pulse shape will become nonsymmetric due to the presence of this perpendicular magnetization component.

As previously pointed out, it is found that for longitudinal recording on thin media, the amount of perpendicular magnetization is quite small, and therefore we are justified in ignoring H_y when estimating the spread of the readback pulse. However, a small amount of signal distortion arises if M_y is present.

(2) $y' < g$.

Figure 5.4 shows a qualitative illustration of the functions H_x and H_y for a value of $y' < g$. In this case, H_x and H_y are shown as functions of x rather than u, because the approximations of equations (5.3) and (5.4) are no longer valid. The general forms of these fields can be quickly sketched, recalling the expressions previously developed for H_x in terms of the subtended angle and

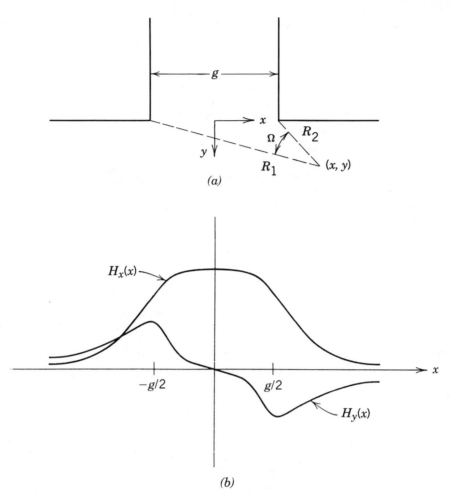

FIGURE 5.4 Fringing field components H_x and $H_y(y' < g)$.

H_y in terms of distances, both functions being defined in terms of the field point relative to the gap corners (this form was obtained from the magnetic charge model and, as previously mentioned, differs by a factor of 1/2 from the Karlqvist expressions). Here, we choose to set $H(0,0)$ equal to the deep gap field H_g to agree with the Karlqvist forms:

$$H_x = \frac{H_g}{\pi}\Omega \quad \text{and} \quad H_y = \frac{H_g}{2\pi} \ln \frac{R_1}{R_2}$$

where Ω, R_1, and R_2 are defined in Figure 5.4a. The curves of H_x and H_y in Figure 5.4b are representative of the general nature of the magnetic field functions in this near zone.

It can be seen from the strong variations in the fields near

$$|x|/g = 0.5$$

that the gap length is the predominant spatial parameter setting the shape and pulse half-width of the fringing field. H_x is the key function for longitudinal recording, and under the condition $y'/g \to 0$, the gap primarily determines the recording resolution. Hence, a reduction in gap size gives an almost proportional reduction in pulse width for a step change in horizontal magnetization.

The parameters g, δ, and d should be of the same general magnitude, since improving the magnetic coupling resolution can essentially be viewed as a scaling down of the recording geometry. Clearly, the fringing field directly scales with the coordinates. However, g must be large enough to overwrite data and δ appears associated with M_r in the signal amplitude expression as $M_r\delta$ and therefore must be large enough to provide an adequate signal-to-noise level. Reduced spacing is always desirable, if reliable performance is possible.

5.1.3 Additional Pole-Tip Geometries

The ideal head model is the most common method to represent ferrite heads, as their pole pieces gradually recede from the plane of the storage medium over distances long compared to the gap.

In addition to this widely used ring head model, several other geometries have been designed into recording systems. In fact, the first disk drive (RA-MAC) used a laminated head with contoured pole tips, providing the same advantages of pulse slimming that are now identified with current thin film heads. Film heads are made using batch fabrication techniques, such as masking, plating, and sputtering, similar to those used in microelectronics (unfortunately, mechanical finishing operations are still required). Ring heads made using these techniques have finite pole tip lengths, as shown in Figure 5.5, where the magnetic potential surface and resulting H_x field are sketched.

The effect of this geometry on the longitudinal field H_x is to cause the field to curve in the reverse direction at the outer pole corners. The resulting shape of H_x leads to negative undershoots on readback pulses, located near the outer edges of the pole faces. These become less pronounced as y increases, and the fields approach those of the approximations presented earlier. To calculate the fields in detail requires the use of some of the techniques described in Chapter 2. Several workers [6, 7] have found closed-form expressions for the fields by using approximations for the magnetic potentials along the head surfaces [Figure 5.5c]. From these boundary potentials the magnetic field components may be derived using an appropriate Green's function.

For perpendicular recording systems, probe heads are commonly used. One configuration uses a double-layered medium in which the perpendicularly oriented recording layer is deposited on a soft magnetic back layer which, in essence, forms a part of the head structure. Probe heads may be fabricated as

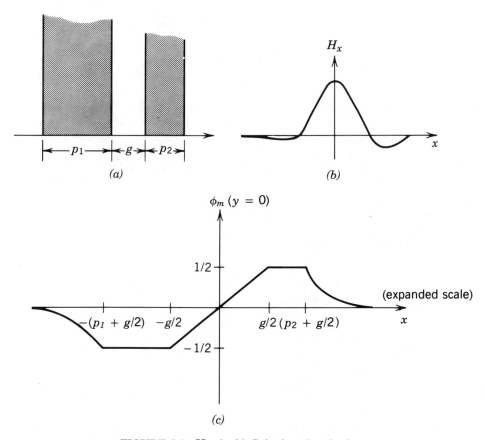

FIGURE 5.5 Head with finite-length pole tips.

film heads with one very thin pole tip—the probe—and a much thicker one that completes the flux path around the head and through the back layer of the medium. Figure 5.6 shows a typical geometry. In perpendicular recording, it is the H_y field that is of interest. A simple approach to estimating the field is to approximate the magnetic charge distribution on the probe by a uniform charge distribution on the pole tip. Expressions are then readily obtained from this charge and its image in the back layer.

Reading Coil Location

Figure 5.7 shows the magnetic potential lines for an entire head structure so that the influence of the coil location becomes evident. From the principle of reciprocity, the coupling of the coil with the medium sets the character of the readback pulse. The magnetic potential lines shown are for the magnetic shell equivalent of the coil and do not give the correct field within the coil. Note that the size and location of the coil on the magnetic core do affect the gross magnetic field distribution of a magnetic head. Usually, the coil location

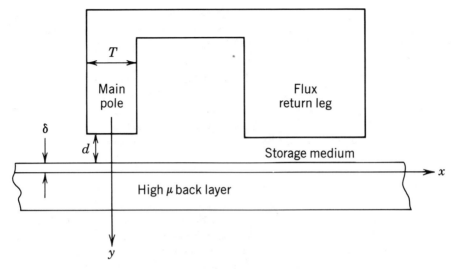

FIGURE 5.6 Probe head for perpendicular recording.

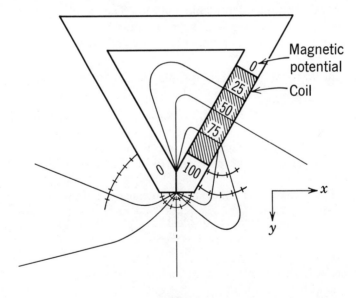

—— Magnetic equipotential lines
⊢⊢⊢⊢Magnetic field intensity lines

FIGURE 5.7 Influence of read coil location on magnetic coupling field.

is not important to pulse shape, since it does not influence the field in the immediate vicinity of the gap. In some magnetic head configurations (such as the one shown in Figure 5.7), however, the position of the coil, through its nonsymmetrical location on the head core, can unbalance the readback pulse "tails" through its modification of the head–surface coupling function outside the immediate gap area. The head structure illustrated reveals the unbalance that can arise in the flux along a plane in front of the head gap from placing the coil on only one leg. In sine wave recording, the location of the coil on the magnetic head core would manifest itself only in the very long wavelength response, that is, where the wavelengths become of the same order as the physical size of the head itself.

To estimate the fringing field outside the immediate gap area, it is advisable to make a coarse magnetic field map that encompasses the entire head geometry, including the actual location and distribution of the read coil windings on the core. This type of magnetic field map is easily constructed by substituting for the coil a magnetic potential source corresponding to the magnetic shell equivalent, as shown in Figure 5.7. Further, this type of mapping can also indicate the magnitude of the nonuseful leakage flux associated with a magnetic head. In general, the magnetic core structure is primarily significant in setting the maximum deep gap field available and the efficiency of the magnetic coupling of the turns to the gap. The magnetic pole faces and gap size set the magnetic coupling characteristics between head and medium.

5.1.4 Magnetic Circuit of the Magnetic Head

Ferrite Core Structures

Figure 5.8 shows a typical magnetic recording head and its magnetic circuit analog. R_g is the reluctance of the read/write head gap and R_{bg} and R_{fg} the leakage reluctances at the back and front of the gap respectively. R_c is the reluctance of each leg of the core and R_b the reluctance of the back gap, often very small.

Recall from Chapter 2 that magnetic reluctance is defined by

$$R = \frac{l}{\mu \mu_o A} \tag{5.6}$$

where l = path length,
A = cross-sectional area of path, and
μ = relative permeability.

The reluctance concept is based on the assumption that the magnetic flux follows the magnetic paths making up the structure or circuit.

Again, key objectives in the design of the magnetic head circuit are

1. To achieve the maximum flux density on writing at the pole tip region of the gap.
2. To minimize the reluctance of the magnetic core compared to that of the gap so that as high a fraction as possible of the ampere-turns applied on

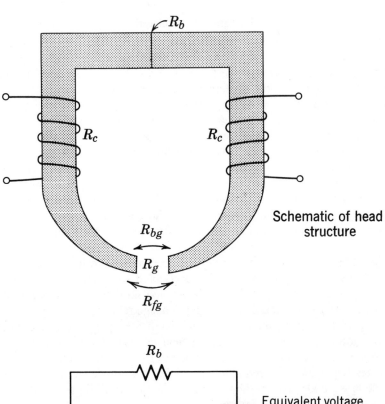

Schematic of head structure

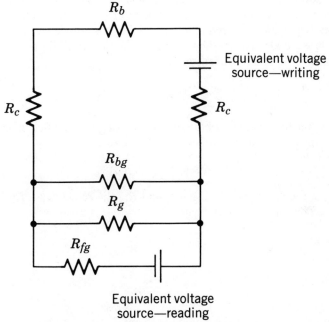

Equivalent voltage source—writing

Equivalent voltage source—reading

FIGURE 5.8 Magnetic head circuit analog.

writing appear across the gap to maximize the coupling of the read/write coil with the storage medium.

The variables in the reluctance terms give the designer a means of having some control in meeting the objectives above. In order to have the maximum flux density occur in the pole tip region, the cross-sectional area of the gap is made less than that of the magnetic core by a forming a "V" notch at the upper throat of the gap, which results in the gap having the minimum cross-section in the magnetic path. This design feature assures that the maximum flux density will occur at the gap and, by increasing the reluctance of the gap relative to the magnetic core, increases the fraction of applied ampere-turns that appears across the gap. A high permeability for the core material and a minimum core length will further reduce the core reluctance (but the core length must provide an adequate winding cross section for the number of turns needed).

Head efficiency is a parameter defined to characterize how effectively the ampere-turns on the magnetic head are coupled to the head gap. The efficiency ε is given by the fraction of the applied mmf that appears across the gap, in the absence of a medium. The gap leakage reluctances are much larger than the gap reluctance (that they parallel) so that the presence of the medium can be ignored. (Although the fringing field associated with R_{fg} in front of the gap is everything in recording!) Though efficiency is defined for writing, it also has application for reading. The higher the efficiency, the greater the flux linking the coils produced by a magnetization pattern on the medium. The expression for the head efficiency is

$$\varepsilon = \frac{H_g g}{NI} \tag{5.7}$$

An expression for ε will be obtained, considering a simplified magnetic head circuit to consist of just the gap and core:

$$NI = \Phi(R_g + R_m) \tag{5.8}$$

where R_g is the reluctance of the gap and R_m the reluctance of the magnetic head core. The mmf across the gap

$$H_g g = \Phi R_g$$

or

$$\varepsilon = \frac{R_g}{R_g + R_m} \tag{5.9}$$

which can be rewritten in the following form:

$$\varepsilon = \frac{1}{1 + \dfrac{1}{\mu} \dfrac{l_m}{g} \dfrac{A_g}{A_m}} \tag{5.10}$$

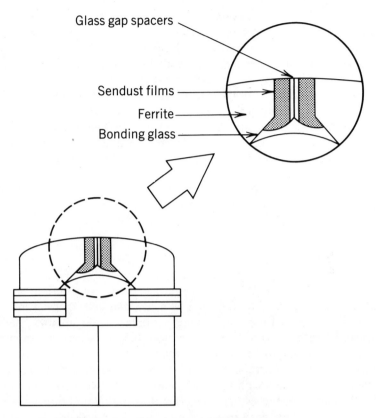

Glass gap spacers

Sendust films

Ferrite

Bonding glass

FIGURE 5.9 Metal-in-gap (MIG) head structure.

It is clear that for a high head efficiency we desire a short magnetic core path length, a high permeability, and a small ratio of gap-to-core cross section. The somewhat more detailed magnetic circuit of Figure 5.8 includes the back-gap (that is, where the two pole pieces join) and the leakage fluxes associated with the read/write gap. Inclusion of these associated reluctances refines the analysis leading to (5.10). In the usual magnetic head the efficiency is between 70 and 90 percent.

Metal-in-Gap Ferrite Head

A modification of the ferrite head is to include on one (the trailing leg) or both inner gap surfaces a thin metal layer of magnetic material (Figure 5.9). The flux densities of magnetic films can be several times that of ferrite and this is the reason such a film is used. In a head core fabricated from one material, saturation first occurs at the pole tip corners, and therefore limiting the write fringing field to a value less than that associated with the bulk material. By placing a thin film layer on the inner face of the trailing gap leg, with a saturation flux density two or more times that of the body of the core, early pole tip saturation at the trailing leg region (where writing occurs) can be avoided. A larger write field as well as a greater field gradient (from the localization of the enhanced flux density along the pole face) is the result. The motivation for the MIG head design comes from the availability of newer recording media with much higher coercivities and hence linear density possibilities. Sendust or AlFeSi is a popular material choice for this film. One magnetic design problem is that if the magnetic interface between the metal film and ferrite is imperfect, a "secondary gap" is created. The significance of this secondary gap can be estimated by comparing the fringing field at the medium along this "gap" centerline with that from the actual head gap along its centerline at the medium for the same H_g. Owing to this secondary gap, the readback pulse will exhibit a corresponding secondary readback peak. Normal specifications for such heads are that any such peak be less that 5 percent of the main peak of the signal.

Thin Film Heads

The magnetic circuit of a thin film head is quite different than that of the standard ferrite head. To date, these heads are plated on a substrate in a fashion that deposits one leg or pole, followed by a pancake coil, then an insulation layer that also provides for the function of a nonmagnetic gap, and finally the second magnetic pole. There is relatively more pole leakage (flux shunted by the magnetic legs) than in ferrite heads, which have a much larger opening for the insertion of turns. In the case of ferrite heads, a magnetic circuit analog is usually adequate, while with thin film heads a distributed transmission line model is generally used to estimate the flux distribution and efficiency of the structure. Jones [4] developed this approach in connection with the early thin film head work. Another major difference is the narrow pole tips. To be sure that the pole tips are the location where saturation of the head occurs first (and hence where the flux density is a maximum), the throat height must be generally less than the pole tip width, that is to say, considerably less than the throat height of a ferrite structure; this makes the fabrication of the device more challenging, since the mechanical finishing operations connected with achieving a head mounted in an air-bearing slider occur on the gap face. See Figure 5.10a, where a film head cross section is shown. Clearly, one advantage of this thin-film magnetic circuit structure is that the narrow pole tips improve the resolution of the device. However, as discussed earlier, at the outer corners of the pole tips the fringing field is oriented in the reverse direction to that within the gap region and this leads to negative undershoots on the readback pulse. The pulse features can require greater complication in the readback detection electronics.

The "air gap" reluctance term R_g is not frequency dependent, but the reluctance of the magnetic core R_m will be because of the eddy current and hysteresis energy losses in the magnetic material. Frequency considerations will be addressed later in this chapter, but high-frequency performance is one of the major advantages of thin film structures. The less magnetic material

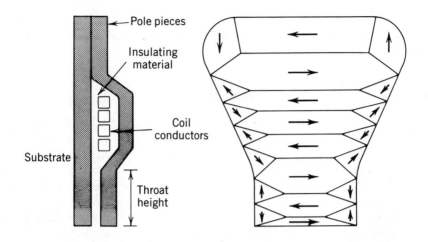

(a) Cross section of head   (b) Pole piece domains, no applied field

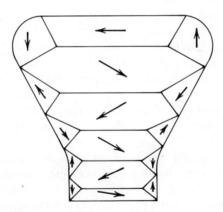

(c) Pole piece domains, peak write current

FIGURE 5.10 Film head showing (a) cross section, (b) pole piece while reading, (c) pole piece while writing.

needed for the core, the less will be the losses and the inductance for a given number of turns, advantages arising from the miniaturized nature of thin film devices.

5.1.5 Domain Structure in Film Heads

Although the magnetic circuit approach is a very effective method for analyzing heads, it is limited to head structures having homogeneous regions, which can be modeled by either lumped circuit reluctance or transmission line models. Film heads often have a rather complex domain structure, as shown in Figure 5.10b. The film shown is anisotropic, with the easy axes of the long domains oriented across the track as shown. Closure domains form at the edges of the head to minimize the total energy, as discussed in Chapter 2. To carry small amounts of flux, while reading for example, the magnetization rotates away from the easy axis. In this mode of operation, under the assumption that there is no domain wall motion, the pole pieces may be considered to be homogeneous with a permeability given by

$$\mu = 1 + M_s/H_k \qquad (5.11)$$

where H_k is the anisotropy field. In this approach, the effective width of the head is smaller because of the closure domains.

When the head is excited by large fields, while writing, there is extensive domain wall motion and the structure might look like that of Figure 5.10c. Analysis is much more difficult for this situation, but still possible using energy methods and numerical analysis. When write currents are removed, the domain pattern may not return to that existing before writing. Consequently, readback waveforms may not be reproducible. Closure domains at the edges of the head are reduced by building up the pole piece from several layers. The flux in one layer can close through adjacent layers so that closure domains are not required.

A radically different thin film head design is the so-called horizontal thin film head. Here, the head is fabricated with the pole faces parallel to the plane of the substrate. Thus, the head gaps and air-bearing surfaces are on the top surface of the wafer. This approach offers the opportunity to ion etch the air-bearing surface and eliminate the mechanical finishing operations associated with the conventional approaches. As the magnetic structure of a head closely resembles that of the standard ring-type structure, the throat height is not nearly so critical. The individual head units would be diced from a wafer. The main advantage seen in this design is the possibility of much lower cost.

5.1.6 Magnetoresistive Heads

Although inductive heads are the most commonly used sensors of information stored on magnetic media, many other modes of sensing are possible. Any

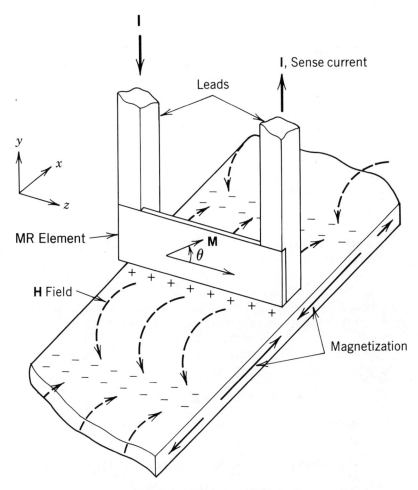

FIGURE 5.11 Magnetoresistive sensor.

physical effect sensitive to the external fields produced by the magnetization patterns written on the medium is a candidate for a read head application. Some of these are magnetic semiconductor, magneto-optic, and magnetoresistive effects. Many laboratory demonstrations have shown the feasibility of noninductive field sensors, but the only widely used phenomenon at present is the magnetoresistive effect used in read heads in magnetic tape storage systems. However, MR heads are under intensive investigation for disk drive applications. We will present the concepts for a simple magnetoresistive head shown in Figure 5.11. Recognize that the MR head is a read-only device and for recording it must be used in conjunction with an inductive write head (or some other device that can suitably magnetize the medium).

The resistance in some magnetic materials depends upon the angle between the current flowing through the material and its magnetization. The orientation of the magnetization changes the lattice configuration slightly and hence affects the scattering of the conduction electrons as they pass through the lattice, thereby changing the resistivity. Although the maximum change in resistivity is small, on the order of several percent, the output signal voltage is proportional to the sense current when the device is driven by a constant current source. By using a very high current density in the stripe, the readback voltage will be larger than that from an inductive head, when size and frequency bandwidth limit the number of turns. The resistivity is greatest when the current is parallel to the magnetization and may be expressed in terms of the angle θ it makes with the magnetization vector as

$$\rho = \rho_0 - \Delta\rho \sin^2 \theta \qquad (5.12)$$

In the simple head geometry of Figure 5.11, the magnetoresistive film is magnetically anisotropic, with easy axis aligned across the track. The current flows parallel to the easy axis. It is assumed that the film is a single domain, and demagnetizing effects are neglected. When a magnetic field source gives rise to a field H_y under the MR film, the magnetization rotates to minimize the total energy, which in this case is the sum of the anisotropy energy and the magnetic potential energy. Recall that in the vicinity of a horizontally recorded transition, the external flux above the storage medium is primarily normal to the surface (y direction in Figure 5.11).

$$U = K \sin^2 \theta - M_s H_y \sin \theta \qquad (5.13)$$

which is minimum when

$$\sin \theta = M_s H_y / 2K \qquad (5.14)$$

K is the uniaxial anistropy constant. Substituting into (5.12), we have

$$\rho = \rho_0 - \Delta\rho (M_s H_y / 2K)^2 \qquad (5.15)$$

If H_s were the desired signal field from the recorded magnetization, it would experience severe distortion from the square law relationship of (5.15). This can be overcome by applying a linearizing, or bias, field to the sensor film so that

$$H_y = H_b + H_s \qquad (5.16)$$

where H_b and H_s are bias and signal fields, respectively, and $H_s \ll H_b$. Under these conditions,

$$\rho = \rho_0 - \Delta\rho (M_s H_b / 2K)^2 (1 + 2H_s / H_b) \qquad (5.17)$$

giving a change in resistivity that is linearly proportional to the signal field. Standard practice is to bias the stripe so that M_s is at a 45° angle with respect to the current (easy axis) to maximize the linearity range. More detailed analysis is required to handle effects of demagnetization, domain wall formation and motion, and film defects. Head engineers have developed many novel configurations of biasing, film geometry, and shielding to enhance magnetoresistive head performance [4]. Reading involves sending a constant current through the MR stripe and detecting the voltage signal due to the resistivity variations. The voltage outputs can be relatively high and they are not sensitive to the head–medium velocity.

Shielded MR Head

An unshielded MR stripe would give poor resolution, since it would couple for a relatively long distance along the medium. By proper equalization and coding, one can compensate this device. Nonetheless, most commonly used MR heads are shielded devices, that is, the MR stripe is enclosed between two magnetic pole pieces, which could be an operative inductive head. Such a magnetic structure can be viewed as two back-to-back ring heads that are differentially coupled. To understand the flux coupling into the stripe, we can imagine a small coil wound around this stripe and look at a structure using the principle of reciprocity. Refer to Figure 5.12. The potential along the pole face $y = 0$ is shown for an idealized head. t is the width of the stripe. Adding to this potential function that for a similar idealized head displaced by $g + t$ but with reversed sign, we get the total potential distribution as shown. But this is exactly the potential we would see if an mmf were placed along the MR stripe. It is also clear that while the flux sensed by the stripe enters in the y direction, its source is a horizontal magnetization transition, as the flux sketch in Figure 5.11 shows. The stripe width is on the order of 50 nanometers or much less than the gap size g.

Using this double gap ring head analogy, we can write the voltage across the hypothetical coil on the stripe (here assuming $t = 0$) as

$$e(\overline{x}) = e_1[\overline{x} + (g/2)] - e_1[\overline{x} - (g/2)] \qquad (5.18)$$

where $e_1(\overline{x})$ is the signal from an inductive head with a gap g. This expression can be rewritten as

$$e(\overline{x}) = g \left[\frac{e_1(\overline{x} + (g/2)) - e_1(\overline{x} - (g/2))}{g} \right]$$

In this form, the term in brackets is an approximation to the derivative of $e_1(\overline{x})$ at $\overline{x} = 0$. This is a reasonable approximation when the voltage pulse is much broader than g, which is usually the case in noncontact recording. Then

$$e(\overline{x}) \approx g \frac{de_1(\overline{x})}{dx} \qquad (5.19)$$

Now the MR head output is proportional to the flux through the stripe, not the rate of change of flux as is the case with the inductive head. Therefore, the output signal is proportional to the integral of the voltage across this hypothetical coil or

$$e(\overline{x}) \approx g e_1(\overline{x}) \qquad (5.20)$$

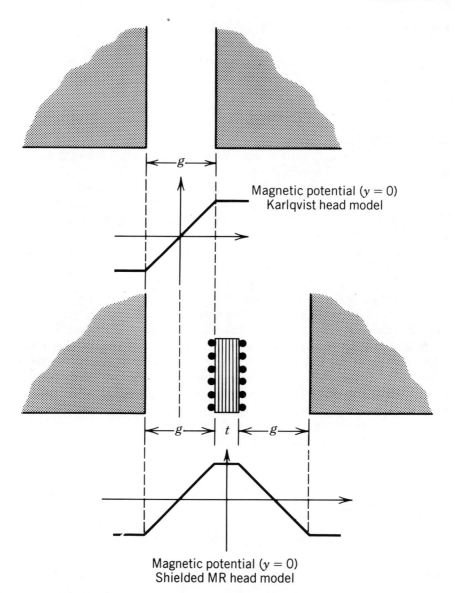

FIGURE 5.12   Shielded MR head.

We conclude that the pulse shape of a shielded MR stripe (centered within a gap of $2g$) is similar to the output signal from an inductive head with gap length g.

The shielded MR stripe not only can offer higher voltage output than an inductive head, when high performance requirements or size limit the number of turns that can be put on the head, but its pulse resolution is at least comparable to inductive head devices. Perhaps most attractive, the MR head is well adapted to designs such as write-wide read-narrow units, which later is shown to be extremely important in reducing misregistration problems limiting track density. Turns on the shielding pole(s) of an MR stripe immediately provide a head unit with both write and read functions.

5.2 ELECTRICAL CHARACTERISTICS OF MAGNETIC HEADS

When we speak of the electrical characteristics of magnetic heads, we are essentially referring to the frequency behavior of the magnetic head transducer and the manner in which it influences design and performance. The frequency aspects of the magnetic head relate to its characterization in the time domain. In presenting the overall recording process performance, including both spatial and temporal effects, a characterization is valid only for a specific head surface velocity through the expression $f = v/\lambda$.

Basically, two types of magnetic materials, ferrites and metallic films, are available for magnetic head construction. Both the magnetic and electrical properties of these two categories of materials differ widely. In addition to the influence that eddy current and hysteresis losses have on the frequency response of a magnetic head, we must give attention to the fact that these energy losses may give rise to a measurable thermal heating of the magnetic core. Thus, each of these two types of core materials will be discussed individually in terms of the nature of the influence its class of properties has on the electrical behavior of the magnetic head.

5.2.1 Ferrite Cores

The resistivity of a conventional ferrite material is a million or more times that of the common metallic magnetic alloys, and eddy current losses are negligible. In general, the permeabilities and maximum flux densities are much lower, and the coercivities, while small, are higher than those of metallic magnetic materials. The main disadvantage of ferrites with respect to magnetic heads, however, is the difficulty of fabricating out of this brittle ceramic material, precisely dimensioned head gaps whose edges will not chip, or deform under prolonged abrasion or intermittent impact.

Hysteresis power loss in a ferrite head is important when writing, because at this time a high flux density is required in order to magnetize the recording medium. Losses become worse when writing at high pulse rates. As demonstrated in Chapter 2,

$$P_h \propto f \int H \, dB \qquad (5.21)$$

where P_h is the hysteresis power loss and the integral represents the area of the B–H loop traversed during each frequency cycle. The presence of this latter term makes evident the reason writing is of concern. A ferrite material with a low coercivity is highly desirable to minimize the hysteresis integral.

Attention must also be given to the possibility of appreciable heating of the magnetic head core produced by hysteresis effects on writing. Special design precautions may be necessary to assure that the thermal energy generated is effectively conducted away, recognizing the insulator qualities of ferrite. Elevated temperatures of ferrite core may not only damage the coil-winding insulation and perhaps the recording surface and its free movement (if intermittent contact occurs), but can also reduce the ferrimagnetic properties of the magnetic head core to a marked degree, even to the point of rendering it completely ineffectual if the Curie temperature of the material is approached.

For the read process, the small-signal permeability of the ferrite core determines the electrical equivalent circuit. When the ferrite core is excited by a small, sinusoidally varying field, the permeability is constant with frequency until a certain cutoff frequency f_c is reached, after which it decreases rapidly. Figure 5.13 shows the behavior qualitatively.

The cutoff frequency is related to the ferrimagnetic resonance effect, caused by electron spins precessing about the easy axis of magnetization in individual domains. The more tightly coupled the magnetization is to the easy axis, the higher the natural frequency of precession. This coupling is measured by the anistropy field H_k, and the permeability cutoff frequency is roughly proportional to H_k. On the other hand, the small-signal permeability at low frequencies is inversely proportional to H_k. To first order, then, the product of low-frequency permeability times the permeability cutoff frequency is a constant, given by Snoek's limit.

$$\mu f_c = 4000 \text{ MHz} \tag{5.22}$$

When the ferrite core is excited at frequencies close to f_c, there is interaction between the precessing electron spins and the applied field, which leads to an absorption of power from the applied field. This power dissipation in the ferrite can be accounted for by assigning a complex permeability to the material:

$$\mu = \mu' - j\mu'' \tag{5.23}$$

where μ' accounts for the magnetic energy storage property of the ferrite and μ'' its power dissipation. The variations of both μ' and μ'' with frequency are shown in Figure 5.13, and they are related. Roughly speaking, μ'' is proportional to the negative derivative of μ' with respect to frequency. This is a behavior characteristic of many physical *dispersive* phenomena such as wave propagation in dielectric and magnetic media.

5.2.2 Metallic Head Cores

The most frequently used metals for magnetic head cores are magnetic alloys, such as nickel–iron, used as films or thin laminations. These magnetic substances have higher saturation magnetizations than ferrites, making them

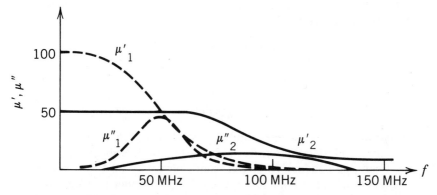

FIGURE 5.13 Plot for two different materials of ferrite complex permeability versus frequency.

attractive for writing on high-coercivity media. They also have some advantages for ease of fabricating film head cores, being made by techniques similar to those used in batch processing of semiconductors. Unfortunately, magnetic heads differ radically from semiconductor devices in that individual head devices must be incorporated in an air-bearing slider (carrier), which requires precise mechanical contouring and surface finishing to assure proper flying. While the mechanical operations on the head/slider are also required for ferrite and MIG heads, they are much more critical for film heads in that they minimize the advantages ordinarily associated with batch fabrication. Now beginning are investigations of planar thin film heads, heads in which the gap pole faces lie in the plane of the wafer, which offer the possibility of fabricating an entire head and slider through electrodeposition and eliminating any mechanical finishing steps. The metallic alloys have very high permeabilities and comparatively low resistivities (or high conductivities), and they are used in the form of thin sheets or laminations to minimize eddy current losses. Usually, with metallic magnetic materials, the eddy current loss will be much greater than the associated hysteresis loss, even for the operation of writing. This results in part from the redistribution of flux in the core produced by the eddy currents.

We will in brief form develop the relations that govern the influence of eddy currents on the magnetic behavior of the head core. As an approximation, we can consider that the flux in a film or lamination varies with only one dimension. Then, to derive the frequency characteristic of the magnetic head caused by induced eddy currents, we can solve

$$\frac{d^2B}{dx^2} = j\omega\mu_0 B \tag{5.24}$$

subject to the boundary conditions imposed by the choice of lamination thickness t. This equation, developed in Chapter 2, gives the space–time behavior of the magnetic flux density in a conductor material for a time-periodic field of angular frequency $\omega(\omega = 2\pi f)$. The solution is

$$B = B_0 e^{-x/\delta} e^{-jx/\delta} \tag{5.25}$$

where

$$\delta = \frac{1}{\sqrt{\pi f \mu_0}}. \tag{5.26}$$

The parameter δ has the dimensions of distance and is familiarly known as the depth of penetration, or skin depth, in describing the skin effect in current-carrying conductors. Recall from Chapter 2 that for a semi-infinite block the depth of penetration is the depth from the outer surface, where the source field is applied, at which the flux intensity B would decay to $1/e$ (or 36.7 percent) of its value at the surface. We can write the following expression for the flux carried per lamination:

$$\Phi = 2 \int_0^{t/2} B_0 \, dx = 2B_0 \int_0^{t/2} e^{-(1+j)x/\delta} \, dx \tag{5.27}$$

where B_0 is the applied surface flux density on either side of the lamination. Or we have

$$\Phi = \frac{2B_0\delta}{1+j} \left[1 - e^{-(1+j)t/2\delta} \right] \tag{5.28}$$

For $\delta \ll t$ the flux is given by

$$\Phi = \frac{2B_0\delta}{1+j} \tag{5.29}$$

Note that the flux does not depend on t at these frequencies where the skin depth is much less than t. For low frequencies (i.e., very small t/δ),

$$\left[1 - e^{-(1+j)t/2\delta} \right] \approx \frac{(1+j)t/2}{\delta} \tag{5.30}$$

Thus, as expected at dc, $\Phi(0) = B_0 t$. Therefore, the ratio of flux carried by the lamination at high frequencies to that under static conditions is

$$\frac{\Phi(f)}{\Phi(0)} = \frac{2\delta}{(1+j)t} = \frac{\sqrt{2}\delta}{t} \angle -45° \tag{5.31}$$

For a given applied field the reluctance of the magnetic core varies inversely with the flux, and its value compared to the gap reluctance depends on frequency.

For high frequencies, almost all the magnetic head flux during both reading and writing is carried by the surface layers of the laminations. Even so, if

$$R_m(f) < R_g$$

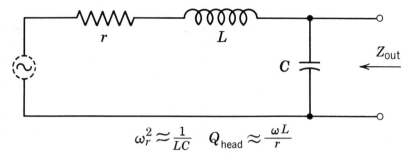

$$\omega_r^2 \simeq \frac{1}{LC} \qquad Q_{\text{head}} \simeq \frac{\omega L}{r}$$

FIGURE 5.14   Simplified equivalent electrical circuit of magnetic head.

in this frequency range, the head sensitivity will not be significantly reduced, because the head reluctance is dominated by the air gap reluctance. If the magnetic core reluctance were to dominate, then

$$e \propto \omega \Phi \qquad \text{or} \qquad e \propto f^{1/2}.$$

This frequency loss characteristic is similar to that of an inductance that is dominated by eddy currents in its core. But note that these are time and not wavelength-dependent effects and on readback occur in addition to the wavelength loss factors already described. Where they fall on a density curve depends on the medium velocity.

The above analysis is applicable to homogeneous single sheets or laminations as well as multilayered geometries. For small skin depths it also describes thick layers as in the MIG head constructed by forming metal pole tips in a ferrite head core. In film heads, there are additional loss mechanisms associated with damping of domain wall motion and micro eddy currents, but the classical eddy current treatment serves as a starting point for further analysis.

5.2.3 Equivalent Lumped-Constant Electrical Circuit of the Magnetic Head

The output voltage on reading and the magnetizing force on writing (for a given current) are both proportional to the number of turns on the read/write coil(s). This indicates that it should be advantageous to make the number of turns N as large as practical. The inductance of the magnetic head is proportional to N squared, however. Furthermore, the stray capacitance associated with the coil winding increases with N. Accordingly, the larger the value for N, the lower the resonant frequency of the magnetic head and the greater the time constants associated with its transient electrical response. The lumped-constant circuit shown in Figure 5.14 will normally suffice to represent the equivalent electrical circuit of the magnetic head for the electrical design aspects of the digital magnetic recording system. In Figure 5.14, C is the effective shunt capacity associated with the magnetic head and includes not only the contribution from the head coil but also the lead capacity between the head and the first stage of electronics. Both the resistance r and the inductance L will be functions of frequency whenever it is necessary to account for the frequency loss function of the magnetic head core in the circuit design.

As an example, we calculate the impedance of a ferrite head using the magnetic circuit and complex permeability concepts developed earlier. The inductance L is given by

$$L = N^2/(R_g + R_m) \tag{5.32}$$

in terms of the number of turns and the head reluctances. R_m is now complex:

$$R_m = l_m/\mu_0(\mu' - j\mu'')A_m \tag{5.33}$$

or

$$R_m = R_m'/(1 - j\mu''/\mu') \tag{5.34}$$

where R_m' is the reluctance calculated using the real part of the permeability only. After substituting equation (5.34) into (5.32), we obtain a complex inductance,

$$L = L' \left[\frac{(1 - j\mu'/\mu'')}{1 - (j\mu'/\mu'')\left(\dfrac{R_g}{R_g + R_m'}\right)} \right] \tag{5.35}$$

where $L' = [N^2/(R_g + R_m')]$. When the air gap reluctance dominates, L reduces to L', but when the core reluctance becomes greater, the imaginary part of the inductance introduces a resistance into the equivalent circuit. The impedance Z_L of the inductor for $R_m' \gg R_g$ is

$$Z_L = j\omega L = \omega L'(\mu''/\mu') + j\omega L' \tag{5.36}$$

The total resistance r of the equivalent circuit includes the winding resistance plus the resistance introduced by the lossy ferrite core material (first term in Z_L). Note that the latter varies with frequency. Similar analyses can be carried out to derive equivalent circuits that include hysteresis losses and eddy current effects.

Usually, the quality factor Q (defined in Figure 5.14) of a magnetic head is quite low (less than 10). The inductance L is relatively low compared to its associated coil resistance because of the inherent air gap(s) in the magnetic circuit of a magnetic head (recall that $L \propto 1/R_h$ where R_h is the total reluctance of the magnetic head circuit). Thus, a magnetic head typically has a broad frequency resonance peak. For digital recording, one customarily operates below resonance frequency ω_r, that is, where the head impedance is still inductive in character. This procedure minimizes spurious output signal oscillations on readback.

In high-frequency digital magnetic recording heads, the effective output impedance of the head, Z_{out} of Figure 5.14, may be on the order of 10 to several hundred Ohms. Normally then, during readback the head is terminated with a relatively low impedance, for example, 1000 Ohms. This resistance is chosen to minimize noise in the preamplifier and to provide some circuit damping, in order to reduce or eliminate any pulse overshoots (or ringing) that is, waveform distortion associated with the electrical characteristics of the head.

5.2.4 Cross Talk and Interhead Shielding

Cross talk refers to the magnetic coupling between magnetic heads mounted in close proximity, and it is of concern when the heads must be simultaneously operated. The most obvious example is recording in parallel on a group of tracks with a set of magnetic heads arrayed in a common mounting block.

For high frequencies, effective shielding can be achieved through enclosing or separating the head from its environment by a shield of a high-conductivity material such as copper. The screening action results from the induced eddy currents in the conductor surface. Here, we deliberately seek an eddy current effect, and the thickness of the shield should be several times the depth of penetration for the frequency range for which the shield is to serve, if it is to be fully effective. For low frequencies, the most effective magnetic shielding approach is to insert two or three high-permeability magnetic screens, with intervening spacers, between heads to act as shunts for the flux tending to spread from one magnetic head to the other. It can be proved that several such magnetic shields, separated from each other by nonmagnetic layers, are much more effective than one single shield of equivalent net thickness.

Thus, in general, one will find that where excellent magnetic shielding between heads is required, a sandwich composed of alternate layers of copper and some high-permeability magnetic material is inserted between the groups of magnetic head laminations in the head stack.

5.3 HEAD-TRACK REGISTRATION

In digital magnetic recording, the importance of high storage density places emphasis on track density as well as bit density. The surface area information density in bits per square inch is equal to the product of track density times bit density. Head-to-track registration tolerances are necessary in any mechanical structure designed to operate with track seeking and following. With a single read/write head element it is necessary, in order to accommodate the lack of precise registration, to accept during readback signal interference components, arising from residual patterns at the track edges from previous and adjacent track recordings. A track must then be wide enough (at the price of track density) to provide an adequate "desired" signal-to-noise (SNR) ratio to yield a suitable error rate. In Chapter 8 track misregistration issues for a single read/write head are discussed. A dual-element head unit is a special means to help compensate for track misregistration tolerances.

A dual-element head structure could be a write-wide read-narrow head unit or a wide-erase narrow-read/write unit. In these units the individual elements

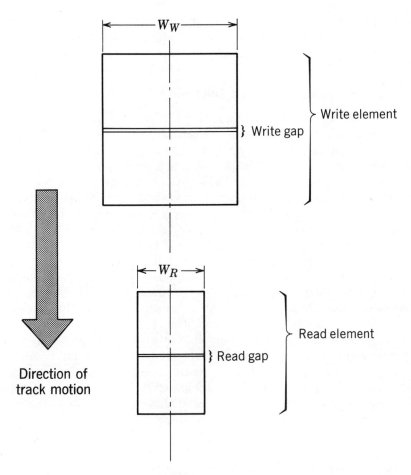

FIGURE 5.15 Write-wide read-narrow head.

are aligned along a common centerline (see Figure 5.15). The advantage to be gained by this head arrangement can be seen by reference to Figure 5.16 where the write-wide read-narrow configuration under worst-case track registration conditions is shown.

Let

$\pm P$ = head-to-medium lateral registration tolerance and

W_R = read head width

W_W = write head width

On each writing operation, the write head records a "band" of new information where

$$W_W - 2P$$

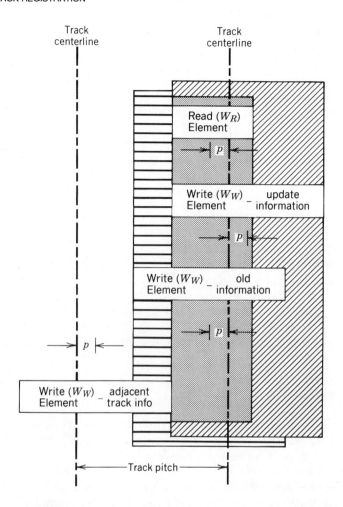

FIGURE 5.16   Write-wide read-narrow positioning tolerance.

is the guaranteed width of the updated recording band under any combination of mispositioning errors. Moreover,

$$W_R + 2P$$

is the width of the guaranteed band within which the read-element sensing will occur. By requiring the following inequality:

$$W_R + 2P \leq W_W - 2P \tag{5.37}$$

the read element is constrained to fall always within the updated information band. This relation gives

$$W_W \geq W_R + 4P \tag{5.38}$$

as a restriction on the minimum width of the write element relative to the read element to eliminate any sensing of old or adjacent track information for the given positioning tolerance P. The larger the ratio W_R/P, the higher the SNR. This dual-element type of head unit assures that no output signal interference will arise from variations in lateral track registration up to a misregistration tolerance of $\pm P$. A low error rate performance, comparable to that obtainable from perfect track alignment, then could be expected if these conditions are met.

The minimum track spacing or pitch is W_W. Therefore, the maximum track density (tracks per inch = tpi) achievable under the above positioning constraint from such a dual-element head configuration is

$$\text{tpi} = 1/W_W \tag{5.39}$$

where W_W is given by equation (5.38). The minimum acceptable "on-track" signal sets W_R. With the read head width thus set, formula (5.38) gives the write head width, and hence from equation (5.39) we have an estimate for the maximum track density that can be realized under the imposed conditions. In general, not only does the maximum desired signal decrease with off-track misalignment, but disturbances from both old information and adjacent track information increase and cause the effective readback SNR to deteriorate. Since these undesired signal sources are not directly correlated, their contributions to noise (voltage) tend to add as the square root of the sum of the squares, similar to random noise sources. The off-track capability significantly influences linear density limits. In many disk drives the system must meet the design error rates with up to a 15 percent track misregistration tolerance.

References

1. "Magnetic Data Recording Theory: Head Design," A. S. Hoagland, *Commun. Electron. (AIEE)*, pp. 506–513, November 1956.
2. "High-Resolution Magnetic Recording Structures," A. S. Hoagland, *IBM J. Res. Dev.*, Vol. 2, No. 2, pp. 90–105, April 1958.

3. "High Density Magnetic Head Design for Noncontact Recording," L. F. Shew, *IRE Trans. Electron. Comput.*, Vol. EC-11, No. 6, pp. 764–772, December 1962.

4. *Magnetic Recording*, Vol. I: *Technology*, C. D. Mee and E. D. Daniel, McGraw-Hill, New York, pp. 244–336, 1987.

5. *Introduction to Magnetic Recording*, R. M. White, IEEE Press, New York, 1985, pp. 22–24.

6. "Analytic Expressions for the Fringe Field of Finite Pole-Tip Length Recording Heads," R. I. Potter, *IEEE Trans. Magn.*, MAG-11, pp. 8000–8081, January 1975.

7. "Analytic Expressions for Field Components of Non-Symmetrical Finite Pole Tip Length Head Based on Measurements on Large-Scale Models," T. J. Szczech, *IEEE Trans. Magn.*, MAG-15, pp. 1319–1322, September 1979.

8. "On the Characteristics of the Pole-Keeper Head Fields," J. C. Mallinson and H. N. Bertram, *IEEE Trans. Magn.*, MAG-20, pp. 721–723, September 1984.

9. *Ferrites*, J. Smit and H. P. J. Wijn, Wiley, New York, 1959.

10. "Calculation of the Magnetic Field in the Ferromagnetic Layer of a Magnetic Drum," O. Karlqvist, *Trans. Roy. Inst. Technol. Stockholm*, No. 86, 1954. Reprinted in *Introduction to Magnetic Recording*, R. M. White, Ed., IEEE Press, New York, 1985.

11. "Studies on Magnetic Recording," W. K. Westmijze, *Philips Res. Rep.*, Part II, Vol. 8, No. 3, pp. 161–183, June 1953. Reprinted in *Introduction to Magnetic Recording*, R. M. White, Ed., IEEE Press, New York, 1985.

12. "High-Density Magnetic Recording Heads," F. J. Jeffers, *Proc. IEEE*, Vol. 74, No. 11, pp. 1540–1556, November 1986.

13. "Magneto-Optic Determination of Magnetic Recording Head Fields," M. E. Re, R. R. Katti, S. L. Zeder, and M. H. Kryder, *IEEE Trans. Magn.*, MAG-22, pp. 840–842, 1986.

14. "A Magnetoresistive Readout Transducer," R. Hunt, *IEEE Trans. Magn.*, MAG-7, pp. 150–154, 1971.

15. "A New Thin Film Head Generation IC Head," J. P. Lazzari and P. Deroux-Dauphin, *IEEE Trans. Magn.*, MAG-25, pp. 3190–3193, 1989.

CHAPTER 6

MAGNETIC RECORDING MEDIA

Magnetic recording media find a wide range of usage in digital magnetic recording products. The three principal classes of product are tape, rigid disk, and flexible disk. These, in turn, cover a host of application and performance specifications, requiring special properties of magnetic materials, binders, coatings, and substrates. This chapter will address the principles by which magnetic media affect the recording process but will not treat the many complex material fabrication processes that the production of recording media entails. Needless to say, the development and production of magnetic recording media as storage densities move above 10^8 bits per square inch represent an enormous challenge.

6.1 GENERAL FEATURES OF RECORDING MEDIA

6.1.1 Magnetic Properties and Design Considerations

In distinction to the "soft" magnetic material properties of a magnetic head, the recording medium is a "hard" magnetic material. The readback signal voltage in the magnetic head on readback in saturation recording is proportional to M_r, the residual or remanent intensity of magnetization of the storage medium after being recorded. Thus, a large value for M_r is indicated. A relatively large coercive force H_c is also desired for a magnetic recording medium. A large coercive force will provide for stability of the magnetization against stray and self-demagnetizing fields. However, the choice of H_c is limited in magnitude by the fact that it must be compatible with the means available for magnetizing the medium. As mentioned in Chapter 5, head materials are limited in their saturation magnetization, which limits the writing field strength and gradient. A rectangular hysteresis loop like that shown in Figure 6.1 is advantageous in binary recording to improve the definition of the two discrete magnetization states used and assures the switching will be localized in the vicinity of $H = H_c$. These M–H loop properties are frequently described in terms of remanence squareness M_r/M_s and the switching field distribution (SFD). This function measures the narrowness of the range over which the domains or particles reverse or switch as a function of H. The switching field distribution function is often characterized by plotting the derivative dM/dH of the hysteresis loop centered about H_c. The half-amplitude width of this curve, ΔH, when normalized by H_c, is a measure of the distribution function. An alternative definition is given by

$$SFD = \frac{[H(-M_r/2) - H(M_r/2)]}{H_c} \tag{6.1}$$

The SFD is a means to characterize the squareness of any recording medium loop, giving the fractional change in H_c that will switch half the material. The smaller the SFD, the more square the loop. Another term commonly used to characterize the distribution of switching fields is coercivity squareness S^*, which is defined for a hysteresis loop such that at $H = -H_c$

$$\frac{dM}{dH} = \frac{M_r}{(1 - S^*)H_c} \tag{6.2}$$

A typical magnetic recording material will have M_r/M_s and S^* values of approximately 0.9. The mean switching field can be characterized by the remanence coercivity H_{cr}, illustrated in Figure 6.1. If the applied field is reduced to zero after reaching $-H_{cr}$, the magnetization will decrease to zero along the minor hysteresis loop shown; that is, there is no magnetization remaining after a field reversal of amplitude H_{cr}.

In Chapter 4 we obtained the following expression for the transition parameter due to self-demagnetizing effects:

$$a_m = \frac{M_r \delta}{2\pi H_c} \tag{6.3}$$

Now consider the terms in this relationship. The potential gain in pulse resolution from a decrease in recording surface thickness, through a reduction in the magnetic coupling region along a track between head and surface, has been described previously. The signal output is essentially proportional to $M_r \delta$ as long as $\delta < d$ such that the writing field $H(x,y)$ within the medium is essentially uniform through its thickness. The related bit density increase offered by going to thinner magnetic films usually more than justifies the loss in readback signal amplitude that results. As a consequence, the major direction of development efforts in magnetic recording media is to achieve ever thinner magnetic recording media. Therefore, to obtain a satisfactory signal

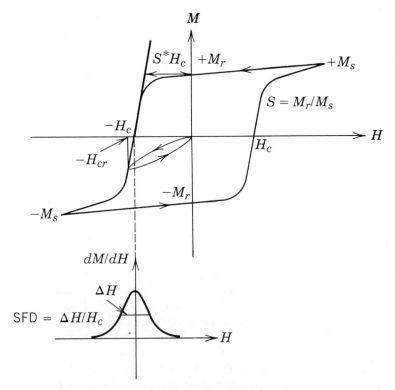

FIGURE 6.1   Hysteresis loop showing magnetic medium parameters.

level, media with high values of M_r, associated with a large M_s and a high degree of loop squareness, are desirable. However, where a high demagnetizing factor exists, M_r can be limited and proportional to H_c. Given the need to achieve a small value for the transition parameter, the coercive force also must be increased, as indicated by the above expression. The ability to make metal films that are extremely thin and offer very wide choices for H_c and M_r has increasingly made this form of storage material the one of choice for high-density recording.

Another important attribute of a recording medium is the preferential orientation of the medium magnetization which is related to the anisotropy of the material used. For normal longitudinal recording, the easy axis of magnetization is chosen to be in-plane to favor alignment of the magnetization in the direction of the desired head coupling field. An orientation in the direction of track motion will further increase signal output. As a consequence, the output pulse from a transition will be similar to the H_x fringing field along the track, and hence, fairly symmetric and narrow. For perpendicular recording, on the other hand, the anisotropy of the film is chosen to be normal to the film plane, since in this form of recording the objective is to minimize transition demagnetization by having oppositely magnetized regions aligned antiparallel to one another rather than "head-to-head," as with in-plane magnetization. Further, with some such films a soft magnetic underlayer is included to increase the coupling of flux through the head–medium magnetic circuit when pole heads are used.

6.1.2 Noise Characteristics

The noise characteristics of the media are extremely important as we go to higher densities, and the medium noise properties are quite different between particulate and thin film media. Track density increases require narrower tracks. The signal will be proportional to track width, the voltage from differential widths of the track adding coherently. If the medium noise is random and uncorrelated, then medium noise powers will add, and the medium root-mean-square (rms) noise voltage will vary as the square root of track width. (Signal power adds as the square of the sum, while noise power adds as the sum of the squares.) This leads to a 3 dB SNR voltage loss with a halving of the track width. The signal and medium noise are both affected similarly by the wavelength characteristics of the recording channel. On the other hand, there are other sources of noise and interference (head, electronics, and electromagnetic radiation), so that the actual role of media noise in setting performance is a system issue. Another important source of errors in data storage is media defects. The frequency of occurrence and size distribution of defects in the film or coating are very much a function of the processing of the medium.

6.1.3 Mechanical Properties

Actually, the most important properties required of a recording medium are mechanical in nature. For rigid disk drives, the substrate and magnetic and nonmagnetic layers put down in forming the recording surface must allow flying heights of 0.2 microns or less at high surface speeds with no performance degradation due to wear. This places very challenging requirements on flatness and surface smoothness. Further, the recording surface must be able to tolerate temperature and humidity changes as well as shock and vibration. In addition, the drives are subject to start–stop operations that bring the head in contact with the disk during landing and taking off. Many thousands of start–stops are part of a product specification. This requirement leads to the mechanical and tribological challenges in dealing with stiction and friction.

Hence, the disk represents a complex and critical element in the recording system. In tape and flexible disks the challenges are similar except that the applications here are for removable storage and the design criteria recognize the acceptance of some wear. Consequently, flexible media devices normally specify a minimum number of "passes" of the medium by the head (for which the medium is warranted) and beyond which it should be replaced by copying the data to a new medium. Moreover, head life is similarly stated in terms of number of hours of use before replacement.

6.2 PARTICULATE MEDIA

Particulate media are composed of magnetic particles embedded in a binder. The magnetic-binder formulation can be considered similar to a paint and is coated on the substrate surface. When dry and set, the typical coating has a particle volume packing fraction of approximately 30 to 40 percent. The magnetization M is expressed in magnetic moment per unit volume:

$$M = \lim_{\Delta v \to 0} n_v \sum_{i=1}^{i=N_{\Delta v}} m_i \qquad (6.4)$$

where m_i is the moment of the i'th particle, n_v is the particle volume density, and Δv is an elemental volume. The summation is over all particles in the volume $N_{\Delta v}$. Thus, we essentially deal with the magnetic material in terms of its macroscopic properties as if it were continuous. At the increasing densities now being pursued, micromagnetic modeling is becoming more common. In magnetic recording, extremely small particles are needed to minimize media noise, because the higher the particle density the lower will be the noise from a statistical point of view. Therefore, in all advanced digital magnetic recording applications the individual particles can be regarded as single-domain particles.

The magnetic behavior of an individual particle can be examined in terms of energetic considerations. The dominant terms are the crystalline anisotropy, shape anisotropy, exchange energy, and magnetostriction. To control magnetization orientation, for example, to achieve in-plane magnetization, the particle shape is chosen to be acicular with a length-to-breadth ratio on the order of 10 to 1. Then the shape anisotropy will cause the magnetization to align itself with the major axis of the particle, and the easy axis then coincides with the particle axis. The difference in demagnetizing field energy perpendicular and parallel to the particle axis constitutes the uniaxial shape anisotropy energy density. If the particle shape is assumed to be a prolate spheroid with magnetization M_{sp}, the corresponding anisotropy field can be expressed as

$$H_s = (N_b - N_a)M_{sp} \qquad (6.5)$$

where $N_b = N_c$ are the demagnetizing factors in the directions transverse to the particle's long axis, and N_a is the demagnetizing factor in the direction of the particle axis. Recall that $N_a + N_b + N_c = 1$, so that $N_b > N_a$ for acicular particles. With strongly acicular particles, the shape anisotropy field can be made dominant in terms of the magnetic characteristics of the single particle.

With an applied field parallel to the particle axis, the coercive force based on shape anisotropy is $H_c = H_s$. If a particle becomes too small, that is, having a diameter on the order of 10 nanometers, it will become superparamagnetic and lose its hysteretic properties. Thermal energies are enough to reverse the magnetization during time periods on the order of a minute. Fortunately, this limit is well below the dimensions at which storage densities are today or are expected to reach in the coming decade. Actual particle assemblies will always have a distribution of the direction of the particle axes, and this angular distribution is important in understanding H_c. Stoner and Wohlfarth [4] have shown that for particle axes distributed in random orientations and switching through coherent rotation, the average coercive force determined by shape anisotropy is given by

$$(H_c)_{Av} = 0.48(N_b - N_a)M_{sp} \tag{6.6}$$

Measured coercivities for particulate media are generally lower than predicted by Stoner–Wohlfarth theory. The main reasons are that switching mechanisms other than coherent rotation occur and the particles do interact. In order to maximize the alignment of the particles in the plane of the medium, thereby increasing the coercivity, most coating processes use aligning magnets and mechanical orienting operations. In addition to shape anisotropy, crystalline and strain anisotropies can also be used to control particle coercivity.

So far, we have discussed particulate media as though the particles behaved independently when magnetized. In practice, particle-to-particle magnetostatic interactions will influence the manner of magnetization reversal. While studies of the subject are complex, a number of self-consistent magnetization models take particle interaction fields into account. In modeling the write process, these fields are included to determine M at each point through an iterative process. Essentially, the effect of increasing particle packing density is to lower the coercive force of the macroscopic aggregate below that of the single particle. With increased packing density, particles are closer together, increasing the effects of particle interaction.

Particles that have been widely used in recording media are gamma iron oxide, cobalt-modified iron oxide, chromium dioxide, metal particles, and barium ferrite. The advantages of higher coercive force have led to progress following the sequence above. However, the advantages of barium ferrite are somewhat unusual. This particle is actually in the form of a platelet, with the easy axis normal to the plane of the crystal. A coating prepared from such particles can possess good magnetization characteristics in both the longitudinal and perpendicular directions. It is believed that by having both longitudinal and perpendicular components recorded in the medium, the low frequencies are favored by a longitudinal orientation and the high frequencies by a perpendicular orientation, since the demagnetizing effects are less as the length of individual magnetized regions is reduced. Accordingly, a wider band signal may be recorded and read, even with a somewhat lower coercive force.

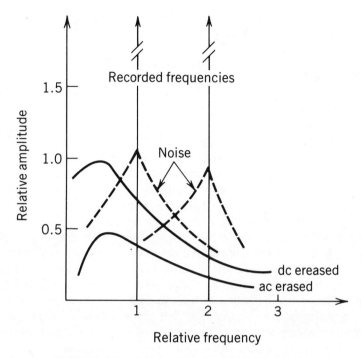

FIGURE 6.2 Noise spectra for particulate media.

6.2.1 Signal-to-Noise Factors

Noise in particulate media is of two types—additive and multiplicative. The additive noise characteristics tend to be like white noise, with a wavelength characteristic measured at the readback head similar to that of the signal. Both signal and noise pass through the recording channel transfer function. When the output noise is corrected for the channel transfer function, the resulting flux noise from the medium should have a flat power spectral density if the noise is entirely additive. This result will be derived in Chapter 8.

Multiplicative, sometimes called modulation, noise results from correlation of the noise from different groups of particles. It can be caused by chaining or clumping of particles as well as other mechanical features such as surface roughness. Multiplicative flux noise power spectral density is nonuniform, tending to increase at longer wavelengths. In general, multiplicative noise depends upon the recorded signal, both amplitude and wavelength.

Figure 6.2 shows typical noise spectra from particulate media as measured at the head output. Multiplicative noise leads to increased noise in a dc erased medium. When a sine wave is recorded the multiplicative noise is shifted up in frequency, appearing as noise sidebands about the signal, which acts as a carrier frequency. As seen in the figure, the overall noise spectrum is relatively independent of signal frequency. The multiplicative noise is simply shifted, and the noise power remains constant.

6.3 THIN FILM MEDIA

Thin film media have been around for many years but were essentially used only in special device applications until recently. All the early thin film media were made by plating. In the 1950s the UNIVAC system used plated drums. Again, the advantages for film media have long been evident. The long period before general acceptance can be attributed to process problems and corrosion concerns, but much more importantly, to the continuous progress being made in particulate coatings. This made it possible to extend an existing production process to continue the advances being achieved in storage density and drive performance, and at a lower cost. Thin film technology received a major boost with the great interest that developed in perpendicular recording in the late 1970s. In perpendicular or vertical recording it is essential to obtain a uniaxial orientation normal to a storage plane. The use of sputtering techniques provided a ready method to achieve such films with cobalt chromium materials and triggered a great deal of thin film media activity. The most important factor leading to a move from particulate to thin film, however, was the increasing density demands that were now becoming much easier to meet with thin films. Now almost all advanced disk drives use thin magnetic films, both plated and sputtered. Both technologies are improving process control, leading to higher production of thin film metallic media.

Both crystalline and shape anisotropy can be used to control coercivity in thin films. In addition, processes and choices of materials affect the magnetic properties of the fabricated medium.

6.3.1 Signal-to-Noise Factors

A thin film medium is made up of a domain structure and there can be very significant effects from domain interactions and domain wall formation. The so-called zigzag transition shown in Figure 6.3 is a good example of this.

At a magnetization transition boundary the minimum energy condition causes the transition to follow a zigzag path across the track. On readback the result is that there are timing shifts in the signals readback by the elemental head sections across the track. These lead to a broadening of the readback pulse and a shift in its peak location. Because of the apparent random nature of the zigzags, there are noise contributions introduced by the presence of transitions. In terms of the spectral response of the noise from a thin film medium, we find that the noise is a minimum under the dc erased condition and increases with signal frequency as the density of transitions increases (Figure 6.4). This indicates that the main source of noise is associated with the transitions. This behavior may be contrasted with a particulate medium for which the noise remains constant as signal frequency increases. One approach

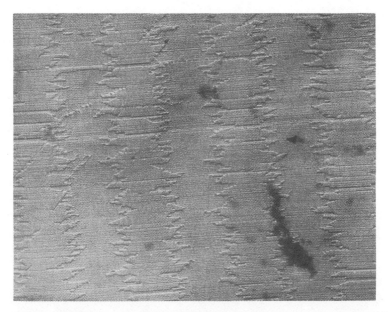

FIGURE 6.3 Zigzag transitions in a thin film disk at an average spacing of 2.5 μm between transitions. Photograph courtesy of T. C. Arnoldussen.

to reducing the noise associated with the zigzag transitions is to reduce domain interaction, or, stated another way, to make the thin film surface appear as if composed of small discrete domains or "particles." Significant progress has been made here [9].

6.4 NONMAGNETIC MEDIA CHARACTERISTICS

The mechanical requirements in disks are such that all surfaces have a very thin lubricant layer on the surface. The role of this lubricant is to minimize contact start–stop problems. All drives also are designed to tolerate a small degree of intermittent contact arising from debris getting on the disk or mechanical motions that temporarily destabilize the air bearing. Below this lubricant will be found an overcoat on metal films to protect the magnetic layer from impact and retard corrosion. The standard overcoat is carbon. Needless to say, both these overcoats are extremely thin, since, being nonmagnetic, they add to the effective spacing between head and magnetic medium. Under the magnetic layer on thin film disks will be found a thin layer of chromium or some metal that will help promote the desired crystal structure growth. Below this layer is a thick plating of nickel phosphorus that covers the aluminum substrate and is needed to achieve the necessary smoothness free from substrate defects. This layer will be textured, that is, made slightly wavy, since if the

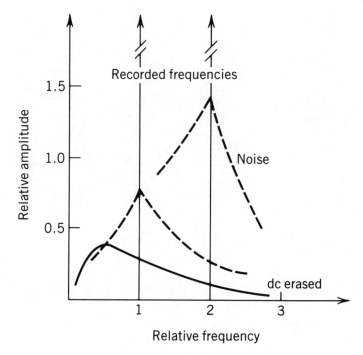

FIGURE 6.4   Signal and noise spectra for thin film media.

recording surface were perfectly smooth the head could stick to the surface. This is an effect similar to that obtained when two very smooth blocks are pressed together.

On particulate coatings, alumina (3 to 5 percent) is added to the coating mix. The alumina is very hard relative to the binder coating and provides a bearing surface for the head to minimize medium wear from intermittent contact or start–stop operations. The usual particulate coating is thick enough to fill in and conceal substrate asperities and pinholes.

It can be seen that the magnetic disk is indeed a high-technology product requiring a broad range of expertise to develop and manufacture a viable component for a magnetic storage device.

REFERENCES

1. *Magnetic Recording*, Vol. I: *Technology*, C. D. Mee and E. D. Daniel, McGraw-Hill, New York, pp. 98–244, 1987.
2. "Particulate Recording Materials," G. Bate, *Proc. IEEE*, Vol. 74, pp. 1513–1525, November 1986.
3. "Thin-Film Recording Media," T. C. Arnoldussen, *Proc. IEEE*, Vol. 74, pp. 1526–1539, November 1986.

4. "A Mechanism of Magnetic Hysteresis in Heterogeneous Alloys," E. C. Stoner and E. P. Wohlfarth, *Phil. Trans. Roy. Soc. Ser. A*, Vol. 240, pp. 599–642, 1948.

5. "Magnetic Properties and Recording Characteristics of Barium Ferrite Media," T. Fujiwara, *IEEE Trans. Magn.*, MAG-23, pp. 3125–3130, September 1987.

6. "Flux Noise in Particulate Media: Measurement and Interpretation," L. L. Nunnelley, D. E. Heim, and T. C. Arnoldussen, *IEEE Trans. Magn.*, MAG-23, pp. 1767–1775, March 1987.

7. "Measurement of Noise in Magnetic Media," R. A. Baugh, E. S. Murdock, and B. R. Natarajan, *IEEE Trans. Magn.*, MAG-19, pp. 1722–1724, September 1983.

8. "Zigzag Transition Profiles, Noise, and Correlation Statistics," T. C. Arnoldussen and H. C. Tong, *IEEE Trans. Magn.*, MAG-22, pp. 889–891, November 1986.

9. "Physical Origin of Limits in the Performance of Thin-Film Longitudinal Recording Media," T. Chen and T. Yamashita, *IEEE Trans. Magn.*, MAG-24, pp. 2700–2705, November 1988.

10. *Tribology and Mechanics of Magnetic Storage Devices*, B. Bhushan, Springer-Verlag, New York, 1990.

CHAPTER 7

DIGITAL RECORDING TECHNIQUES

7.1 THE DIGITAL MAGNETIC RECORDING CHANNEL

The general aspects of magnetic data recording and the consequent character-ization of the digital magnetic recording channel are presented in this section. The key performance criteria are the bit density in bits per inch (bpi) along a track and the track density in tracks per inch (tpi). While SI units are em-ployed extensively in this book, the measurement of linear and track densities in inches is so ingrained that it would be a disservice to the reader to de-part from this convention. The product of these two factors is the data storage density per square inch of the recording medium. The more effective the uti-lization of the available storage surface area, the more favorable are the stor-age capacity to access time relationships associated with any given mechanical structure used for data storage. Track density is a function of component and mechanical tolerances as well as the servo positioning technology available to control head tracking. At present, bit densities exceed track densities signif-icantly, often by an order of magnitude or more. Here we will examine the linear density issues where we assume perfect tracking. In Chapter 8 we will add track misregistration and off-track problems to expand our understanding of the actual data recording channel. In the previous chapters we have dealt at some length with the overall magnetic recording process and the relation of flux changes per inch (or, equivalently, the transitions per inch) and record-ing resolution to the magnetic recording system parameters. Linear bit density is not only related to the overall resolution of a given recording system, but also the digital recording techniques used to store an input binary data stream on writing and reconstruct this binary sequence from the output waveform on

159

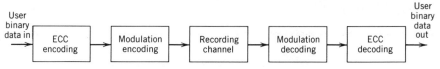

FIGURE 7.1   Digital magnetic recording channel.

reading. This chapter will extend the previous developments to treat the basic principles of digital magnetic recording techniques for binary data. To best utilize the recording "channel," modulation encoding techniques are used to transform the user input data (in bits or bytes) to coded data bits. From the device level, the term "bits per inch" refers to user data bits, while the term "flux changes per inch" (fci) defines the density of the coded bits. In both cases the binary patterns contain the information of interest. The context of the material should make it clear which usage the word "density" is referring to and, when necessary, the distinction will be made explicit.

A fundamental feature of digital magnetic recording is the precise, quantitative measure of performance reliability on a bit-by-bit basis. Each recorded bit is individually detected and interpreted, providing a continuing check on every region of the storage medium. Thus, the objective of achieving a high data storage density always involves striking a balance between bit density per se and the associated performance reliability. For this reason, redundancy is generally included in the user data to provide a degree of automatic error detection and correction (ECC). This subject is treated in Chapter 8 to identify the techniques used to secure satisfactory operational performance, providing an additional dimension to the relation between the transition density characteristics of a magnetic recording device and the actual data storage density from the perspective of a user.

A magnetic recording system can be viewed as a communications channel. If we ignore the time delay between the writing and reading of a given information block, caused by the motion time necessary to permit rescanning this section of track, we have essentially an input/output data transfer channel (Figure 7.1). This perspective is instructive, for it provides a familiar reference point and furthermore will clearly reveal the aspects of the digital magnetic recording process that are unique as compared to conventional communications channels. The physical characteristics of the digital magnetic recording channel will be first elaborated; equalization, encoding techniques, and signal detection methods will then be discussed. The objective of this chapter is to provide an insight into the subject of digital recording techniques rather than merely a compilation of methods that have been used.

7.1.1 Qualitative Features of Digital Recording

Data in digital magnetic recording is coded in a binary notation. For example, in the binary coded decimal (BCD) code, a six would be written as 0110. Our interest here, then, is specifically in the recording, both writing and reading, of arbitrary sequences of ones and zeros. In cases where recording is done in parallel on a group of tracks, the nature of the data signals associated with any single track is still characterized by varying patterns of ones and zeros.

Only two distinguishable states of magnetization are necessary for the storage of digital data. Generally, two opposing senses of saturation magnetization are used in digital magnetic recording to achieve the maximum differentiation between storage states as well as take advantage of the natural simplicity of modifying stored data. The digital magnetic recording channel concept will be developed on this basis. Saturation recording exploits the nonlinear saturation characteristic of the magnetic recording medium. The magnetic surface provides an inherent limiting action through the phenomenon of saturation, to define and establish consistently a region of the surface magnetized in either of two stable magnetic states. This self-regulating feature can occur, even with variations in parameters such as writing current, spacing, and so on, by proper design. Hence, the saturation characteristic of the digital magnetic recording channel can be favorably exploited.

The input current waveform on writing is most often continuous, and, if so, it will be constant in magnitude and will alternate in polarity ($I = \pm I_s$ where I_s is the saturation current). The writing current could also consist of positive and negative current pulses of amplitude I_s. Another possibility would be to have the current continuously saturate the medium in one direction for zeros and use current pulses to record ones. Figure 7.2 gives examples of these three types of input current waveforms, although, as stated, the predominant method for data recording is to change the direction of current saturation to record a coded one.

It is necessary to make a distinction between a "1" and "0" in the user data and the recording waveforms used to store this data. By convention the recorded binary information is coded data and an encoding and decoding process is used to translate between user data bits and code bits. Ordinarily, a transition in either direction (and hence an output pulse) is associated with a coded "1" bit, and the absence of a transition (or output pulse) during a code bit interval with a "0." The minimum distance of unidirectional magnetization is referred to as a bit cell, although it cannot be related directly to a user data bit.

The output voltage waveform for a step change in magnetization characterizes the recording system and is a pulse; not surprisingly, it is often referred to as the isolated pulse response, as it is associated with a single transition. Such a "characteristic" voltage pulse is illustrated in Figure 7.3. In saturation recording, the magnetization written on the medium has roughly the same shape as the writing current waveform. A continuous writing current waveform, most commonly used in practice, consists of a succession of alternating step changes in current. Therefore, the associated output voltage waveform will inherently consist of an alternating pulse sequence (Figure 7.3). This feature can be used to enhance readback reliability by taking advantage of this a

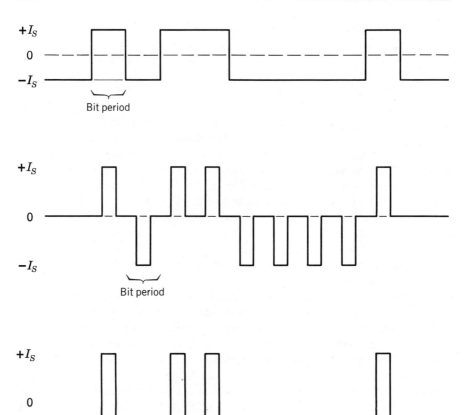

FIGURE 7.2 Write current waveforms for recording binary data.

priori knowledge of the character of the readback waveform. Accordingly, the maximum value of the output signal is the peak amplitude of the voltage pulse from a single current (i.e., magnetization) reversal.

For a recorded current pulse, the output voltage signal will be a dipulse, as shown in Figure 7.3. This waveform arises because a single current pulse records a discrete cell on the surface, having two closely spaced but oppositely directed magnetization transitions at its edges. One of these magnetization changes arises from the trailing leg field and one from the leading leg field of the magnetic head. The magnetization change produced by the leading leg of the head is a consequence of removing the write field, which preserves the transition created on the leading gap leg. (With continuous current recording, the transitions that may be produced under the leading leg of the head will be rewritten by the field at the trailing leg.) A dipulse signal is the result, accord-

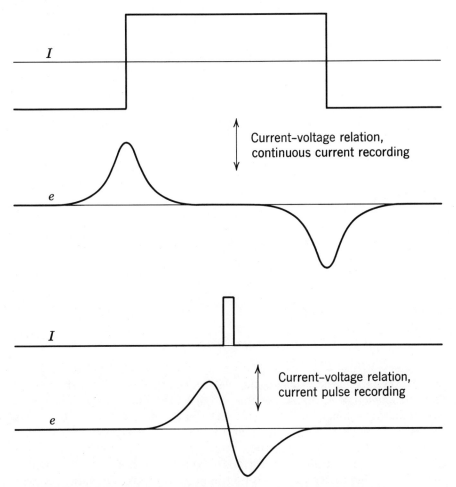

FIGURE 7.3 Current–voltage relations, digital magnetic recording.

ing to the general theory developed in previous chapters, of the superposition of two immediately adjacent pulses of opposite polarity, which correspond to the two oppositely directed magnetization reversals produced. However, here, in contrast to a continuous current input only switched in direction, the separation of these magnetization reversals is fixed by the head–surface geometry and the current pulse duration rather than the bit rate.

The digital magnetic recording process for the longitudinal recording mode may be represented by the channel block diagram(s) shown in Figure 7.4. The write current waveform switches between two fixed values at predetermined times to produce a magnetization pattern on the medium of the same form. The "input" to the recording system is a current reversal. A current reversal produces a finite write transition, as described in Chapter 4. Two views

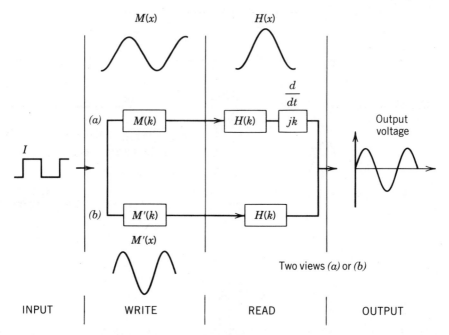

FIGURE 7.4   Block diagram of recording channel model.

can be now taken. The magnetization pattern can be convolved with the head sensitivity function to obtain the flux through the head. Then this operation is followed by a functional block that includes the differentiation operator to produce the output voltage waveform. Exactly the same result is obtained as shown in Figure 7.4 if we view the current reversals as producing a sequence of magnetization transitions, characterized by the derivative of the magnetization pattern. The derivative of this transition sequence is then convolved with the head sensitivity function to obtain the output voltage signal. The derivative of the magnetization pattern, assuming ideal step function transitions, will be a sequence of impulses of fixed amplitude $2M_r$, alternating in sign and occurring at the x values corresponding to write switching times. In either manner, the write process can be then included in the overall recording channel block diagram. A writing "loss" will be associated with the spreading of the actual transition from an ideal step change in magnetization.

A functional block (not shown) including μ_0, head efficiency, track width, number of turns, medium thickness, and head–medium velocity will scale the voltage waveform to the correct amplitude in the time domain.

7.1.2 The Characteristic Voltage Pulse

In Chapter 3, the following formula was derived, giving the relation between the output voltage signal and the recorded magnetization. It is assumed here that the magnetization is in-plane and uniform through the recording layer thickness δ, that is, $M = M_x$ and is only a function of x.

$$e(\overline{x}) = K v N \int_{\delta}^{\delta+d} \int_{-\infty}^{+\infty} \frac{\partial M_x(x - \overline{x})}{\partial x} H_x(x,y) \, dx \, dy \qquad (7.1)$$

For a thin medium H_x will vary little through the medium thickness. Earlier we found that $y = y' = \sqrt{d(d + \delta)}$ (or the geometric mean between the top and bottom) medium surfaces was an appropriate choice for an "effective" spacing, coming from the calculation of the pulse half-width PW_{50}. Then, assuming a thin medium, we can replace the integration over the medium thickness δ by the factor $\delta H_x(x,y')$.

Now setting

$$\frac{\partial M_x}{\partial x} = M'_x \qquad (7.2)$$

we can write

$$e(\overline{x}) = K v N \delta \int_{-\infty}^{+\infty} M'_x(x - \overline{x}) H_x(x) \, dx \qquad (7.3)$$

In this form, $e(\overline{x})$ is expressed by a superposition integral. H_x can be regarded as a weighting function applied to an excitation function M'_x. In this sense, H_x is similar to an aperture or window by which M'_x is scanned. The voltage $e(\overline{x})$, as previously demonstrated, is identical in form with H_x for an impulse of M'_x. The parameter PW_{10} has been used already to designate the spread of the magnetic head fringing field H_x. PW_{10} is a measure of the resolving power of the magnetic head, that is, a head with a reading resolution of PW_{10} can resolve individual step changes in saturation magnetization up to a linear density of approximately $1/PW_{10}$. In the limit, if H_x were to approach an impulse, $PW_{10} \to 0$, corresponding to infinite resolving power.

Then,

$$e(\overline{x}) \to K_1 M'_x \qquad (7.4)$$

where K_1 is a constant. In other words, the output voltage waveform would approach the derivative of the recorded magnetization, and the pulse width would be set only by the transition width. For example, a ramp function magnetization reversal gives for M'_x a rectangular pulse of amplitude $2M_r/x_1$ and width x_1, which would be the pulse width.

The actual output pulse width will reflect both the readback geometrical parameters and, for an arctangent model, the write transition width parameter a. In Chapter 4 the following expression for the pulse half-width was obtained which includes all these parameters:

$$PW_{50} = [(g)^2 + 4(d + a)(d + a + \delta)]^{1/2} \qquad (7.5)$$

If we describe the magnetization input function in terms of the arctangent write parameter a, and the head sensitivity function in terms of the three

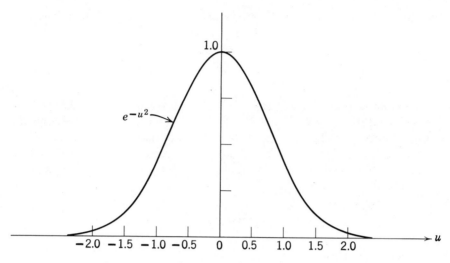

FIGURE 7.5   Gaussian pulse response waveform.

geometrical factors (g, d, and δ), we are led to the following useful waveform approximation for the "characteristic" output pulse:

$$e(u) = \frac{E_m}{1 + u^2} \tag{7.6}$$

where

$$u = \frac{x}{PW_{50}/2}$$

Another analytic "pulse" shape that is very useful is the Gaussian or normal probability density function. This expression can generally provide a good-to-excellent fit to experimentally obtained isolated voltage pulses. This normalized waveform is shown in Figure 7.5 and is given by

$$e(u) = e^{-u^2} \tag{7.7}$$

The pulse skirts of this Gaussian pulse decay much more rapidly than the term $1/(1 + u^2)$ as u increases. The Gaussian curve is therefore more bell-shaped and can serve as a better mathematical approximation for the near-zone head field. More complex formulations can be developed using the Karlqvist expression for the fringing field, but at this stage it may be appropriate to go to full computer simulation with the growing processing capabilities becoming available.

7.1.3 Pulse Superposition Theory

In digital magnetic recording there is a wide array of recorded patterns, related to the variety of binary sequences that may be stored. We are hence dealing with a multitude of output voltage waveforms arising from the possible alternating sequences of recorded magnetization changes. The readback process can be considered linear, as discussed previously. Thus, the principle of superposition can be applied. The net voltage (or flux) caused by a sequence of magnetization changes on the recording medium is then obtained by the linear combination of their individual voltage (or flux) contributions. The utilization of the principle of superposition will be valid as long as the density of saturation reversals does not exceed the limit for the writing of independent saturation reversals. With a separation between current reversals of less than the transition width, it is clear that a magnetic transition region would be modified by the reversed writing field established for an immediately subsequent magnetization change. At this point the nonlinear behavior in writing transitions would invalidate a description of the input–output relations in terms of superposition of characteristic pulse responses. Predictable bit shift behavior can be accommodated. The performance limits set by read resolution usually occur well before a density is reached at which the use of superposition for waveform analysis becomes questionable. Using superposition, we can directly determine the output voltage waveforms as a function of encoding method and maximum transition density. We shall use the symbol PW'_{10} to define the voltage pulse width from an actual magnetization transition, including the effects of both transition length and head reading resolution. PW_{10} remains the width of H_x, and $PW'_{10} = PW_{10}$ when the transition is a step function. Figure 7.6a shows the read voltage e_1, from the superposition of the characteristic pulses from a series of magnetization transitions at constant linear density. The parameter h defines the bit interval or cell length, that is, the minimum spacing between current reversals. In this instance, the number of cells or pulses per inch (ppi) = $1/h$. Figure 7.6b gives a curve of the peak output voltage versus ppi, obtained by superposition. Several observations may be made. If each pulse is to have its individual integrity preserved,

$$h \geq PW'_{10}$$

or

$$(\text{ppi})_{\text{max}} = 1/PW'_{10} \tag{7.8}$$

The output voltage peak amplitude will remain constant until adjacent pulse interference extends to the pulse centers. Interference from adjacent pulses is subtractive, causing the amplitude to fall or roll off with increasing transition density. The "breakpoint" or commencement of roll-off in the voltage amplitude curve of Figure 7.6b occurs at approximately

$$\text{ppi} = 2/PW'_{10} \tag{7.9}$$

The precise shape of the amplitude roll-off with increasing density will depend on the actual waveform of the isolated voltage pulse. If the pulse response from an isolated transition has a sharp peak and broad skirts, the amplitude drop-off will be gradual; for a characteristic pulse, which is more bell-shaped, the amplitude roll-off curve will drop much more rapidly.

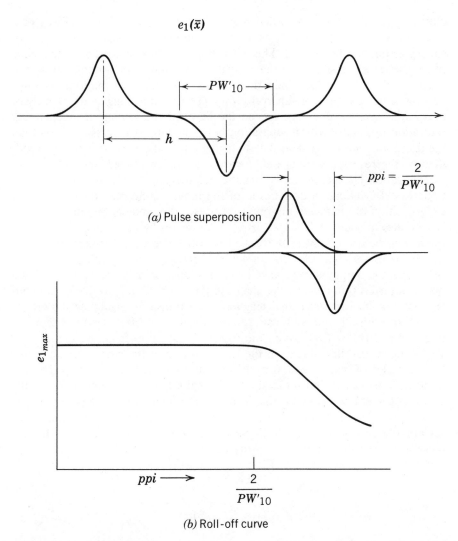

$e_1(\bar{x})$

(a) Pulse superposition

$ppi = \dfrac{2}{PW'_{10}}$

(b) Roll-off curve

FIGURE 7.6 A roll-off curve of output voltage amplitude versus pulse (transition) density.

Pulse Crowding—Examples

In digital recording, a large number of output pulse patterns arise. At low densities each pulse is individually resolved. With higher densities, pulse crowding, or intersymbol interference, occurs. The consequent signal distortion that arises will be illustrated for several selected cases. These examples are worst case for specific forms of waveform distortion.

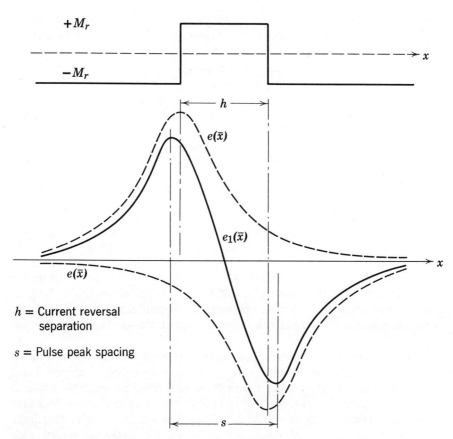

FIGURE 7.7 Two adjacent saturation reversals and resultant signal showing peak shift effect.

(1) Two Adjacent Saturation Reversals

Figure 7.7 illustrates the output signal when there is an isolated pair of magnetization changes separated by a distance h appreciably less than PW'_{10}. The individual signal from each saturation reversal is shown as well as the resultant voltage, obtained by the superposition of the individual pulses.

As seen in Figure 7.7, there is a peak shift effect produced by pulse interference, indicated by the fact that the separation between the peaks in the output voltage waveform is greater than h, the separation between the corresponding reversals in write current. This peak displacement phenomenon gives rise to a discrepancy in pulse location timing with respect to the original clock time period on writing.

For any characteristic pulse waveform, the pulse separation s in the output waveform from two current reversals will approach a finite lower limit as h approaches zero. The signal $e_1(\bar{x})$ is obtained by the subtraction of the characteristic pulse e, offset by the distance h, from itself. This procedure amounts to an approximation method for differentiation of the reference pulse through a finite difference technique except for the division of the difference by h. Then as $h \rightarrow 0$,

$$e_1(\overline{x}) \rightarrow h \cdot e'(\overline{x}) \tag{7.10}$$

where

$$e'(\overline{x}) = \frac{de(\overline{x})}{d\overline{x}} \tag{7.11}$$

The signal $e'(\overline{x})$ is a dipulse, and the locations of its pulse peaks are at positions $\overline{x}$ where its derivative $e''(\overline{x})$ is equal to zero.

Consider, for example, the following characteristic voltage pulse:

$$e(\overline{x}) = \frac{1}{1 + \overline{x}^2} \tag{7.12}$$

(Here $PW_{50}/2 = 1$.)

Carrying out the calculations outlined above, we obtain $s = 1.15$ as the lower limit of s for the assumed characteristic pulse, which has a PW'_{10} of approximately six. The peak shift phenomenon is quite sensitive to the nature of the peak of the basic readback pulse, a cusplike waveform minimizing this effect.

As h becomes smaller, the output signal amplitude will approach zero, but the separation between the two pulse peaks, corresponding to the recorded saturation reversals, approaches the finite limit defined above. This situation is shown in Figure 7.8. The onset of peak shift begins as h becomes less than three, which corresponds to $PW'_{10}/2$, the point at which the peak amplitude curve begins to roll off. As illustrated by Figure 7.8, interpulse interference has a significant effect on the pulse timing with a continued reduction in h. For $h \geq 3$ in this example, the output pulse separation is essentially identical to the interval between current reversals, and no peak shift problem arises.

(2) Three Adjacent Saturation Reversals

Figure 7.9 shows the output waveform resulting from three adjacent magnetization transitions when there is pulse crowding. Two effects are immediately obvious. First, the central pulse suffers a relatively greater attenuation than the other pulses. The amplitude of the center pulse peak is

$$e_1 = e(0) - 2e(\overline{x} = h) \tag{7.13}$$

In fact, this particular sequence is especially unfavorable to the amplitude of the central pulse. If an additional pulse were located on either end (or pulses on both sides of this pattern), their individual signal contributions would tend to increase the amplitude of this center pulse because of the inherent alternating nature of successive pulses in saturation recording. A second point that

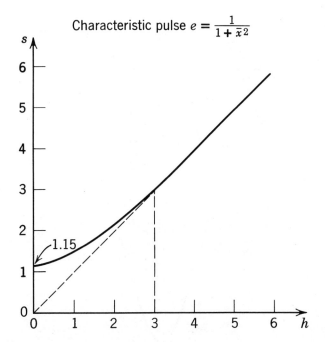

FIGURE 7.8 Pulse peak spacing s versus current reversal interval h.

can be noted is the shifted baseline of the resultant signal. The readback signal undergoes a positive displacement through the central region of the output waveform. e_1 contains a dc component over this pulse grouping because of the odd pulse count.

(3) Four Successive Saturation Reversals

Figure 7.10 shows the output signal with pulse crowding when four successive saturation reversals are recorded. In this case, because of symmetry, the two outer pulses are of the same amplitude and the two inner pulses are also equal in magnitude. The inner pulses are each surrounded by two adjacent pulses of opposite polarity and therefore are reduced in peak amplitude to a greater degree than the pulses on the waveform extremities. The net effect is to give the waveform the appearance of a "droop," as shown. It is clear that here also there is a baseline shift, up for the first half of the waveform, and down for the second.

Pulse Interference—General Aspects. The interval extending $h/2$ on both sides of a current reversal (in time the interval $\Delta t = h/v$) is the length uniquely allotted to this switching change. This interval can also be identified in terms of the associated output signal, as extending $\pm h/2$ on either side of the peak

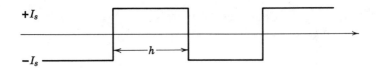

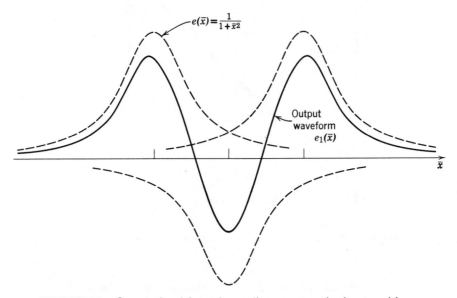

FIGURE 7.9 Output signal from three adjacent magnetization transitions.

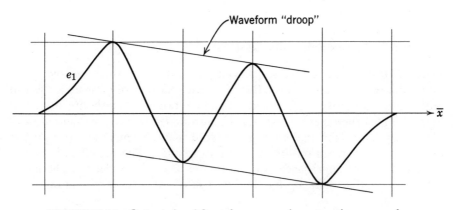

FIGURE 7.10 Output signal from four successive saturation reversals.

of the pulse $e(\overline{x})$. The readback voltage waveform $e_1(\overline{x})$, during such an interval, or time slot, will be increasingly distorted by interference from pulses at neighboring saturation reversals, as the separation h between adjacent step reversals in write current is decreased below PW'_{10}. The actual voltage waveform in the cell assigned to a possible pulse position will depend on the particular pattern of saturation reversals recorded in its immediate environment. Figure 7.11 shows the number of unique binary patterns leading to distinct waveforms in the interval h, when pulse interference extends to include the two nearest neighboring pulses that may be present on either side of the given pulse. In this case, there are 10 distinct waveforms. As the degree of pulse crowding is increased, the number of different signals that will be encountered in a given bit period or interval h goes up rapidly. Because of the validity of the application of the principle of superposition, these waveforms can be generated or synthesized directly for any given value of h by applying graphical or numerical techniques to the characteristic pulse $e(\overline{x})$. There are an identical number of still different output waveforms corresponding to the absence of a recorded pulse in a selected bit cell. To distinguish the presence of a recorded magnetization reversal, we must essentially be able, correctly and unambiguously, to classify all readback waveforms arising within a bit interval into the appropriate one of these two possible sets.

An expression for the degree of pulse interference may be obtained by reference to Figure 7.12. For a magnetization transition located n intervals distant from the point in question,

$$nh - PW'_{10}/2 \le h/2 \qquad (7.14)$$

is the inequality relating h and PW'_{10} which determines whether the output signal from this magnetization change will interfere with the signal in the reference interval. For example, for $n = 3$,

$$h \approx PW'_{10}/5$$

or

$$1/h = \text{ppi} \approx 5/PW'_{10} \qquad (7.15)$$

The "breakpoint" on the roll-off curve of Figure 7.6 occurs at $\text{ppi} = 2/PW'_{10}$. Thus, we see that with pulse crowding of degree $n = 3$ we are already far out on the roll-off curve, where appreciable amplitude reduction occurs. Consequently, in practice we may neglect transitions beyond the next nearest neighbors of the bit cell under consideration.

Write Precompensation. As was pointed out, the pulse peaks will shift from the transition location due to intersymbol interference. In the case of the dipulse, the peak separation increases owing to the proximity of the transitions. The binary sequence surrounding a given bit is known and this informa-

0	0	1	0	0						
0	1	1	1	0						
1	1	1	1	1		Equivalent				
1	0	1	0	1		binary configurations				
0	0	1	0	1	=	1 0 1 0 0				
0	0	1	1	0	=	0 1 1 0 0				
0	0	1	1	1	=	1 1 1 0 0				
0	1	1	0	1	=	1 0 1 1 0				
0	1	1	1	1	=	1 1 1 1 0				
1	1	1	0	1	=	1 0 1 1 1				

1 = Saturation reversal
0 = No change in current

FIGURE 7.11 Unique saturation reversal combinations about given current switching point, including two nearest neighbors on both sides.

tion can be used to modify the timing of the write current changes to cause the transition locations to be offset in a manner that reduces the relative bit shift of the pulse peaks. For example, for the dibit pattern 000011000, the transition of the first one bit could be written slightly later than its normal clock time and the transition of the second bit slightly earlier in time. This precompensation would have the effect of reducing the bit shifts of the two pulse peaks (relative to the clock window centers). By using the information in the incoming bit stream to be recorded, a set of precompensation rules can be implemented to deal with those patterns that create the greatest problems. It is noted that here a controlled amount of intersymbol interference is being used to improve the overall readback performance.

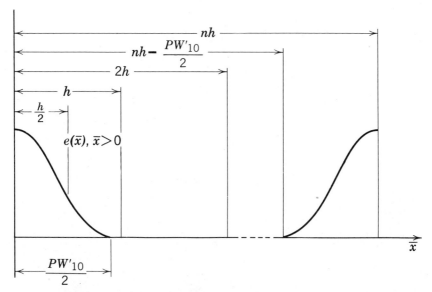

nh = Location of possible saturation reversals (n = 0, 1, 2 $\cdots$)
PW'_{10} = Pulse spread (isolated saturation reversal)

FIGURE 7.12 Pulse interference in terms of pulse width and pulse density.

7.2 EQUALIZATION OF THE DIGITAL MAGNETIC RECORDING CHANNEL

We have seen how the tails of the readback voltage waveform produce adjacent pulse interference as the distance h between write current reversals is decreased. Such interference is often referred to as intersymbol interference. Is it possible to produce from the given readback pulses, output voltage waveforms that have minimum intersymbol interference? This is a classical problem from communications theory, and Nyquist [2] showed that there is a class of signals that have zero intersymbol interference at regularly spaced signaling points. Suppose that signals may occur at times $t = NT$, where N is an integer and T is the clocking period for data transmission. Nyquist's class of signals with zero intersymbol interference have the property that their Fourier transforms have odd symmetry about the frequency $1/2T$. Figure 7.13 shows transforms and waveforms for two example pulses. The familiar $(\sin x)/x$ pulse is a member of Nyquist's class.

As illustrated in Figure 7.4, the recording channel may be modeled by a linear system knowing the impulse response to a reversal in write current. An equalization block connected at the output of the channel can shape the overall frequency response to approximate a Nyquist characteristic, symmetrical about $f = 1/2T$ and having linear phase variation with frequency. Intersymbol interference at sample times will be significantly reduced.

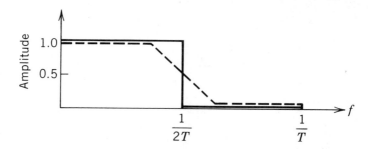

Frequency spectra

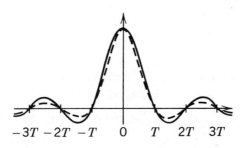

Pulse shape

FIGURE 7.13   Examples of Nyquist pulses having zero intersymbol interference.

Many electrical designs can produce a desired equalization. As an example, consider the transversal filter, or tapped delay line circuit of Figure 7.14. The circuit delays the input signal by multiples of the clock period T, multiplies the delayed versions by coefficients α_i, the tap weights, and sums them to produce the equalized output signal. Design of the circuit involves choosing the α's to minimize intersymbol interference at a finite number of points in the time domain or to shape the overall frequency response in the frequency domain. Both amplitude and phase response can be equalized by the transversal filter. As an example of a three-tap design, where a high frequency boost is needed to attain the desired Nyquist shape, the equalized output e_e might be written

$$e_e(t) = -0.5e(t) + e(t - T) - 0.5e(t - 2T) \qquad (7.16)$$

Taking the Fourier transform to get the frequency response and recalling that a delay in time T in the time domain corresponds to multiplying by $e^{-j\omega T}$

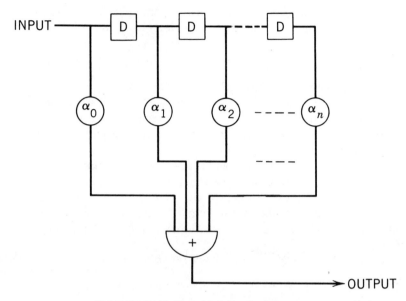

FIGURE 7.14 Tapped delay line equalizer.

in the frequency domain,

$$E_e(j\omega) = [-0.5 + e^{-j\omega T} - 0.5e^{-j2\omega T}]E(j\omega)$$

$$= [1 - \cos(\omega T)]e^{-j\omega T}E(j\omega) \tag{7.17}$$

This equalizer increases the amplitude of the high frequencies, a feature often required in recording channel design. There is an extensive literature on equalizer design. Many refinements are possible, including the ability for the recording system to be equalized adaptively, as the channel parameters change with time.

Another approach to equalization is simply to increase the bandwidth of the readback signal by compensating for the loss in high frequencies produced by the recording channel. The increased bandwidth results in a narrower pulse in the time domain. This kind of equalization is sometimes called pulse slimming.

From the channel block diagram, we can express the output voltage for longitudinal magnetization in terms of Fourier transforms as

$$E(j\omega) = M'(j\omega)H(j\omega) \tag{7.18}$$

$E(j\omega)$ is the Fourier transform of e, $H(j\omega)$ the Fourier transform of $H(x)$, and $M'(j\omega)$ the Fourier transform of $M'(x)$. The x subscripts have been dropped. The same analysis can be applied to perpendicular magnetization using the y components of H and M. In equation (7.18), the angular frequency

$$\omega = \frac{2\pi v}{\lambda} \tag{7.19}$$

where λ is the recorded wavelength. Of greatest importance, the frequency spectrum associated with the waveforms is only absolutely related to distance, not time, because the recording process is directly related to the recording geometry and λ is the fundamental spatial wavelength parameter along the track coordinate x.

Now we can modify the input–output relation of equation (7.18) by insertion of an electrical equalizer with transfer function $G(j\omega)$ at the head output. The electrical parameters of the magnetic head can be viewed as also incorporated into the design of the inserted equalizer transfer function $G(j\omega)$. The output voltage $e(x)$ is then related to the input $M'(x)$ by the following transfer function:

$$E(j\omega)/M'(j\omega) = T(j\omega) = G(j\omega)H(j\omega) \tag{7.20}$$

Theoretically, if $G(j\omega)$ could be chosen such that

$$H(j\omega)G(j\omega) \approx 1.0$$

over the read signal bandwidth, then $E(j\omega)$ would be identically equal to $M'(j\omega)$ or

$$e(\overline{x}) = M'(\overline{x})$$

Thus, in the limit, with complete compensation of the readback channel, the overall digital recording performance would be set solely by the magnetization reversal distance on writing, x_1. Since the unequalized output pulse width is considerably greater than x_1, that is, $PW'_{10} > x_1$, there is considerable gain in bit density that may be realized by electrical equalization of the digital magnetic recording channel.

As an example of pulse-slimming equalizer design, let us take

$$H(x) = e^{-a^2 x^2} \tag{7.21}$$

where from now on, $H(x)$ can be viewed as also representing the characteristic pulse response. This fringing field function is a Gaussian distribution curve. As previously mentioned, this general waveform can frequently be closely fitted to both field plots of H_x and experimentally obtained output voltage pulses. Further, its mathematical form makes it very amenable to design calculations. The corresponding characteristic voltage pulse, normalized to a peak amplitude of 1.0, will be

$$e(x) = e^{-a^2 x^2}$$

Taking the Fourier transform of $H(x)$, we get

$$H(j\omega) = H(\omega) = \frac{\sqrt{\pi}}{a} e^{-\omega^2/4a^2} \tag{7.22}$$

Note that $H(j\omega)$ is also a Gaussian function. The transform of $H(x)$ has no phase variation with frequency because $H(x) = H(-x)$. Now we can set as a design goal the insertion of a linear equalizer with gain to obtain the following characteristic pulse output:

$$e(x) = e^{-c^2 x^2} \tag{7.23}$$

This signal is of the same form and peak amplitude as the original pulse. For $c > a$, the width of the pulse from the compensated channel is less than the pulse width of the original signal. Accordingly, by choosing $c > a$, we will improve the reading resolution of the system. The principle of superposition remains valid for the equalized readback channel because $G(j\omega)$ is a linear network. Since the basic output signal waveform has been retained, we can apply directly to this new characteristic output voltage the same analysis and evaluation criteria for intersymbol interference previously discussed. Therefore, projections are straightforward on the bit density gains that can be realized, with respect to limitations arising from interbit interference or pulse crowding. If the original output pulse is reduced in pulse width by 50 percent, then a 100 percent improvement in bit density is potentially possible with the same detection method.

For the pulse-slimming output signal transformation just described, we require

$$T(\omega) = H(\omega)G(\omega) = \frac{\sqrt{\pi}}{c} e^{-\omega^2/4c^2} \tag{7.24}$$

$T(j\omega)$ is functionally similar to $H(j\omega)$ because we chose to preserve the shape of the original output pulse waveform. Then

$$G(\omega) = \frac{T(\omega)}{H(\omega)} = \frac{a}{c} e^{[(c^2-a^2)\omega^2/4c^2 a^2]} \tag{7.25}$$

The electrical network synthesis problem is concerned with the realization of $G(j\omega)$. Figure 7.15 shows a graph of the function $|G(j\omega)|$. $G(j\omega)$ is not physically realizable, and therefore we must approximate this frequency function over a finite bandwidth, for example, with a linear passive network plus a broadband linear amplifier. The need for gain arises because in the formulation of the problem we chose to set the peak output amplitude of the compensated pulse at the same signal level as held before the introduction of the equalizer. That is, both voltage pulses are normalized to 1.0. The restoration of signal level is necessary before it passes into the detection circuitry.

An interrelation between output pulse width and signal-to-noise ratio is involved with this approach to increasing bit density. To clarify this relation we shall carry this analysis through a specific example. Suppose we attempt to halve the basic readback pulse width. Narrowing the pulse response to this degree offers a possibility for doubling the bit density. In this case,

$$c = 2a \tag{7.26}$$

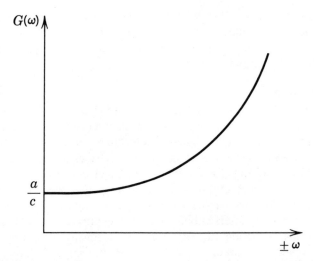

FIGURE 7.15 Frequency response of pulse-slimming equalizer.

or

$$G(\omega) = \tfrac{1}{2}e^{(3/4)(\omega/2a)^2} \tag{7.27}$$

To proceed further we must select a bandwidth criterion. In order to reproduce adequately a Gaussian voltage pulse, we shall set $\omega = 0$ as the low-frequency limit and define the high-frequency cutoff as that frequency at which the relative amplitude of the Gaussian signal-frequency spectrum drops to $1/e$ times its low-frequency value. This bandwidth will include approximately 95 percent of the signal energy in this pulse. Specific design figures depend on the bandwidth definition used, but this criterion is a reasonable requirement and provides some simplicity in calculation. Then for the cutoff frequency of $T(j\omega)$, we have

$$\omega_c = 2c \tag{7.28}$$

The uncompensated transfer function $H(j\omega)$ would reach a relative attenuation of $1/e$ in its frequency response at the frequency

$$\omega = 2a = \omega_c/2 \tag{7.29}$$

Thus, we are effectively doubling the bandwidth of the overall input–output channel, which directly corresponds to our objective of reducing the output pulse width by a factor of 2. This simple relation holds because the output pulse width is inversely proportional to the overall transfer function bandwidth when the input signal is assumed to be an impulse of $M'(x)$.

Figure 7.16 shows the frequency spectra $H(j\omega)$ and $T(j\omega)$ for this problem, the transformation of $H(j\omega)$ into $T(j\omega)$ being achieved by the equalizer $G(j\omega)$.

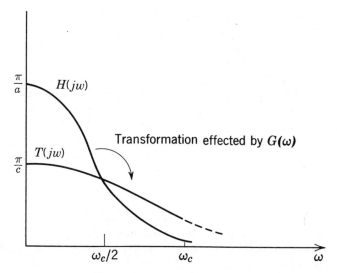

FIGURE 7.16 Unequalized and equalized frequency spectra.

To find the gain required of $G(j\omega)$, we substitute $c = 2a$ and $\omega = \omega_c = 2c = 4a$ into equation (7.25) to get

$$G(\omega_c) = \tfrac{1}{2}e^3 \approx 10 \tag{7.30}$$

Moreover, at very low frequencies

$$G(0) = \tfrac{1}{2} \tag{7.31}$$

Using the property that $G(j\omega)$ varies exponentially with frequency squared, we can now write

$$G(\omega) \approx \tfrac{1}{2}[20]^{(\omega/\omega_c)^2} \tag{7.32}$$

where ω_c retains the definition of equation (7.28).

$G(j\omega)$ may consist of a passive equalizer network, approximating the desired equalizer frequency response out to $\omega = \omega_c$, followed by an amplifier flat out to at least ω_c. The passive circuit then attenuates the low frequencies $(\omega = 0)$ relative to the high frequencies $(\omega = \omega_c)$ by a factor of 20. A voltage gain of 10 is required to preserve signal amplitude.

The signal-to-noise ratio (SNR) will be decreased by the high-frequency equalization of the digital magnetic recording channel. Hence, there is a trade-off of SNR for bandwidth. Assuming white noise, the output noise voltage contribution arising from a noise source located at the input of $H(j\omega)$ will be proportional to the square root of the bandwidth. For the example given, such a noise component would be increased by the square root of 2. The added amplifier will introduce an additional noise source that could be significant. Further, consider noise that may be introduced into the system at the magnetic head output terminals, that is, prior to $G(j\omega)$. While the passive equalizer section reduces the readback signal amplitude by a factor of roughly 10, it will pass a considerable percentage of the noise energy in the frequency band $0 < \omega < \omega_c$, particularly at the high-frequency end. The seriousness of the net reduction in SNR depends on the margin existing in the original SNR of the unequalized digital magnetic recording channel.

If we desired to extend the bandwidth by another factor of 2 by this technique, looking to a potential improvement of 4 in bit density, we would require a gain of approximately

$$\tfrac{1}{2}[20]^4 = 80,000$$

for amplitude restoration, based on equation (7.32). Therefore, because of the nature of the required $G(j\omega)$, channel equalization in digital magnetic recording for pulse width reduction can very rapidly degrade the SNR if one attempts to secure much more than a factor of 2 improvement.

7.2.1 Time Domain Factors

$G(j\omega)$ characterizes an electrical network in a frequency domain corresponding to an inverse transform in the time domain. However, we have seen that for $M'(x)$ and $H(x)$ the frequency transformation gives a frequency variable equal to v/λ, where v is the relative velocity between the head and surface and lambda is a spatial wavelength of magnetization along the track. We must then set $f = v/\lambda$. This implicit mixture of the time and space domains in the overall transfer function requires, in order to match frequencies correctly, that the surface velocity v remain constant within a very small percentage tolerance. A slight change in speed will proportionately shift the frequency spectra of $M'(x)$ and $H(x)$. $G(j\omega)$ is, of course, unaffected by variations in surface velocity. Thus, whenever v departs from its design value, $G(j\omega)$ will no longer be matched to the magnetic recording channel. The resulting frequency equalization under this condition is off-design. The output signal distortions that may result—especially if appreciable speed changes occur—could actually degrade the overall performance of the compensated channel below that of the uncompensated system. This sensitivity to velocity is a major reason why the equalization of the digital magnetic recording channel has not yet been exploited more intensively for disk storage systems even though it has had many successful applications in tape systems. (In disk drives the velocity of a given track varies directly with the radius of that track.)

7.2.2 Electrical Equalization: Summary

The principal limitations that show up in the consideration of this technique will be briefly restated. The velocity v must be very stable to maintain proper compensation, since $H(j\omega)$ is velocity dependent (ω is proportional to v) while $G(j\omega)$ is a time domain filter and independent of the surface velocity. In general, $G(j\omega)$ is not physically realizable, and suitable approximations are fairly intricate because of the required frequency characteristic. Hence, an actual equalizer may introduce some baseline pulse distortion, such as overshoots and so on. This signal-waveform distortion may seriously impair the performance obtainable from the signal detection stage. The equalizer design is based on a given $H(x)$, and therefore any perturbations in spacing or the other spatial parameters will also disturb the matching of the equalizer to the recording channel transfer function, which includes spacing loss and other variable parameters. Finally, a loss in SNR must be accepted. Although the SNR should nominally be high, it can be rapidly reduced as pulse width is decreased. Nonetheless, equalization has great potential for reduction of intersymbol interference, and certainly merits consideration where high-density storage is of prime importance.

7.3 CHANNEL MODULATION CODING

On writing, the data stream containing binary digits 0 and 1 must be converted into a corresponding pattern of states of magnetic surface saturation separated by transition regions. This process maps the data stream into the write current waveform required to produce the desired magnetization pattern on the storage medium and is known as channel, or modulation, coding. Many channel codes have been developed in order to optimize performance of particular digital magnetic recording systems. Only a few will be presented to demonstrate some of the principles involved in choosing a channel code. The so-called NRZ and phase modulation methods were among the earliest codes used, before this topic developed a mathematical formalism. As background and to provide a historical perspective, these methods will be covered first.

7.3.1 NRZ Methods

Perhaps the most straightforward way to view writing of binary data is to associate the direction of medium magnetization with "1's" and "0's." For example, a 1 would be represented by a region magnetized to the right and a 0 by a region magnetized to the left. This is precisely the manner in which the NRZ (non-return-to-zero) method coded user data. The relation between the binary data and the write current waveform, corresponding to medium magnetization, for NRZ recording is illustrated in Figure 7.17. The direction of writing current is reversed for every change in the binary sequence (1 followed by 0 or vice versa). One direction of surface magnetization corresponds to a 1, whereas the opposite direction of magnetization corresponds to a 0, and the magnetization waveform is the same as the data pattern. In the modified non-return-to-zero, or NRZI, encoding method the current is reversed every time

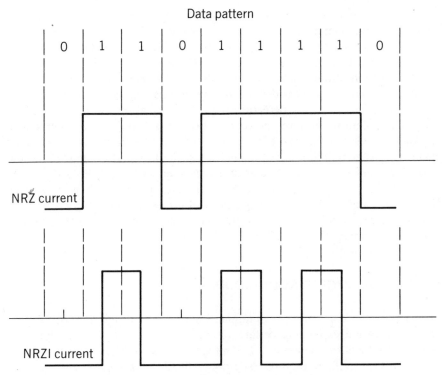

FIGURE 7.17   NRZ and NRZI binary coding.

a 1 is to be recorded. The presence of a 1 signal on readback will be indicated by either a positive or a negative output pulse in the NRZI method of encoding and a 0 by the absence of a pulse. Also shown in Figure 7.17 is the NRZI current waveform for the same data pattern used to illustrate the NRZ recording method. These two methods are the same in their basic input–output signal characteristics, and therefore only one of them needs to be examined in any detail. The significance of the NRZI interpretation is that if a bit is misread, only that bit is in error. On the other hand, with NRZ coding, if a bit is in error, the error will propagate indefinitely.

The NRZ recording method uses at a maximum one saturation reversal (and provides one output pulse) per bit of information. This maximum occurs only when an alternating sequence of 1's and 0's is recorded. For NRZI, the corresponding pattern is all 1's. These NRZ schemes impose absolutely no constraints on the recorded binary input signal waveform. Also, it would not be possible to record binary data in which all possible patterns are allowed, with any fewer current, or magnetization, reversals. Not every bit is identified by an output pulse, and hence accurate clocking is necessary to interpret the recovered waveform correctly, particularly to read those data bits where a signal may not be sensed over several bit periods. In the NRZ method bpi (bits

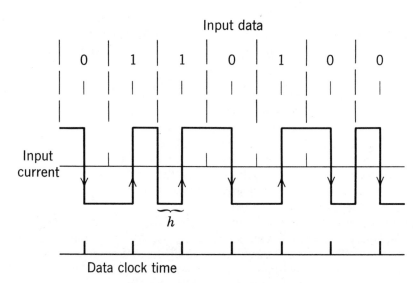

FIGURE 7.18   Phase-encoding waveforms.

per inch) $= 1/h$, and the maximum value of the output pulse density in pulses per inch, corresponding to flux changes per inch, is just equal to the recorded bit density.

7.3.2 Phase Encoding

Within a short time span another binary coding technique came into use. This technique, which addressed the self-clocking weakness of NRZ, came to be variously referred to as phase encoding, frequency modulation, biphase, and a few other more infrequently used terms. The term "phase encoding" will be used here to identify this basic digital recording technique. This method also involves a continuous writing current. Figure 7.18 illustrates the relationship between binary input data and the associated write current waveform for a typical binary pattern. As originally envisaged, a 1 is written by a positive current reversal or positive transition at the center of the bit cell, while a 0 is recorded by a negative transition. It can be seen that current reversals must occur at cell boundaries when successive 1's or 0's are in the data stream. This write current coding technique can be viewed as a phase modulation process where a square wave with one cycle per bit has one phase for 1's and the opposite for 0's.

Phase encoding provides more waveform redundancy than the NRZ method, since an output pulse is guaranteed to occur every data bit period. As we saw with NRZ, several current waveform identifications may be made for the binary digits in phase encoding, but the particular code and signal properties illustrated here are generic to this class of recording techniques. When recording using phase encoding, the discrimination between a 1 and 0 involves in principle only detection of pulse polarity. The maximum number of input current reversals, or output pulses, per bit is equal to two, and in fact

$$bpi \leq ppi \leq 2 \, bpi \qquad (7.33)$$

where again bpi = bit density in bits per inch, a constant, and ppi = output pulses per inch, a variable that is a function of the binary input data stream. Because both 0 and 1 bits provide read pulses, there is at least one output pulse per bit interval. This feature makes it easy to generate a clocking signal continuously from the output. Although this feature is advantageous for coping with bit synchronization problems in readout, a price is paid by additional pulse crowding, as described below.

In recording with phase encoding, the bit density is equal to $1/2h$. Thus, phase-encoded output signals will encounter pulse crowding at lower bit densities than the NRZ method. Examination of Figure 7.18 reveals, however, that the number of pulse environments for a given bit signal is highly restricted in the phase-encoding technique. Consider the two nearest-neighbor pulse locations on either side of a given output pulse, and let P = pulse (or current reversal) present and N = no pulse present. We obtain the following limited set of distinct waveforms associated with the chosen reference bit pulse:

PN<u>P</u>NP

PP<u>P</u>NP

PP<u>P</u>PP

Compared with the NRZ method, with its many possible pulse patterns over the same interval, the variation of the output signal waveform in a given bit interval $2h$ will be far less for a given degree of pulse crowding. The presence of a nearly symmetrical alternating pulse environment surrounding any output pulse tends to minimize the problem of pulse location timing. With the phase-encoding technique, every bit gives a pulse with its rise and fall sharply delineated by zero crossover points, which are the best preserved waveform features in the presence of considerable pulse interference. As shown in Figure 7.18, the waveforms are also readily amenable to ac coupling at both input and output.

7.3.3 Formal Characterization of Codes

Because of the large number of codes used or proposed for magnetic recording and their differences in performance, it is useful to have a system for characterizing them for comparison purposes. As seen in the descriptions of coding methods above, there are two important code properties, the minimum distance between output pulses or write current reversals and the maximum distance. The minimum distance is a measure of susceptibility to pulse crowding effects, while the maximum indicates performance with respect to clock recovery and low-frequency signal content which can cause errors in bit detection. A special class of codes with respect to low-frequency behavior is called dc free, that is, the write current waveform has zero average value. A modulation code places constraints on the binary sequences that can be recorded to secure these features. For example, if the user data consisted of 10 bits, there would be 2^{10} possible binary combinations of 1's and 0's that are possible. However, if we map the 10 bits of user data into 20 coded bits, we need use only a subset of the total number of code bit patterns to represent all combinations of the user bits. The code bit sequences used can then be chosen to meet conditions we want to impose on the selection of recording patterns. Thus, modulation codes involve encoding groups of data bits into different-length groups of coded bits which in turn are used to generate the write current waveform. If m is the number of data bits and n the number of code bits, clearly n must be greater than m to provide the opportunity to constrain the acceptable recording sequences.

A code may be described as an $m/n(d,k;c)$ code where the parameters describe the characteristics of the code. An additional parameter arises for variable block-length codes where the number of user data bits grouped for encoding into coded bits can vary with the input data bit sequence. For fixed block-length codes, m data bits are grouped and coded into n code bits. The ratio m/n is the code rate, which must be less than one. d is the minimum number of 0's between two consecutive 1's in the *coded sequence*. k is the maximum number of 0's between two consecutive 1's in the *coded sequence*. Here, a 1 corresponds to a recorded transition and a 0 to the absence of a recorded transition at a write clock time. Therefore, d impacts the pulse crowding associated with the code, since the larger the value of d, the greater the spacing between current reversals (or transitions). k is related to the ease of clock synchronization. The smaller the value of k, the more frequently will a pulse occur from which the clock generator can be resynchronized. For finite k, the code is called run-length-limited. The parameter c is the charge constraint or digital sum variation. The running digital sum or accumulated charge is generated from the write current waveform by discrete integration. The charge in a coded bit cell is taken to be either $+1$ or -1, depending upon the current polarity. c is defined as the magnitude of the maximum value of charge or running digital sum that can occur for a given code. Codes with finite c are dc free. Figure 7.19 illustrates several codes and compares them for the same input user data. For the two codes previously discussed, the code descriptions are

$$\text{NRZI} : 1/1(0,\infty;\infty)$$

$$\text{PE} : 1/2(0,1;2)$$

Additional parameters that are very useful for describing and evaluating codes may be defined in terms of the basic parameters, m, n, d, k, and c. Let

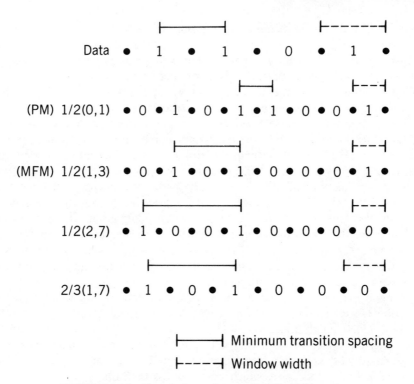

FIGURE 7.19   Comparison of several RLL (d,k) codes.

T be the clock period of the user data bit stream. Then the clock period for the code bits is

$$\frac{m}{n}T$$

This time interval is the time of the window within which the code bit must be detected. Therefore,

$$T_w = \frac{m}{n}T \tag{7.34}$$

where T_w is the detection window. Let $T_{\min}$ be the minimum time interval between transitions. Then

$$T_{\min} = (d + 1)T_w \tag{7.35}$$

where, again, d is the minimum number of 0's between 1's for all possible code bit sequences. Similarly, the maximum time interval between pulses is $T_{\max}$ where

$$T_{\max} = (k + 1)T_w \tag{7.36}$$

The density ratio is defined as the ratio of bit density to the maximum flux reversal density (bit density referring to user bits). Then

$$\frac{\text{bpi}}{\text{fci}_{\max}} = \frac{1/T}{1/T_{\min}} = (d + 1)\frac{m}{n} \tag{7.37}$$

In addition, the ratio of the all-ones high frequency f_h to all-ones low frequency f_l is

$$\frac{f_h}{f_l} = \frac{k + 1}{d + 1} \tag{7.38}$$

The selection of a code involves engineering trade-offs or compromises and this will be seen in looking at some common codes in use today.

7.3.4 Additional Codes, Including MFM, 2,7, and 1,7

The modified frequency modulation (MFM) code, often referred to as the Miller code, has been widely used in both tape and disk recording systems. We describe it here as an example of code characterization. The MFM code is a $1/2(1,3;\infty)$ code. It has the same maximum ppi as NRZI, but k is finite, making clock synchronization much easier. Each data bit is coded into two code bits according to specific coding rules. Accordingly, the clock period for a code bit is one-half that of a data bit. The generation of code bits from an incoming stream of data bits is illustrated by the use of a state diagram, as shown in Figure 7.20.

To follow the state diagram, choose an initial state, say A, and then move to the next state (including remaining in the same state), depending on the following input data bit. The corresponding code output is associated with this next state. For example, an all-ones data pattern will send the system to state A, where it remains with the coded output being a sequence of 01's. Similarly, an all-zeros data pattern will result in state C, with coded output a string of 10's. Note the similarity to the phase-encoding system, for which 01 and 10 are the two phases. The role of state B is to handle the transition from state A to state C in such a way that no input sequence can produce a coded output with successive 1's. Consequently, d must be greater than zero, and, in fact, is equal to one, as seen after a little study of the state diagram and the encoded binary sequence that is generated. The maximum number of 0's between 1's (k) is three, corresponding to the input data pattern 101. The charge constraint c is unbounded. For example, the data pattern 101, when coded, produces a net charge of -2, assuming that the initial current step is downward. Repeating this pattern continuously produces negative charge growing without bound. As mentioned previously, coded 1's correspond to recorded transitions (or the write current could be viewed as generated from the coded data by using the NRZI mode as shown). Note that even though d is one for the MFM code as opposed to zero for NRZI, the maximum ppi for the two codes is the same because d is stated in terms of the coded bit cell length, which for Miller code is half that of NRZI.

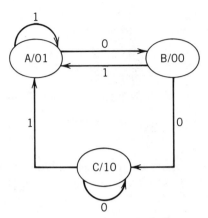

State diagram (states A, B, C)

Example:

Data: ● 1 ● 1 ● 0 ● 0 ● 1 ● 0 ● 1 ● 0 ● 0 ●

MFM coded: ● 01 ● 01 ● 00 ● 10 ● 01 ● 00 ● 01 ● 00 ● 10 ●

FIGURE 7.20   State diagram and code generation for MFM code.

While many different channel, or modulation, codes have been developed for digital magnetic recording products, the $1/2(2,7;\infty)$ and the $2/3(1,7;\infty)$ codes have been extensively adopted in high-performance disk drives.

The 2,7 code has become widely used in magnetic disk drives since its introduction by IBM on the 3380. This is a variable-block code, that is, groups of data bits are collected into blocks of varying length before coding. Each block of user bits is always coded into twice that number of code bits. Hence, the code rate m/n is one half. The use of variable blocks greatly simplifies the implementation of the code.

If the user data clock period is T, then the code bit interval is $T/2$, which will also be the detection window for the code bits. The minimum number of zeros between ones (or transitions) is two or the minimum time between transitions is

$$\frac{T}{2}(d + 1) = 3T/2$$

and the maximum time between transitions is

$$\frac{T}{2}(k + 1) = 4T$$

In addition, the density ratio

$$\frac{\text{bpi}}{f\,ci_{\max}} = (d + 1)\frac{1}{2} = 1.5 \tag{7.39}$$

and

$$\frac{f_h}{f_l} = \frac{7+1}{2+1} = \frac{8}{3} \qquad (7.40)$$

Thus, compared with the MFM code, we see that the bit density is 3/2 times the maximum transition density. If minimum transition spacing is fixed due to intersymbol interference, changing to the 2,7 code can allow a 50 percent increase in linear density with the same recording components. However, the increased data density associated with this capacity gain reduces the detection window by a third, and if the system margins are not high a loss in reliability will result. Another trade-off is to use the 2,7 code at the same linear storage density and reduce intersymbol interference problems. The d choice is made to limit pulse crowding and the k choice to assure clocking capabilities.

The 1,7 code becomes attractive where margins are stressed, as it provides a larger detection window at the same density. That is,

$$T_w = \tfrac{2}{3}T$$

On the other hand,

$$T_{min} = T_w(d + 1) = \tfrac{4}{3}T$$

compared to $(3/2)T$ for the 2,7 code. Therefore, for the same user data density there will be greater pulse crowding with the 1,7 code. Here,

$$\frac{f_h}{f_l} = 4$$

The 2,7 and 1,7 codes have contributed a great deal to the gains in the use of the magnetic recording channel for data storage and retrieval. Much current interest is being focused on coding procedures that will combine both modulation and error correction features in a single development.

7.4 READBACK DETECTION TECHNIQUES

The reading operation is concerned with the reconstruction of the original coded input binary sequence from the output voltage waveform. The decoder converts this coded data back to the original user data that was encoded. Each written bit must be properly detected. This subject will be presented primarily in terms of generalized principles with emphasis on bit density limitations. The functional nature of detection techniques and their relation to the readback waveforms are fundamental to the digital magnetic recording channel, whereas specific electronic circuit implementations are in a continual state of evolution because of the constant stream of new electronic circuits appearing.

The output signal interval within which a binary decision or choice between the two possible values 0 and 1 must be made is the coded bit interval or detection window. The range of signal waveforms in the code bit interval for any given maximum flux density and recording method is, as we have seen, highly dependent on the overall characteristics of the magnetic recording system and the channel coding technique. Before any decision can be made about the signal in a given bit interval, the bit interval must be defined by the generation of a clocking window.

Clocking—Clocking of coded data refers to the defining of the boundaries (location) of each bit interval. All high-density recording systems rely on some form of self-clocking. The term "self-clocking" is used to describe reading methods in which the basic clock is derived from the data itself. The generation of a precise clock from the recorded data is greatly facilitated by frequent resynchronizing pulses. Consequently, a run-length-limited channel code must be used. A minimum frequency for the occurrence of pulses or 1's in the code bit sequence is achieved through the choice of k, placing a limit of the maximum time delay in the resynchronization of the clock. Self-clocking still, of course, requires a reasonably uniform relative velocity between medium and head during reading. With a velocity mismatch, the timing errors will be cumulative over the span of 0's. The time slots for the bit sequence must be generated by the electronic clocking circuit from the resynchronization provided by the last previous 1.

Since each recorded track clocks itself, there is no inherent barrier to recording in parallel on a group of tracks. However, in order to bring the respective output bits from such a group of tracks into time alignment, de-skewing buffer storage may be required. Skew refers here to the lack of time synchronization between simultaneously operating recording tracks.

Noise Sources—The use of signal-to-noise ratio (SNR) in digital magnetic recording requires special clarification. The normal signal level compared to random or statistical noise is relatively high, although as track widths are reduced, data rates increase, and bit cell sizes decrease, the media, head and electronic noise sources become of much greater significance. However, there are many sources of signal distortion that do introduce serious problems in achieving detection reliability; for example, intersymbol interference, or pulse crowding, and overwrite limitations.

When amplitude detection is used, a common cause of a readback error is a missing bit or "dropout." A dropout is a temporary loss of signal strength, caused by a transient increase in the head-to-medium spacing, which is sufficient to cause reading errors. The sources of spacing fluctuations are found in particles, dust, or surface asperities that pass between the head and recording medium and in mechanical and air bearing dynamics. An extra bit usually arises from pinholes and other media defects that create an unwanted change in magnetization.

The most common method of detection is peak sensing and here an error arises from the shifting of the pulse peak outside its window, to be detected in a window not associated with a transition. Then error sources are identified and understood in terms of their potential contributions to bit shift. Peak detection is covered later in this chapter.

In disk drives head-to-track registration tolerances introduce limitations that further lower the density. On readback, at high track densities, the track registration tolerances result in the head simultaneously sensing (1) the desired (most recently written) data pattern; (2) previously written "old information," due to misregistration on the previous overwrite; and (3) an adjacent track signals. Moreover, these undesired signal sources represent interference since the signals from old and adjacent track recorded information have attributes similar to those of the desired signal from the most recent update. Any off-track positioning both reduces the desired signal and increases these undesired "noise" sources. Thus, high linear density is limited by such track density factors to less than the limits normally associated with the standard "channel" design. More will be said about overall recording performance in Chapter 8.

7.4.1 Amplitude Detection

The most direct method of reading output waveforms from the head is simply to sense the amplitude of the output voltage. Consider the NRZI code. We choose a threshold voltage e_T and, by sampling the magnitude of the output signal at the center of each bit interval, we can define the value of the output in terms of e_T as follows (let e_t be the total signal and e the signal from an isolated readback pulse):

$$|e_t| < e_T, \qquad \text{code bit} = 0$$
$$|e_t| \geq e_T, \qquad \text{code bit} = 1 \tag{7.41}$$

We shall assume that there is an accurate clock source for sampling the output voltage at the center of each bit interval. Furthermore, the peak amplitude of the characteristic pulse will be considered normalized to 1.0, that is, $e(\bar{x} = 0) = 1.0$. In terms of readback systems it is appropriate to use the time domain. Here, we want to focus on the characteristic pulse which is inherently related to the recording geometry and not make the analysis specific to any particular modulation code. Therefore, we again define h as the minimum transition spacing.

The largest "0" signal will result from the worst-case pattern, $\ldots0000\underline{1}00\ldots$ (where the underline indicates the particular bit under investigation). Then

$$e_t\big|_{\max}("0") = e(\bar{x} = h) \tag{7.42}$$

At low densities where $h > PW_{10}'$, this "0" voltage is equal to or very nearly zero. As h becomes less than $PW_{10}'/2$, the amplitude of this "0" signal begins to rise significantly. In order to read this "0" correctly, e_T must be greater than $e(\bar{x} = h)$. The minimum "1" signal will occur with the worst-case pattern $\ldots0011100\ldots$. Here, the adjacent 1 pulses subtract from the "1" signal of concern. Then

$$e_t \big|_{\min} (\text{``1''}) = 1 - 2e(\overline{x} = h) \tag{7.43}$$

This voltage is approximately equal to one until $h < PW'_{10}/2$, at which point the adjacent pulses begin to reduce the peak signal of the central "1" pulse markedly. e_T must be less than $e_t \mid \min(\text{``1''})$ in order to read this pulse properly as a 1 bit.

Now it is necessary that

$$e_t \big|_{\min} (\text{``1''}) \geq e_t \big|_{\max} (\text{``0''}) \tag{7.44}$$

to discriminate correctly 1's from 0's with amplitude detection. It is seen that e_T must fall within these two voltage bounds, which in turn are a function of the degree of pulse crowding and hence bit density.

The theoretical bit density limit can be found by substituting and equating the voltages corresponding to these two limits. That is, setting

$$1 - 2e(\overline{x}) = e(\overline{x}) \tag{7.45}$$

where here $\overline{x} = h_{\min}$. Then $e(h_{\min}) = 1/3$. For $h = h_{\min}$, the maximum zero signal is equal to the minimum one signal and correct bit discrimination is no longer possible. Further, since $bpi_{\max} = 1/h_{\min}$, then at this bit density limit, e_T must equal $1/3$. To determine signal margins and density limitations with this simple amplitude detection method, we must choose a specific waveform for $e(x)$. Let, for example,

$$e(\overline{x}) = \frac{1}{1 + (\overline{x})^2} \tag{7.46}$$

This characteristic pulse has its amplitude normalized to 1.0 and its pulse width to $PW'_{10} = 6$ and has been seen to be a common form of approximation. We can now solve for $h_{\min}$ by setting

$$\frac{1}{1 + h^2} = \frac{1}{3} \tag{7.47}$$

We get

$$h_{\min} = \sqrt{2}$$

or

$$bpi_{\max} = 0.7 \tag{7.48}$$

Since $2/PW'_{10} = 0.33$, the maximum density limit is slightly greater than twice the bit density at which the peak amplitude of a sequence of 1's begins to fall noticeably (Figure 7.6). Figure 7.21 illustrates graphically the variation of $e_t \big|_{\max} (\text{``0''})$ and $e_t \big|_{\min} (\text{``1''})$ with bit density for this particular characteristic pulse. The shaded band designates the acceptable range for e_T as a function of bit density.

In practice, to allow for parameter variations and provide reliability, one could not actually expect to record up to this bit density limit. Given specified

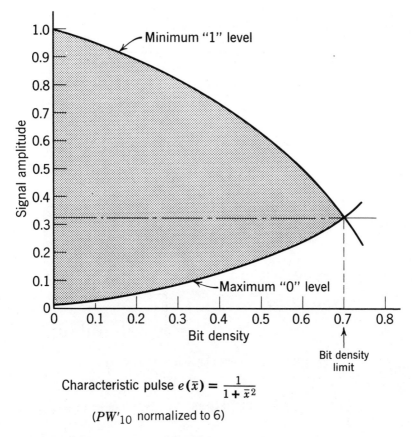

FIGURE 7.21   Threshold detection limits for amplitude detection of NRZI signals.

signal tolerances one could, from curves like those in Figure 7.21, establish both the maximum usable density and the optimum setting for e_T.

7.4.2 Peak Detection

Because of the shape of the characteristic readback pulse, it is possible to detect the presence of a 1 by determining if a pulse peak occurred during the bit interval of interest. Because the derivative of the signal will be equal to zero at the peak, peak detection is implemented by differentiating the signal and detecting zero crossings. Figure 7.22 shows a block diagram for detecting peaks. The zero-crossing detector generates a pulse for each zero-crossing at its input. Note that during intervals of no readback signal, corresponding to 0's recorded, the zero-crossing detector could generate spurious output pulses. The detector must discriminate against these, and the lower path in the block

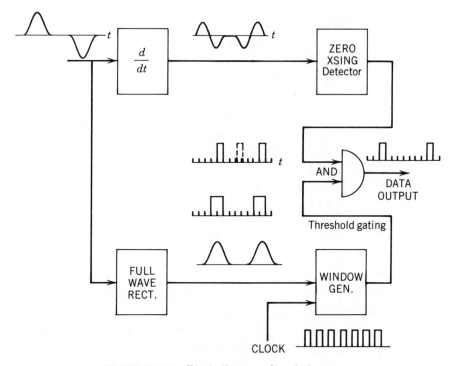

FIGURE 7.22 Block diagram of peak detector.

diagram generates a gating signal that checks for zero-crossings only when a signal above a certain threshold level is present. Note that this particular detector also uses amplitude information, but it is far less sensitive to signal amplitude variations than the pure amplitude detection described above. Pulse timing rather than pulse amplitude limits the detector performance. An error will occur when the zero-crossing from a recorded 1 falls outside of the detection window.

The differentiator analog output signal is the reference for estimating bit shift due to "unwanted" signals. Any corrupting signal will cause a time shift in the occurrence of the zero-crossing. Such "noise" sources will either raise or lower the differentiated signal waveform in the detection window, and the resulting shift in the position of the zero-crossing will be a function of the amplitude and slope of the differentiated signal in comparison with these sources. The greater the signal amplitude, the steeper will this waveform go through zero and hence the less time shift there will be for a given "noise" contribution.

Figure 7.23 shows the standard single-element read/write head illustrating the effects of head mispositioning which were discussed earlier. Shown is the track where the previous or old information was recorded, the adjacent track position, and the track on which the updated information was

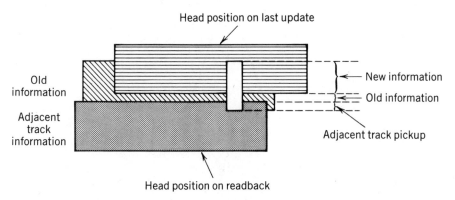

FIGURE 7.23   Signal distortion from tracking tolerances.

written. The current location of the head is the location of the head when reading.

Peak detection then is analyzed in terms of the contributions to bit shift of all sources of signal disturbances. Major sources of bit shift include pattern-induced bit shift, overwrite-induced bit shift, actual noise-induced bit shift, and adjacent-track-induced bit shift. Figure 7.24 illustrates the character of a differentiated readback waveform and the sensitivity of zero-crossing detectors to bit shift arising from various "unwanted" signal sources. The probability of the zero-crossing actually being shifted outside the detection window must be sufficiently small to meet the error rate criteria for the storage device. In Chapter 8 the relation between soft error rate and these sources of bit shift will be discussed in terms of margin analysis.

Owing to the greater immunity of peak detection from signal amplitude variations from component tolerances and when recording at different radii (and thus velocities), peak detection has been found to offer a higher linear density potential than straight amplitude detection.

Additional Detection Methods—With the development of ever more sophisticated signal processing techniques having implementation in large-scale integrated circuits, rapid progress has been made in detection methods for digital communication systems—correlation detectors, Viterbi detectors, and others [7]. A number of these are beginning to find application in digital magnetic recording [11]. While today the focus is on RLL coding and peak detection, more and more investigations are being made into partial response (Class IV) maximum likelihood (PRML) methods. By better matching the signal spectrum to the channel characteristics and exploiting a priori waveform information (rather than examining each bit as an entity in itself), it is possible to gain a 3 dB SNR advantage. This gain translates into significant improvement in error rate with higher densities. PRML was a technique used in a gigabit per

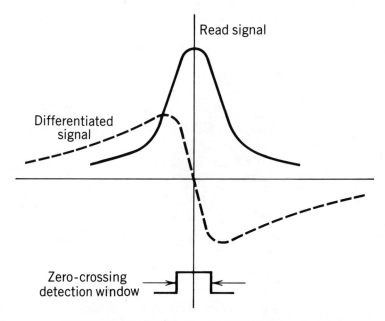

FIGURE 7.24   Differentiated signal zero-crossing.

square inch demonstration system in 1990. It will be some time, however, before these more sophisticated concepts enter into the general disk drive design world.

REFERENCES

1. *Principles of Data Communication*, R. W. Lucky, J. Salz, and E. J. Weldon, Jr., McGraw-Hill, New York, 1968.
2. *Introduction to Signal Transmission*, W. R. Bennett, McGraw-Hill, New York, pp. 78–92, 1970.
3. *Magnetic Recording Handbook: Technology and Applications*, C. D. Mee and E. D. Daniel, McGraw-Hill, New York, pp. 722–739 and 1115–1131, 1987.
4. "Theory of Linear Superposition in Tape Recording," J. C. Mallinson and C. W. Steele, *IEEE Trans. Magn.*, MAG-5, pp. 886–891, 1969.
5. "Algorithms for Sliding Block Codes," R. L. Adler, D. Coppersmith, and M. Hassner, *IEEE Trans. Inf. Theory*, IT-29, pp. 5–22, 1983.
6. "Recording Codes for Digital Magnetic Storage," P. H. Siegel, *IEEE Trans. Magn.*, MAG-21, pp. 1344–1349, 1985.
7. *Digital Communications*, S. Haykin, Wiley, New York, 1988.
8. "Logical Reading System for Nonreturn-to-Zero Magnetic Recording," A. S. Hoagland, *IRE Trans. Electron. Comput.*, EC-4, No. 3, September 1955.
9. "A Self-Clocking System for Information Transfer," L. D. Seader, *IBM J. Res. Dev.*, Vol. 1, No. 2, pp. 181–184, April 1957.

10. "High Density Digital Magnetic Recording Techniques," A. S. Hoagland and G. C. Bacon, *Proc. IRE*, Vol. 49, pp. 258–268, January 1961.

11. "An Experimental Eight-Inch Disc Drive with One-Hundred Megabytes per Surface," R. Wood, S. Ahlgrim, K. Hallamasek, and R. Stevenson, *IEEE Trans. Magn.*, MAG-20, pp. 698–702, September 1984.

12. "Application of Partial-Response Channel Coding to Magnetic Recording Systems," H. Kobayashi and D. T. Tang, *IBM J. Res. Dev.*, Vol. 15, pp. 368–375, July 1970.

CHAPTER 8

DIGITAL RECORDING: NOISE SOURCES, ERROR RATES, AND ECC

In this chapter we discuss readback error sources, the manner in which the bit error rate is related to these error sources, and then the use of error correction to deal with these problems to allow a significant improvement in overall storage device reliability.

Storage device systems strategies also provide methods to enhance overall reliability. For example, a standard technique is to map out bad areas of storage media, both initially and as indicated over time. Storage locations with permanent defects—for example, those caused by a surface scratch—possibly could be tolerated if sufficient data redundancy is provided. However, normal practice on tape is to mark the edges of such a region by recording special signals to delete it from the usable storage area. On magnetic disk drives bad sectors are identified and their addresses are removed from the file allocation table and directory structure. This strategy increases the effectiveness of the error correction system over the remaining track sections which are free from such defects.

One automatic procedure that is commonly employed on detection of a readback error in digital magnetic recording is to initiate a reread cycle. A second or even third attempt will be made to read the data correctly. On disk drives the magnetic head may be offset slightly first in one and then the other direction to see if the data can be successfully read. If the data is read correctly on one of these tries (in terms of simple error detection and without the need to invoke error correction), then the data is accepted and data transfers continue. If the checks fail, then the system is alerted. The controller or host computer system then has the option of invoking the designed-in error correction and accepting the data if this procedure is successful. In any event, the controller will likely mark this as a bad sector and withdraw it from use. Soft bit errors are those that occur due to transient and noise effects and would not be seen on a second read pass. Hard bit errors are those associated with disk defects and are permanent. It is apparent that if the error rate is not extremely small, these additional reads cause the performance of the drive in terms of access rate to decrease markedly.

Another common procedure in digital magnetic recording on tape devices is to make an immediate readback check after writing. This operation is easy to implement on tape owing to the head–medium mechanics of a sequential scanning device. This procedure assures that the new data was correctly recorded, while the original information is still readily available in the computer in the event a second attempt to write is required. With tape, where contact recording leads to some wear, this is a direct method to increase reliability. Furthermore, unlike disk, where it is recognized that as standard operating procedure the data on disk must frequently be backed up on tape, tape itself is viewed as off-line archival-type storage. On tape, defect areas are skipped when the tape is written rather than, as in the case with disk, preformating the medium into sectors and mapping out bad regions mapped during this operation. These approaches reflect both the differences in the head–medium interface as well as the sequential versus direct access nature of the devices and consequently the way they are utilized.

Many other system strategies can be employed, but the fundamental measure of the reliability of the storage device will be found in the basic design and margins of the components and their integration.

8.1 ERROR SOURCES

There are error sources that may be broadly classified as noise sources and interference sources. Noise arises from random processes that can only be characterized by their statistics. Interference, on the other hand, is deterministic and can in principle be predicted completely. For example, the random fluctuation of domain walls in a film head is a noise process, whereas the voltages induced in the head windings from power line fields and fields from high-speed logic switching currents are interferences—in this case, electromagnetic interference. In digital magnetic recording, the most important noise sources come from the heads, electronics, and recording media. Along with electromagnetic interference, intersymbol interference, unwanted signals from adjacent track data, and previous information not completely overwritten are important sources of interference. Because the data patterns and other deterministic mechanisms producing interference are so complex, they often may be analyzed as if they were random signals. Nonetheless, it's important to maintain the distinction between noise and interference because the nature of the errors produced by the two may be very different, depending upon the design of the storage system.

8.1.1 Head Noise

The noise generated by a magnetic head can be determined from the real part of the head impedance. Johnson noise (often called thermal noise) is associated with all lossy mechanisms that can be modeled as linear resistors. Johnson [1] first observed the open circuit noise voltage across the terminals of a resistor at absolute temperature T in thermal equilibrium with its surroundings. Einstein had predicted that this phenomenon would be produced by the Brownian motion of the charge carriers. Using the methods of statistical thermodynamics, Nyquist [2] derived the expression for the power spectral density of Johnson noise. Under the conditions encountered in digital magnetic recording, Johnson noise is "white," that is, it has a constant power spectral density with frequency. The common way for dealing with Johnson noise is to represent a noisy resistor R in thermal equilibrium at temperature T by a noiseless resistor of the same value in series with a noise voltage generator with mean-squared value:

$$\overline{e_n^2} = 4K_BTBR \qquad (8.1)$$

where K_B is Boltzmann's constant, $1.38 \cdot 10^{-23}$ J/K, and B is the bandwidth in Hertz. Figure 8.1 shows the equivalent circuit and noise power spectral density. Johnson noise is uncorrelated, so that noise voltages add on a mean-squared basis.

Using these concepts, we see that the available noise power from a resistor R, that is, the power delivered to a matched load resistor, is K_BTB, which is independent of the value of R.

Using the Johnson noise representation, head noise is easily determined from the real part of the head impedance, derived in Chapter 5. In general, this equivalent resistance includes all loss mechanisms in the head and its windings and is a function of frequency. Consequently, the open circuit noise voltage across the head windings is not "white" noise, but depends upon the loss mechanisms and reactive components of the head.

8.1.2 Electronics Noise

Electronics noise is associated with the electron devices used in the circuits that process the readback signal from the head. The main contributor is the first device in the head preamplifier. Shot noise, associated with the normal thermal fluctuations of carrier energies, is usually the predominant noise mechanism. As with Johnson noise, electronics noise can be modeled by equivalent circuits, the general representation being a noise voltage and noise current source with a correlation coefficient between them [3]. For a given noise equivalent circuit representation of the head and preamplifier, there is an optimum impedance level for interfacing the head to the preamplifier to achieve best noise performance.

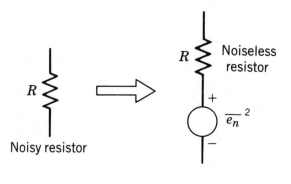

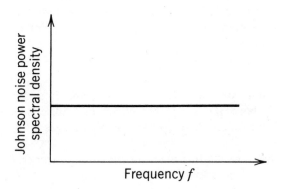

FIGURE 8.1 Johnson noise equivalent circuit and noise power density.

8.1.3 Medium Noise

Medium noise will be treated in somewhat more detail, as the ultimate limits in magnetic storage are perceived as related to the inherent signal to noise capabilities of the media. There are several mechanisms contributing to medium noise, and the weighting of these in overall noise performance depends on the nature of the medium and its manner of use. Some of these mechanisms are random fluctuations in particle position, particle magnetization, particle density, domain wall configurations in film media, and so forth. Because of the nonlinear, hysteretic nature of recording media and possible correlations among noise mechanisms, medium noise depends upon the state of the medium such as ac erased, dc erased, recorded signals at various bit densities. Noise can be categorized as additive or multiplicative depending upon the absence or presence of a recorded signal.

As an example of a medium noise calculation, we present the treatment of additive noise in a particulate medium following the development of Mallinson [4]. Assuming that noise from the individual particles is uncorrelated, the power spectral density of the magnetization noise is found. Then, using the concept that noise powers add, the readback channel transfer function can be applied to the magnetization noise to get a power spectral density for the voltage output noise. This result can be compared with the signal voltage spectrum to find signal-to-noise ratios—both narrow-band, or "slot," and wideband.

The assumptions made in the analysis are that

- The medium supports longitudinal magnetization (x direction) only.
- All particles are dipoles with length l and magnetic moment p.
- There are n particles per unit volume.
- Particles are oriented in the $\pm x$ direction at random.

To calculate the power spectral density of the magnetization, use is made of the Wiener–Khintchine theorem [5], which states that the power spectral density of a noise process is the Fourier transform of its autocorrelation function. The autocorrelation function of a function $f(x)$ is $R(x_0)$,

$$R(x_0) = \lim_{x \to \infty} \frac{1}{x} \int_{-x/2}^{x/2} f(x)f(x - x_0)\,dx \tag{8.2}$$

To calculate R for the magnetization, f is constructed by carrying out the integral over all possible combinations of the individual particle magnetizations ($\pm x$ orientation), and then these results are averaged (ensemble averaging). Because of the assumption that there is no correlation between particles, the only contribution to the autocorrelation function comes from the correlation of each particle magnetization with itself. Thus, the noise is related to the sum of the squares (i.e., np^2), while the signal is related to the square of the sum [i.e., $(np)^2$]. When the linear density of the particle moment is assumed to be a constant over the length x, as shown in Figure 8.2, the autocorrelation function is triangular, and its Fourier transform has a $(\sin x/x)^2$ form. Consequently, the power spectral density of the magnetization noise may be expressed as

$$\overline{M_n^2}(k) = n\frac{p^2}{2\pi}\left(\frac{\sin kl/2}{kl/2}\right)^2 \tag{8.3}$$

Further calculations are greatly simplified if we assume that $kl/2$ is small, that is, the wavelengths involved are greater than the particle length. Then $(\sin x/x)^2 \approx 1$, and the power spectral density is flat with wave number k, that is, "white" noise.

Next, we calculate the noise power spectral density for the voltage output from the head by using the reciprocity theorem, with the methods of Chapter 3, but remembering that noise voltages must be treated in terms of their mean-squared values. Further, if we neglect gap loss effects, we may write

$$\overline{E_n^2}(k) = n\frac{p^2}{2\pi}W \int_d^{d+\delta} (\mu_0 N v k e^{-ky})^2\,dy \tag{8.4}$$

$$= n\frac{p^2}{2\pi}W(\mu_0 N v)^2\frac{k}{2}e^{-2kd}(1 - e^{-2k\delta}) \tag{8.5}$$

which includes spacing and thickness effects.

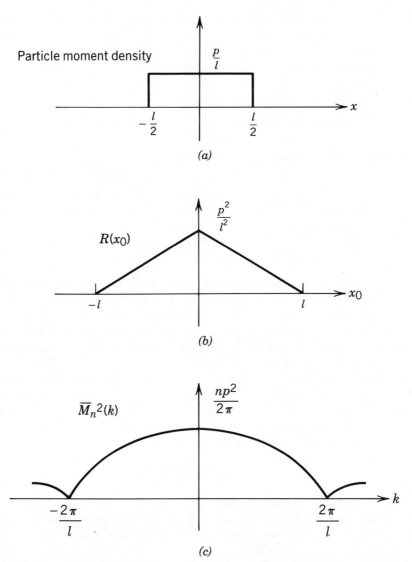

FIGURE 8.2 Magnetization noise power spectral density. (*a*) Particle magnetic moment. (*b*) Moment autocorrelation function. (*c*) Power spectral density.

To find the output signal, under the assumption that the magnetization pattern has flat wavelength distribution, observe that the peak signal amplitude occurs when all of the particles are lined up, $M = np$. Using the results from Chapter 3 gives for the square of the signal voltage

$$\overline{E_s^2}(k) = n^2 \frac{p^2}{2}(W\mu_0 N v)^2 e^{-2kd}(1 - e^{-k\delta})^2 \tag{8.6}$$

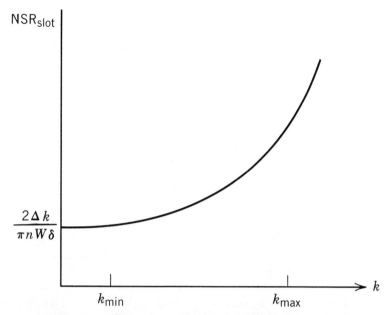

FIGURE 8.3   Slot noise-to-signal ratio versus wave number k.

Comparing equation (8.6) to (8.5), we see that signal and noise both vary in the same way with particle moment, head turns, velocity, and head-to-medium spacing. Differences occur with respect to particle density, track width, wave number, and medium thickness.

These differences arise from the fact that signal adds coherently on a voltage basis, while noise adds incoherently on a power- or voltage-squared basis. To see the implications of these differences on system design, we next find the overall signal-to-noise ratio.

Dividing equation (8.6) by (8.5) will give the signal-to-noise ratio (power) in a band or slot of wave numbers Δk:

$$\text{SNR}_{\text{slot}}(k) = \frac{\pi n W}{\Delta k} \frac{(1 - e^{-k\delta})^2}{(1 - e^{-2k\delta})} \tag{8.7}$$

To find the wideband signal-to-noise ratio, it is easier to work with the noise-to-signal ratio. The slot noise-to-signal ratio,

$$[\text{SNR}_{\text{slot}}(k)]^{-1}$$

is sketched in Figure 8.3. Integrating this curve and then inverting gives

$$\text{SNR}_{wb} = \pi n W \left[\int_{k_{\min}}^{k_{\max}} k \coth(k\delta/2)\, dk \right]^{-1} \tag{8.8}$$

In the high bit density limit, $k\delta \gg 1$, and

$$\text{SNR}_{wb} = 2\pi nW[(k_{max})^2 - (k_{min})^2)]^{-1} \qquad (8.9)$$

Often, $k_{max} \gg k_{min}$, giving

$$\text{SNR}_{wb} \approx nW\frac{(\lambda_{min})^2}{2\pi} \qquad (8.10)$$

This compact result has an interesting physical interpretation with important implications for systems design. Note that the wideband medium SNR for additive noise in the medium is equal to the number of particles in a volume of size

$$(W)\left(\frac{\lambda_{min}}{\pi}\right)\left(\frac{\lambda_{min}}{2}\right)$$

as shown in Figure 8.4. This is the effective medium volume sensed by the read head on playback, limited by track width, the thickness factor (most of the signal arises from the medium within λ/π of the top surface), and the minimum length of a unidirectional saturated region. At short wavelengths $2/\lambda_{min}$ corresponds to the maximum number of flux reversals per unit length. For example, 1000 particles in this sensed volume would give an SNR of 30 dB. Equation (8.10) also suggests that if the recording system is medium noise limited, from SNR considerations it is better, when operating in a short wavelength regime (where a 6 dB loss in SNR occurs per octave in frequency), to pursue higher areal storage densities by increasing track density rather than linear bit density. Suppose a doubling in areal density is obtained by halving W. The degradation in SNR is 3 dB. If λ_{min} is halved in order to double areal density by doubling linear bit density, SNR degrades by 6 dB.

In magnetic disk devices media noise has not yet been the dominant factor setting performance, and the maximum flux reversal rate is usually chosen to be no more than 3 dB down on the signal roll-off curve due to limitations arising from other error sources, principally track misregistration. Increasing linear density depends on reducing flying height, from which dramatic improvements in resolution are possible, while increasing track density is related to improvements in servo systems and narrower head widths. To date, reductions in spacing have been the driving force in the advances made in storage density. Many design factors in addition to medium noise dictate the directions pursued for increasing areal density.

Recall that an important assumption in the above development was that there was no correlation among particles. This allowed us to add noise powers directly, the appropriate treatment for additive noise. When there is correlation between particles, the analysis is very complicated and, as yet, not completely well understood [6]. The correlated noise is known as multiplicative or modulation noise and is strongly affected by the presence of a signal.

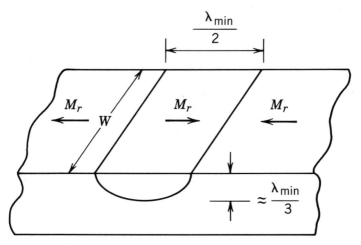

FIGURE 8.4 Effective medium volume sensed by head.

8.2 BIT ERROR RATE

Bit error rate is defined in terms of a hard error rate and a soft error rate. A hard error can arise from a medium defect and each time this region is read an error will be detected. A soft error is an error that arises from noise or other disturbances not regularly repeated on reread. A reread operation conducted with system perturbations such as a small track offset is often done in the hope of compensating for a small mispositioning error. The soft bit error rate is the parameter commonly used to describe overall error performance of a storage system. As mentioned above, both noise and interference (from intersymbol interference, overwrite performance, and track misregistration, etc.) can cause bit errors.

8.2.1 Noise-Induced Bit Shift

The relationship between noise, characterized by a SNR, and bit error rate can be derived for a peak detection circuit as follows [7]. In peak detection, as developed in Chapter 7, the signal is differentiated and the detector looks for a zero-crossing corresponding to the presence of a peak inside of the detection window T_w. In a perfect system, noise- and interference-free, the zero-crossing would occur in the center of the window. Defining $t = 0$ in the center of the window, noise voltages add to the differentiated signal to produce a shift t_s in the zero-crossing, as seen in Figure 8.5. An error will occur when $|t_s| > T_w/2$, shifting the zero-crossing outside of the detection window. There may be two errors if the shifted zero-crossing is detected in the next window where no transition was intended.

Differentiated signal

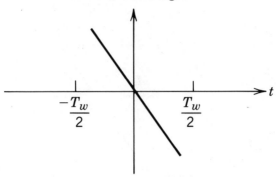

Noise voltage

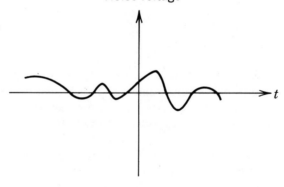

Signal + Noise

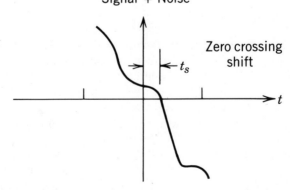

FIGURE 8.5 Shifting of peak detector zero-crossing by noise.

Assume that the noise voltage e_n is white, Gaussian noise where σ_n is the standard deviation of the noise distribution, which is also the root mean-squared value of the noise voltage e_n. The zero-crossing shift t_s as a consequence will also have a Gaussian distribution σ_t.

The probability of an error occurring is just the probability that the zero-crossing will fall outside a detection window T_w. Now the probability distribution of t_s is

$$p(t_s) = \frac{1}{\sqrt{2\pi}\sigma_t} e^{-(t_s/\sqrt{2}\sigma_t)^2} \tag{8.11}$$

And therefore

$$p_{\text{error}}(T_w) = 2\int_{T_w/2}^{\infty} p(t_s)\,dt_s \tag{8.12}$$

Setting

$$u = \frac{t_s}{\sqrt{2}\sigma_t}$$

we can rewrite p_{error} in terms of this new variable as follows:

$$p_{\text{error}}(T_w) = \frac{2}{\sqrt{\pi}}\int_{T_w/2\sqrt{2}\sigma_t}^{\infty} e^{-u^2}\,du \tag{8.13}$$

Using the complementary error function defined as

$$erfc(z) = \frac{2}{\sqrt{\pi}}\int_{z}^{\infty} e^{-u^2}\,du \tag{8.14}$$

We find then

$$p_{\text{error}}(T_w) = erfc\left(\frac{T_w}{2\sqrt{2}\sigma_t}\right) \tag{8.15}$$

The shift in the zero-crossing caused by the noise voltage is a function of the slope of the signal voltage waveform at the zero-crossing. In the presence of noise, the zero crossing will occur at (here e_s is the signal after differentiation)

$$e_s + e_n = 0$$

Take a linear approximation to the signal waveform in the vicinity of $t = 0$ or

$$e_s = -Kt$$

Then substituting in the equation above we have

$$t_s = \frac{e_n}{K}$$

We can conclude

$$\sigma_t = \frac{\sigma_n}{K} \tag{8.16}$$

Now we define the voltage signal-to-noise ratio as

$$\text{SNR} = \frac{E_{pk}}{\sigma_n} \qquad (8.17)$$

in accord with common practice in digital magnetic recording. While this definition applies prior to the differentiation of the signal, we assume here that the signal-to-noise ratio at the input to the zero-crossing detector has the same value. Then

$$\sigma_n = \frac{E_{pk}}{\text{SNR}} \qquad (8.18)$$

and we have

$$\sigma_t = \frac{1}{K} \frac{E_{pk}}{\text{SNR}} \qquad (8.19)$$

To determine K we need to find an expression for the signal voltage as it goes through zero in the detection window. First we assume a Lorentzian isolated pulse shape on readback.

$$e_s = \frac{E_{pk}}{1 + [t/(PW_{50}/2)]^2} \qquad (8.20)$$

where PW_{50} is in units of time. Taking the derivative with respect to t and writing the expression for the scaled voltage in the vicinity of $t = 0$, we have

$$e_s = -\frac{4}{PW_{50}} E_{pk} t \qquad (8.21)$$

And

$$K = -\frac{e_s}{t} = \frac{4}{PW_{50}} E_{pk} \qquad (8.22)$$

If we were to use a sine wave approximation for the voltage signal into the zero-crossing detector, we would have near a zero-crossing

$$e_s = -\omega E_{pk} t \qquad (8.23)$$

or

$$K = \omega E_{pk} \qquad \text{where} \quad \omega = \pi(f\,ci)v,$$

v being the relative velocity between head and medium.

Using the Lorentzian model we are now in a position to write σ_t in terms that include the factors of SNR and the recording resolution PW_{50}. Thus, substituting in equation (8.19),

$$\sigma_t = \frac{1}{K} \frac{E_{pk}}{\text{SNR}} = \frac{PW_{50}}{4\,\text{SNR}} \qquad (8.24)$$

With this relation we can finally substitute σ_t into the expression [equation (8.15)] for the probability of error or bit error rate (ber) and have

$$\text{ber} = erfc\left(\frac{T_w}{2\sqrt{2}} \frac{4\,\text{SNR}}{PW_{50}}\right) = erfc\left(\frac{\sqrt{2}T_w\,\text{SNR}}{PW_{50}}\right) \qquad (8.25)$$

where again SNR is defined in terms of peak signal to rms noise voltage. In this form the importance of SNR, recording geometry, and the clocking window width on the bit error rate (ber) can be readily seen.

Now the soft bit error rate is the probability of an random error occurring. Let t_w be considered a window variable that can range from 0 to $T_w/2$, the full half clock-window period. Then the above equation provides a relationship for the bit error rate versus the consumed detection half-window due to noise as a function of signal-to-noise ratio and the readback pulse half-width. If we specify a required soft bit error rate, then the corresponding value of t_w will be called T_{wSNR}, which is the minimum window that could be used if the only source of error were noise and no safety margin was provided.

A soft bit error rate of 10^{-10} and a hard bit error rate of less than 10^{-12} are common for a disk drive. A soft error rate of 10^{-10} corresponds to a value of 4.573 for the complementary error function parameter z. Note that larger values of z are associated with smaller error rates. The fraction of the detection window consumed by random noise for this case can be estimated as follows:

$$z = 4.573 = \frac{\sqrt{2}T_{wSNR}\text{SNR}}{PW_{50}}$$

where again T_{wSNR} is that fraction of the detection half-window that noise "consumes" (i.e., needed window width allocated to noise so that this source by itself will not cause the specified error bit rate to be exceeded).

$$T_{wSNR} = \frac{4.573PW_{50}}{\sqrt{2}\,\text{SNR}} \qquad (8.26)$$

Since with increasing density the width of the clocking window decreases, the importance of a narrow pulse width and a high signal-to-noise ratio to minimize exposure to noise can be readily appreciated. The ber, at very low bit error rates, is extremely sensitive to SNR. An increase in SNR of 0.1 dB would approximately halve a soft bit error rate in the range of 10^{-10}.

When other sources of systematic bit shift are considered, as for example an intersymbol interference component T_p, then any half-window width less that T_p would give an error rate close to 1.0. T_p is then the portion of the half window $T_w/2$ consumed by intersymbol interference. For a specified soft error rate, the sum of the noise- and systematic-induced bit shifts must not only be less than the design half-window width but sufficiently less to assure an adequate performance margin, taking into account all the component mechanical and electrical tolerances of the drive. Figure 8.6 shows a plot of the bit error rate due to noise, intersymbol interference, and overwrite as a function of consumed window. The margin for a selected error rate is illustrated. The higher the signal-to-noise ratio, the steeper the curve. The flatter the top portion of the curve, the greater the intersymbol interference or other systematic error sources.

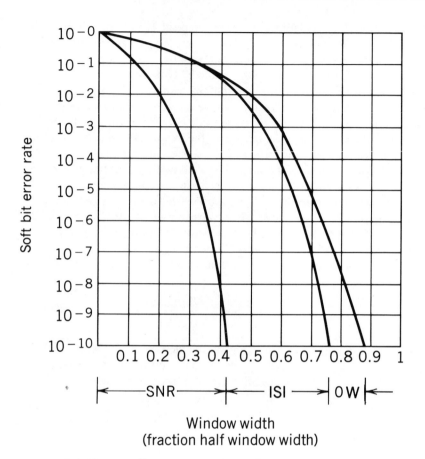

FIGURE 8.6   Soft bit error rate versus detection window.

8.2.2 Intersymbol-Interference-Induced Bit Shift

As previously mentioned, intersymbol interference contributes to the total bit shift. We will develop an estimate for the bit shift due to this source to provide, as we did with noise, a perspective of this error source in terms of its influence on readback reliability. With pulse crowding, the worst-case bit shift arises with the dipulse pattern 00011000. Let D be the minimum transition spacing for a given code. Then

$$e_t(x) = e_0(x) - e_0(x - D) \tag{8.27}$$

where e_t is total signal and $e_0(x)$ is the isolated transition pulse response. One pulse is written at $x = 0$ and the other at $x = D$. Now

$$e'_t(x) = e'_0(x) - e'_0(x - D) \tag{8.28}$$

The location of the pulse peaks occur where $e'_t(x) = 0$. Now the second peak will be shifted later in time so that its location can be written as

$$x = D + \Delta$$

where Δ is the bit shift of this pulse signal.

We can find an expression for the peak shift Δ in terms of the isolated pulse response e_0 by taking the derivative of the signal e_t and using Taylor's series approximations near $x = D$ for both pulses. The derivative of the first pulse is

$$e'_0(x) \approx e'_0(D) + e''_0(D)\Delta \qquad (8.29)$$

and the derivative of the second pulse in this region $x \approx D$ is

$$e'_0(x - D) \approx e'_0(0) + e''_0(0)\Delta \qquad (8.30)$$

Now, substituting into (8.28) with $e'_t(x) = 0$ to find the peak shift Δ,

$$e'_0(D) + e''_0(D)\Delta = e'_0(0) + e''_0(0)\Delta \qquad (8.31)$$

But

$$e'_0(0) = 0$$

so we have for the displacement of the second peak (which, except for direction, is the same as the shift the first peak undergoes)

$$\Delta = \frac{e'_0(D)}{e''_0(0) - e''_0(D)} \qquad (8.32)$$

The significance of this bit shift is of course related to the size of the detection half-window.

Now for a Lorentzian pulse which has the normalized form

$$e_0(x) = \frac{1}{1 + (x/(PW_{50}/2))^2}$$

we can get analytic expressions for the first and second derivatives of the signal pulse waveform and calculate the bit shift, normally expressed as a percentage of the half-window.

The peak amplitude at the highest flux density is given as follows when we take into account the nearest and next-nearest neighbors:

$$e_{pk} = e(0) - 2[e(D)] + 2[e(2D)]$$

Disk drives normally record at densities where the resolution, defined as the ratio of peak signal at the highest flux density to that at the lowest (usually the same as the isolated peak amplitude), is 70 to 90 percent. The above amplitude expression for a Lorentzian pulse then provides a way to estimate D. Then, given PW_{50} we are in a position to estimate the fraction of the window width consumed due to intersymbol interference and hence its contribution to the soft error rate [8].

8.2.3 Other Sources of Bit Shift

A third factor of major importance, in addition to noise and pulse crowding, is bit shift due to overwrite, which was discussed in Chapter 4 where an expression was developed to indicate how a given overwrite performance can be related to bit shift. Still another important source of error is bit shift introduced by head mispositioning, resulting from signal disturbances caused by reading old and adjacent track information. In disk drives off-track tolerance specifications are nominally 15 percent of the track width. Track misregistration (TMR) reduces the effective SNR significantly by lowering the desired signal and increasing "signal disturbances" from the sensing of old and adjacent track information. The side erase phenomena of many magnetic heads can create narrow erase bands on both sides of the head and thereby increase their off track capability. While it is possible to gain physical insight into these and other sources of bit shift through analysis and modeling, empirical methods are essential to secure suitable data for design and evaluation purposes.

8.2.4 Window Margin Analysis

By careful measurements of the bit error rate under stressed conditions with various data patterns, it is possible to quantify the bit shift error sources. An instrument designed to make such measurements is called a window margin analyzer. Figure 8.6 shows typical output that can be interpreted to segregate out bit shift due to pulse crowding, noise, and overwrite modulation. By running these measurements for off-track conditions, an insight can be gained with respect to bit shift associated with head tracking and adjacent track interference.

A brief explanation of the measurement method follows. To determine error rates as low as 1 in 10^{10} would require an inordinate amount of time, even at the data rates of modern disk drives. To obtain accelerated test data, therefore, another technique is required. The implementation techniques can vary but the essential concept is to have an electronically adjustable detection window. When the window is closed, the error rate is 1.0. As the window is incrementally opened, data, in the range of 10^5 bits, is read (say from one track) at each window setting and the bit error rate measured. The logarithm of the soft error rate is then plotted as a function of the half-window size. This curve is then extrapolated to the lower error rates that are of interest. The standard method is to assume the noise has a Gaussian distribution.

When the window is small, the error rate will remain high and relatively flat. The principal cause for this behavior is intersymbol interference, particularly that produced by the dibit pattern. This pattern-dependent component will dominate until the window size exceeds this source of bit shift. As the window opens further, the error rate will decrease and the rate of decrease will primarily be a function of the signal-to-noise ratio. The higher the signal-to-noise ratio, the more quickly the error rate will decrease as the window becomes larger. Other sources of bit shift, such as overwrite, also influence the general character of this log error rate versus window width curve.

The window margin may be defined as the half clock window (for the modulation code under measurement) minus the total consumed window, determined from the measurements and extrapolation, for specified bit error rate. Usually, the margin is expressed as a percentage of the half-window. A typical design objective for the window margin is 25 to 30 percent, which will more than account for component tolerances and so forth and provide a reliable production drive. Other information can be acquired in this kind of stress test. For example, if the error rate were to remain constant as the window size were increased, this would indicate a medium defect for which the track being tested is giving one hard error per revolution.

More studies are also done with this type of testing. By running such tests while also moving the head off-track, doing off-track measurements while "squeezing" in adjacent tracks and so on, track density issues can also be explored. The use of margin testing is to gain design understanding and reliability estimates through meaningful stress testing procedures.

8.2.5 Bathtub Curve and TMR

A so-called bathtub curve gives the soft error rate as a function of the off-track position of the read head. At each point enough data is collected to determine an error rate. Again "old" information across the track region and a "updated" data pattern is first recorded. The TMR (track misregistration) distribution, write-to-read, gives the probability of the read head actually being at each off-track location on positioning. The point by point product of this distribution and the bathtub curve gives the expected error rate at each off-track location. The summation or integral of this expected error curve gives the total soft error rate. In this manner the sensitivity to component tolerances etc. can be studied.

8.3 RELIABILITY THROUGH REDUNDANCY

In digital mass storage, there are several special techniques to improve overall performance reliability with respect to errors caused by noise and interference. Use of these techniques can contribute to the practical utilization of higher bit densities. For example, a parity check bit included within each recorded character (6 to 8 bits) is a standard method of providing single-bit error detection in the character (word). Additional check bits can give the capability for single-bit error correction. These concepts are readily extended through the mathematical foundations of coding theory to handle error detection and correction over large blocks of data. For instance, a burst error correcting code can correct up to a specified number of successive bits in error.

All of the error detection and correction techniques must use redundancy, either in the form of additional hardware or time (additional computer cycles) to store data and execute the algorithms to find and correct errors. To justify the use of some form of redundancy, the benefits must be balanced against and outweigh the additional complexity. Normally, the decision is favorable to the use of redundancy to improve reliability, because data processing systems involve such a large investment in equipment for processing data rapidly that the loss of even a short period of useful time because of storage retrieval errors is extremely expensive.

Trade-offs are inherent with the addition of redundancy. To maintain or even increase capacity with a given level of technology, the addition of redundancy will require a higher recording density. A higher density means a narrower detection window and a lower SNR. These changes by themselves would degrade the bit error rate (ber). However, they can be more than compensated for by the appropriate use of error correction. For example, let p be the probability of a single bit error. Then $1 - p$ is the probability a bit will not be in error. Typically, p will be less than 10^{-7}. As long as $p < 10^{-3}$ the following arguments apply. If we have a code word of length n, then the probability of a code word in error p_r is

$$p_r \approx np(1-p)^{n-1} \tag{8.33}$$

since a single bit error in any one position (or any other combination of errors) will cause the code word to be in error. Now if the code word includes single-error correction capability, then a code word will only be in error if 2 bits (or more) are in error. For this case,

$$p_r \approx \frac{n(n-1)}{2}p^2(1-p)^{n-2} \tag{8.34}$$

where we account for the number of combinations of 2 bits in error possible in a code word of length n. However, in this latter case we must allocate l bits to detect and correct the error. Then the actual number of message bits (and useful information) is $n - l$ and not n. It will be shown later that for a Hamming single-error correcting code one combination is $n = 7$ and $l = 3$. Then for $p = 10^{-5}$ at a given recording density we have, without single-error correction coding, the following probability of a code word error:

$$p_r = 7 \cdot 10^{-5}$$

and with single-error correction

$$p_r = 21 \cdot 10^{-10}$$

which is very much less, but the useful data storage is decreased dramatically in the second case, since only 4 out of 7 bits are being used for user data. To maintain the same capacity we would need to increase the linear density by the factor 7/4. However, if the probability of a bit error, p, increases rapidly with density, there may be little gain or even a decrease in performance. While in general it is obvious that the use of error correction can be of great value, the actual net gain in terms of reduced error rate and improved overall drive performance requires a thorough systems-oriented design analysis.

Error detection and correction codes can contribute immensely to the operational performance of a magnetic mass store. These techniques are invaluable in contending with intermittent errors due to spacing fluctuations and so forth. With higher densities, the burst error correcting codes become particularly attractive. For example, a dust particle, temporarily increasing the head-to-medium spacing, affects a given section of the track and may cause dropouts. At low densities, the dropout distance may correspond to only a few bits, but at high bit densities, a large block of successive bits would be lost. With automatic error correction, a storage system can continue to maintain full operational performance even when encountering errors. Automatic error detection provides a means for the data processing system immediately to initiate programmed procedures, which can attempt to rectify the error.

8.3.1 Error Detection and Correction

Error detection has long been accomplished by parity checking. A parity check bit is added to a data word and is set so that there is either an odd or even number of 1's over the total word, constituting odd or even parity. For example, 1101 is a 4-bit data word. If a fifth bit, the check bit is added and set for odd parity, the new word is 11010. If the word retrieved from storage is 11000, we no longer have odd parity, so we know that the retrieved word is invalid. An error has occurred. This idea can be extended to single-error correction by making a two-dimensional array of data words and checking parity over both rows and columns, as shown in Figure 8.7. Arrays might be formed across multiple tracks as in a tape storage system or by loading data from a single track into a buffer memory. For a single error in the array, both row and column parity checks will point to the bit in error so that it can be corrected. Diagonal parity checks across arrays are also possible, and a very powerful error correction scheme uses this technique [9].

Two examples of applications in which a simple parity check can be applied to do more than merely detect an error are (1) a single track failure (or erasure) on a parallel track magnetic tape and (2) the use of an additional "parity" disk in a disk array used for parallel block transfer. In the first case, if an entire track is lost due to a malfunctioning head (in which case the failed track can be identified by the absence of any signal), no information is lost, since the data recorded on that track can be reconstructed from the parity checks. This is possible because we can identify the failed track; otherwise, we could only conclude that each parallel byte was in error. A bit that we know to be unreliable is called an erasure. An erasure is not as serious as an erroneous bit. In the second example, described in Chapter 1, parity disks can be effectively used in disk arrays, since a malfunctioning drive is readily identified (or, more correctly, provides an indication when it is inoperative).

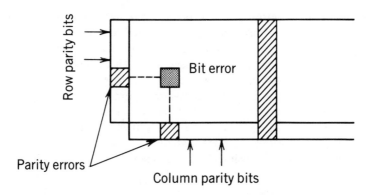

FIGURE 8.7   Two-dimensional parity to correct single error.

When a parity check bit is added to a data word, the number of possible words is doubled. By imposing a parity rule, only half of these are allowed as valid words—the same number as in the data. The other half, which violate the parity rule, are recognized as containing single bit errors. These words differ in one bit location from the allowed words. The allowed words are said to be a Hamming distance of one from the error words, and this permits their detection if they contain a single bit in error. In general, the Hamming distance is the number of bits in which two words differ. This concept leads to a general method for error correction. Instead of doubling the number of allowed words, we increase them many times by adding additional check bits. We do this in such a way that the allowed words corresponding to data, referred to as code words, are spread evenly throughout the entire set of words so that each code word is at least a minimum Hamming distance away from every other code word. Figure 8.8 illustrates this layout schematically. Parity checks are based on the concept that errors are relatively rare and small errors are much more likely than large. Thus, when an error is detected the assumption is that the desired bit sequence is the nearest of the acceptable code words. When the stored code words are retrieved (transmitted and received in communications terminology), errors manifest themselves as received words that are at certain Hamming distances from the code words. As long as these distances are small enough compared with the minimum distance between code words, errors can be corrected by assigning the received word to its nearest code word. For example, if the minimum distance between code words is five, up to two errors in a word can be corrected, because there is always a unique code word that is nearest to the received word containing two errors.

The implementation of this idea, first described by Hamming [10], has spawned the large, active discipline of error correction coding. Activities range from very abstract mathematics to both hardware and software implementation of coding methods. Many of these methods have found application in digital magnetic storage systems. Their details are beyond the scope of this text, but

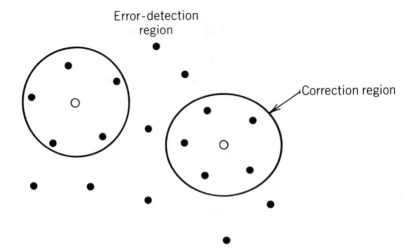

Error-detection region

Correction region

O Code words

● Noncode words

FIGURE 8.8 Layout of code words.

find excellent coverage in several references [11–13]. The Hamming single-error correction code can be expressed as

$$2^{(n-k)} = n + 1 \tag{8.35}$$

where n is the number of bits in the code word, k is the number of message bits, and $n - k$ is the number of parity or check bits. To identify n possible bit error positions as well as the "no-error" state requires the $(n - k)$ check bits be able to indicate $(n + 1)$ conditions, i.e., n possible error locations and the error free condition. For $(n - k) = 3$, $n = 7$, while for $(n - k) = 8$ we have $n = 63$. In the former case the code efficiency k/n, that is, the ratio of the message bits to the length of the code word, is only 0.57, whereas in the latter case the code efficiency is $(63 - 8)/63$, or approximately 90 percent. The advantages of longer code words are apparent.

Design and implementation of codes rely heavily on concepts from linear algebra and modulo-2 arithmetic [14]. Words are represented as vectors in which the bit contents are the components of the vector. There is a null vector, the word containing all zeros, and the operations of vector addition, dot product, and scalar multiplication are defined so that the set of all received words constitutes a vector space. Addition and multiplication are carried out via modulo-2 arithmetic—each result is divided by two successively until there is a remainder of either 0 or 1. This remainder then becomes the final result.

For binary numbers, the addition operation is equivalent to *exclusive or*; multiplication to *and*. This equivalence makes it straightforward to implement the coding and decoding operations in logic circuits.

Hamming codes are included in the class of linear block codes in which blocks of message data k bits long are coded into n bit words that contain the k message bits and an additional $n - k$ parity bits. These codes are characterized as (n,k) block codes. In the Hamming $(7,4)$ code, code words are represented as row vectors x, where

$$x = [p_0, p_1, p_2, m_0, m_1, m_2, m_4] = [p : m] \tag{8.36}$$

p_i is a parity bit and m_i a message bit. Code words are generated by an encoder that generates the $n - k$ parity bits based on the message bits to be coded. The code words are transmitted through the channel and received as the original words plus errors in transmission. In vector notation, we express the received vector y as

$$y = x + e \tag{8.37}$$

where e is an error vector. For no errors in the received code word, e is the all-zeros vector. If there is an error in the ith bit of the received vector y, the ith component of e is 1. The number of error bits in the received word is just the number of 1's in the error vector.

For error correction, the decoder must operate on the received vector y to generate an output vector that will point to the nonzero components of e, that is, the bits in which errors occurred. These bits are then complemented to correct the received message to the original. The receiver decoder consists of a decoding matrix derived from the encoding generator. The example Hamming code is also a cyclic code. Cyclic codes form a subclass of linear block codes. The mathematical properties of cyclic codes lead to some very simple hardware implementations of the encoding and decoding operations. The same general principles have been extended to develop very sophisticated codes tailored to the error sources associated with the application to which they are applied.

In data encoding, long code word lengths have an additional advantage beyond code efficiency. Recording one block of 1000 bits with redundancy allowing the correction of up to 100 random bits (10 percent) in error is much more effective than writing ten 100-bit code words with the same level of correction capability, that is, 10 bits (or 10 percent) per code word. In the latter situation, if readback errors are clustered so that 11 or more occur in any one block, the 10-block group cannot be corrected. With the longer code word length, the same data could be corrected and reliably read.

There are several methods to deal with burst errors, where a burst of length b is defined as a sequence of b bits in which at least the first and last bits are in error. A sequence of bits with some in error can also be viewed in terms of a random error pattern. A burst correction code that can correct up to b successive bits in error is said to have a burst error correction capability of

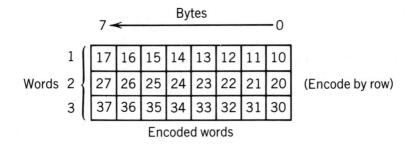

(Encode by row)

Encoded words

Record by column

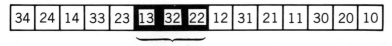

Burst error
recorded data

Readback into columns

(Correct by row)

Readback words single
byte errors are corrected

FIGURE 8.9   Interleaving to improve burst error correction.

b. Interleaving is one approach to provide an improved burst error correction capability to a code word that by itself contains a certain level of error correction.

For example the Reed–Solomon codes [15] are based on symbols rather than bits, and typically a symbol is an 8-bit byte. If a code word is designed to correct 1 byte in error, its burst correction length is only 1 bit, as a 2-bit error sequence that falls at the boundary of the byte symbols would lead to 2 bytes in error, and hence the code word would be uncorrectable. However, if this same code is interleaved to degree three, a burst of up to 17 bits could be corrected. Figure 8.9 is an example of how interleaving is done. Three words with a single-byte error correction capability are encoded and stored in memory by row but are recorded serially by column. A 3-byte error burst will thus be distributed over the three words as shown. On readback the code words are reassembled and their individual error correction capabilities applied. As indicated, this permits a burst longer than that of the code word error-correcting capability to be handled. For example, the IBM 3370 disk storage device uses for error correction a Reed–Solomon code with an interleave factor of 3.

Therefore, it can be seen that in realizing the potential of digital magnetic recording for data storage, error correction and detection methods will become of increasing importance as we go to higher densities where medium defects become of greater importance and a lower SNR must be accepted. The application of more sophisticated error detection and correction opens the way to provide highly reliable data storage using systems with raw error rates on readback much worse than are achieved today.

REFERENCES

1. "Thermal Agitation of Electricity in Conductors," J. B. Johnson, *Phys. Rev.*, Vol. 32, pp. 97–109, 1928.

2. "Thermal Agitation of Electric Charge in Conductors," H. Nyquist, *Phys. Rev.*, Vol. 32, pp. 110–113, 1928.

3. "The Design of Low-Noise Amplifiers," Y. Netzer, *Proc. IEEE*, Vol. 69, pp. 728–741, 1981.

4. "Maximum Signal to Noise Ratio of a Tape Recorder," J. C. Mallinson, *IEEE Trans. Magn.*, MAG-5, pp. 182–186, September 1969.

5. *Data Transmission*, W. R. Bennett and J. R. Davey, McGraw-Hill, New York, pp. 334–341, 1965.

6. *Magnetic Recording*, Vol. I: *Technology*, C. D. Mee and E. D. Daniel, McGraw-Hill, New York, pp. 337–375, 1987.

7. "On Noise in Digital Recording," G. F. Hughes and R. K. Schmidt, *IEEE Trans. Magn.*, MAG-12, pp. 752–754, November 1976.

8. "Effect of Bitshift Distribution on Error Rate in Magnetic Recording," E. R. Katz and T. G. Campbell, *IEEE Trans. Magn.*, MAG-15, pp. 1050–1053, May 1979.

9. "Adaptive Cross-Parity Code for High-Density Magnetic Tape Subsystem," A. M. Patel, *IBM J. Res. Dev.*, Vol. 29, pp. 546–562, 1985.

10. "Error Detecting and Error Correcting Codes," R. W. Hamming, *Bell Syst. Tech. J.*, Vol. 29, pp. 147–160, 1950.

11. *Error Correcting Codes*, 2nd Edition, W. W. Peterson and E. J. Weldon, Jr., MIT Press, Cambridge, MA, 1972.

12. "The Technology of Error Correcting Codes," E. R. Berlekamp, *Proc. IEEE*, Vol. 68, pp. 564–593, 1980.

13. *Error-Correction Coding for Digital Communications*, G. C. Clark, Jr. and J. B. Cain, Plenum, New York, 1981.

14. *A Survey of Modern Algebra*, 3rd Edition, G. Birkhoff and S. MacLane, Macmillan, New York, 1965.

15. "Polynomial Codes over Certain Finite Fields," I. S. Reed and G. Solomon, *J. SIAM*, Vol. 8, pp. 300–304, 1960.

INDEX

A

Access time, elements of, 12–13
Air bearing, for head-medium spacing, 4, 16–17
Alternative storage technologies, 19–20
Ampere's law, 24
Amplitude detection, 193–195
Amplitude roll off, with transition density, 167
Anisotropy, 51
"a" parameter, of arctangent transition model, 97, 98, 101
"a" parameter wavelength dependence, similarity to spacing response, 102
Application characteristics, transaction oriented, batch, 1, 15–16
Arctangent transition model, description of, 97–102
Azimuth alignment, sine wave loss factor, 87

B

Barkhausen jumps, 54
Base-line shift, 171
Bathtub curve, description of, 217
B–H loop, 54–55
Bit error categories, soft, hard, 209

Bit error rate, contribution from random noise, 209–213
definition of, 212
Bit shift:
effect of track misregistration on, 216
from finite current rise time, 106
from intersymbol interference, 214–215
noise induced, 209–213
from overwrite, 104
Boundary conditions, at interface between two magnetic regions, 31
Boundary value problems, at air gaps, 39–43
Burst error correction, interleaving for, 223–224

C

Channel modulation codes:
(1, 7), 191
(2, 7), 190–191
modified frequency modulation (MFM), 189–190
non return to zero (NRZ), 183–185
phase encoding, 185–186
Clocking of data, 192
Code efficiency, definition of, 221

Codes:
   charge constraint for, 187
   detection window for, 188
   formal characterization of, 186–187
Coercive force (coercivity), 54
   of storage medium, 9, 17
Computer data storage, history of, 15–17
Current density:
   conduction, 27
   magnetization, 27

D

Demagnetization, from reversal of medium
   magnetization, 94–95, 98
Demagnetizing factor, 35–36, 52
Demagnetizing field, 35–36, 48, 52
Digital magnetic recording:
   channel block diagram of, 163–164
   current voltage features of, 161–164
Digital recording, use of binary symbols
   in, 9
Direct access disk device (DASD), applied
   to disk drive, 16
Disk drive, *see* Magnetic disk drive(s)
Disk surfaces, defect mapping of,
   201–202
Domain:
   magnetic, 51–53
   single domain behavior, 56–58
Dropout, definition of, 192

E

Eddy currents, 48–50
   in head cores, 137–139
Electrical characteristics:
   ferrite core, 135–136
   of magnetic heads, 135–141
   metallic head cores, 136–139
Electrical circuit, of magnetic heads,
   139–141
Electronics noise, preamplifier major
   contributor to, 203
Energy:
   anisotropy, 56
   in linear magnetic system, 43
   in magnetic circuit, 48
   potential, 57
      of magnetic field, 51

Equalization:
   effect on signal to noise ratio, 179–182
   pulse-slimming, 177–179
   sensitivity to velocity, 182
   transversal filter for, 176–177
   for zero intersymbol interference, 175
Error detection and correction, bases of
   techniques, 219–222
Error sources, definitions for, 202
Exchange forces, 53

F

Faraday's law, 25
Ferrimagnetic materials, 53
Ferrimagnetic resonance, 136
Ferromagnetism, nature of, 50–51
Field:
   from current loop, 25
   from infinitely long straight wire, 27
Field mapping, 40–41
Fields:
   at air gaps, 36–39
   cylindrical, permanent magnet, 29–30
   demagnetizing, 35–36
   from images, 33–35
   from magnetic charge, 33–39
Flux density, magnetic, definition of, 24
Flux leakage, in magnetic circuits, 47–48
Force, on differential length of conductor,
   24
Frequency effects, in magnetic heads,
   139–140
Fringing field, of magnetic head, 66–69

G

Gap loss function, of sine wave response,
   83
Gap size, for writing, 114–115
Gaussian waveform, pulse approximations
   with, 166
Geometrical scaling, significance of, 78

H

Half pulse width (PW50), including both
   writing and reading, 103
Hamming codes, for error correction,
   220–222

Hamming distance, definition of, 220
Hard error rate, definition of, 209
Head fringing field, three dimensional
    aspects, 78–79
Head skew, effect of, 85–88
Head-medium interface:
    contact recording, 14, 19
    non-contact recording, 16–17
Hysteresis loop, 54

I

Idealized ring head:
    gap size for writing, 114–115
    Karlqvist model of, 115
Induction, 44
    magnetic, definition of, 24
    mutual, 44

J

Johnson noise, description of, 203

K

Karlqvist equations, for idealized magnetic
    head, 67

L

Laminations, for head core, 137–139
Leakage flux, in magnetic circuit, 47–48
Linear density, factors influencing, 6,
    14, 17
Longitudinal recording, description of, 6–7
Loss, hysteresis, 55

M

Magnetic charge density, definition of, 28
Magnetic circuit:
    concept of, 45–47
    of magnetic head, 124–127
Magnetic coupling, head to medium,
    63–64
Magnetic coupling reciprocity, principle
    for, 44–45
Magnetic data storage, history of, 15–17
Magnetic disk drive(s):
    access time of, 2
    capacity of, 3, 18

current trends, 17–19
data transfer rate of, 13–14
design aspects of, 12–15
future directions, 19
Magnetic field:
    intensity, definition of, 27
    of permanent magnet, 29
Magnetic field relations, 26–30
Magnetic head(s):
    dual-element structure, 141–144
    effect of reading coil location,
        122–124
    efficiency, 126–127
    electrical characteristics of, 135–141
    far field equations, 68–69, 117–119
    fields in near zone, 119–121
    fringing field of, 112–114
    magnetic charge plane model, 67
    magnetic properties for, 9–10
    magnetoresistive (MR) heads, 130–133
        shielding of, 133–135
    metal-in-gap (MIG) ferrite, 127–128
    probe heads, 121–122
    saturation feature, 114
    shielded MR heads, 133–135
    thin film heads, 121, 128–130
        domain structure in, 130
Magnetic head noise, from head
    impedance, 203
Magnetic medium thickness, effect on
    readback pulse shape, 71, 73
Magnetic particles, used in recording
    media, 152
Magnetic properties:
    for magnetic heads, 112
    for recording media, 147–150
Magnetic recording:
    advantages of, 11–12
    for data storage, 8–11, 61–63
    description of, 4–6
    history of, 4
    input/output transfer function, 61–62, 82
    time domain response, 69–70
    wavelength response, 79–84
Magnetic recording system, as
    communications channel, 160
Magnetic shell, equivalent current loop for,
    31–33
Magnetic tape, usage of, 2, 15

Magnetic tape drive, characteristics of, 15, 16
Magnetic transition, recording of, 90–92
Magnetization, definition of, 27
Magnetization process, 53–58
Magnetization reversal:
readback pulse for finite width of, 74–76
readback pulse for step change in, 69–70
Magnetomotive force, definition of, 47
Mass storage:
operational reliability, 3
organization of, 2–3
use of term, 1
Media noise:
assumptions in calculation, 205
noise power spectral density of, 205
particulate magnetic layer, 204–208
physical interpretation of, 208
signal-to-noise factors, 153–154
Minimum transition length:
from self demagnetization, 98
in terms of "a" parameter, 98
Modes of recording, definition of, 6–8

N

Nature of head fringing field, fundamentals of, 76–78
Non-linear bit shift, from writing process, 104–106
NRZ recording, 183–185
Numerical methods, 42

O

Output waveform, in and out of plane magnetization, 74–75
Overwrite, qualitative description of, 103–106
Overwrite measurement, bit shift relation to, 107–108

P

Parity check, with magnetic tape, 219
Parity check bits, for improving reliability, 219
Particulate media:
additive noise in, 153
coercive force from shape, 152
multiplicative noise in, 153–154
shape anisotropy field of, 151
Peak detection, 195–197
noise induced bit shift, 209–211
Peak shift, from pulse interference, 169
Permeability:
complex, 136
magnetic, 31
Perpendicular magnetization, effect on pulse shape from ring head, 118–119
Perpendicular recording, description of, 7–8
Potential, scalar magnetic, 28, 33
Probability of error, effect of redundancy, 218–219
Pulse crowding:
four adjacent transitions, 171
three adjacent transitions, 170–171
two adjacent transitions, 169–170
Pulse pairing, writing on dc erased medium, 104
PW50, half pulse width, in terms of recording geometry, 71–72

R

RAMAC, description of, 17
Readback detection techniques, 191–198
amplitude, 193–195
peak, 195–197
Readback process, linearity considerations of, 63
Readback signal, general formula for, 65
Reading resolution, measure of, 165
Reciprocity, principle of, applied to head-medium magnetic coupling, 63–65
Recording, magnetic coupling function, 113, 115–121
Recoding media:
magnetization orientation in, 149–150
mechanical properties of, 150–151
noise characteristics, 150
non-magnetic characteristics of, 155–156
self-demagnetizing effects, 148
Redundancy, for increasing reliability, 217–219

Registration, head-to-track, 141
Reliability, techniques to enhance, 217–218
Reluctance, concept of, 47
Remanent induction, 54
Ring head, idealized model of, 66–69
Ring head output pulse, perpendicular magnetization, 70

S

Saturation flux density, 54
Saturation recording:
    description of, 9
    for storing digital data, 161
Sensitivity function, of magnetic head, 69
Shielding, between heads, 141
Side reading, relation to fringing field, 79
Side writing, relation to fringing field, 79
Signal to noise ratio, tradeoff, linear *vs.* track density, 208
Single domain, magnetization process, 56–58
Single error correction, Hamming code for, 222
Skew, definition of, 192
Skin depth, 50, 138
Skin effect, 50
Spacing loss factor, of sine wave response, 84
Squareness:
    coercivity (S*), definition of, 148
    remanence, definition of, 148
Storage hierarchy:
    levels of, 1
    tradeoffs, cost/byte and access time, 2–3
Storage media, magnetic properties for, 9
Superposition, application to readback process, 166–167
Superposition integral, for readback formula, 81
Susceptibility, magnetic, 31
Switching field distribution, definition of, 148

Systematic bit shift:
    from intersymbol interferences, 214–215
    from overwrite limitations, 216

T

Tape devices, read after write check, 202
Thickness, influence on pulse shape, 73
Thickness factor, of sine wave response, 83
Thin film disks, structure of, 155
Thin film media:
    development for perpendicular recording, 154
    noise behavior of, 154–155
    zig-zag transitions in, 154–155
TMR (track misregistration), in performance studies, 217
Torque, 51–52
Track density, factors influencing, 14–15
Transition:
    role of B–H loop, 90, 101
    role of demagnetization, 94–95
    role of head field gradient, 91
Transition calculation, Middleton modification, 101
Transition formation, when head saturation occurs, 103
Transition length, description of, 91
Transition location:
    as function of overwrite, 105, 107–108
    influence of state of medium, 93
Transition shape, arctangent model, 97

U

Units, 30

V

Velocity, as scale factor between time and distance, 61–62
Vertical recording, *see* Perpendicular recording, description of

Voltage pulse:
  characteristic nature of, 76–78, 161,
      164–166
  waveform from current pulse, 162

W

Wavelength response:
  of arctangent transition, 102–103
  recording geometry factors, 81–84
Williams–Comstock model:
  assumptions used, 99
  for determining "a" parameter, 99–101

Window margin analysis:
  for accelerated performance testing, 216
  method for, 216–217
Write loss term, from finite "a" parameter,
      102
Write precompensation, 173–174
Write process, effects when overwriting,
      104–106
Writing:
  formation of transition, 90–93
  gap size influence, 114–115
Writing current waveform, 161